CIGARETTE CARD VALUES

1988 Catalogue of Cigarette and other Trade Cards

NANKI-POO.
"THE MIKADO."

"My catalogue is long, through every passion ranging"
— W. S. Gilbert (The Mikado)

Compiled and published by

MURRAY CARDS (INTERNATIONAL) LIMITED

51 Watford Way, Hendon Central, London NW4 3JH
Tel: (01) 202-5688

Opening hours — 10am-5pm Monday-Friday

Watford Way is the A41 road into London, and is one mile from the end of the M1 Motorway. It can be reached via Hendon Central Underground Station (Northern Line), which is 100 yards away, and is also served by a number of bus routes and Green Line.

     ISBN 0 946942 06 4

Introduction

Our 1987 Catalogue proved to be even more successful than its predecessors, with more than $12\frac{1}{2}\%$ extra sold. The vast majority of collectors and dealers regard our annual production as the definitive work of reference for information about cigarette and trade cards and their values. The Catalogue is also used extensively by most collectors clubs (in Britain and abroad), auction houses, and libraries.

This year a minimal number of changes have been made to the basic appearance of the Catalogue. A number of new trade issues have been added, together with a few new tobacco issues. In addition there has been some change to the information about several series. We always endeavour to make the work as accurate as possible, so that when new data comes to light we amend our records accordingly. If anyone has any corrections to the quantities in the series shown, or the dates of issue, we should be most grateful to learn of these.

The main changes, of course, to the Catalogue are the prices of the cards. 1987 has seen a marked increase in interest in card collecting, and this has undoubtedly been encouraged by the continued insertion of cards with Brooke Bond's Tea, and also by Player and Wills with their various brands of cigars and cigarettes. In addition many more collectors are appearing who are interested in one subject only, and who find that cards are an ideal pictorial record. In particular it has been noted this year that there has been a considerable amount of interest in soccer series, with football statisticians concentrating on the cards of one particular club – this has resulted in our publishing a book which lists all the known soccer related tobacco cards issued up to 1940. The issue of a large number of stickers by the Panini organisation has also resulted in some younger collectors progressing to more conventional series. All these factors have combined to encourage a steady increase in prices once more. It should be noted however that there are still many series, usually the more common type, which have tended to remain constant since the supply is still fairly plentiful. A study of the following pages should reveal just what subjects and series have shown the greatest increase, but the speculator should bear in mind that this year's winner could be next year's also-ran.

Two other developments in the past year have been noteworthy, and these have both sought to satisfy the increasing demand for particular subjects. The first of these is the appearance of a number of commercial issues, prepared solely to be retailed, and not connected with any product. The second is the increasing number of reprints of rare or more common series, now officially blessed by the Imperial Group. In both cases the cards should be treated as acceptable for the information they impart and the colourful pictures, but it must be realised that they are never likely to become of any intrinsic value.

The increased activity of Cartophily is reflected in the proliferation of auctions, with record prices being achieved, and fairs. Our own auctions, held on the third Sunday of every month, have attracted more and more bidders, resulting in satisfied buyers and sellers; in spite of our regular backlog of 4-5 months, vendors consider it well worth the wait in order to achieve realistic returns for their collections, or just unwanted duplicates. The fairs held in conjunction with the auction encompass over 50 dealers tables, and the attendances here too are constantly increasing.

HOW TO USE THE CATALOGUE

The Catalogue is in three parts.

Part I contains all known issues by British-based tobacco companies. Thus all cards by the firm W.D. & H.O. Wills, which was located in Bristol, are shown, even though they may have been issued in a Wills brand abroad. Issues from the Channel Islands and the Republic of Ireland are included in this part. Excluded are most post cards and larger non-insert items.

Part II contains tobacco issues by most of the major manufacturers in the English-speaking world, and a selection of other series, including all the sets readily available to collectors.

Part III comprises series issued with commodities other than tobacco (commonly known as "trade cards"). Although mainly British issues, there are a number of overseas sets included. Each issuer's name is followed by the commodity with which the cards were issued; where the set was not given away free, but produced in order to be sold, the issuer is described as "commercial".

Parts I and III commence with an index of brand names, and the issuer's name under which that item appears. Series are listed in alphabetical order of series title under the issuing firm, regardless of country of origin. Where the issuer was not normally located in the United Kingdom the country of origin is given. In the case of certain larger issuers series have been listed in logical groups so that they may be more readily found.

For each set the following information is given:–

(1) **Size information.** Cards are assumed to be standard size unless otherwise stated. Sizes used correspond to the page sizes used for our plastic albums (see separate notice) i.e. when a letter is used it may be assumed that at least one dimension is greater than the size shown by the previous letter. Abbreviations used are:–

K	smaller than standard.	
B	bigger than standard.	51 x 41 mm.
M	medium size.	80 x 46 mm.
L	large size.	80 x 52 mm.
T	Typhoo/Doncella size.	80 x 71 mm.
X	extra large size.	110 x 54 mm.
P	postcard size.	80 x 110 mm.
G	cabinet size.	165 x 105 mm.
E	too large for albums.	223 x 165 mm.
D	dual (more than one) size.	
S	stereoscopic series.	
F	photographic production.	

(2) **Number of cards in set.** When there are several rare numbers in a set the quantity normally available is shown. Thus 35/37 means that the series consists of 37 cards, but that only 35 are usually obtainable.

(3) **Series title.** Where the set has no name then the title accepted by common usage is given. Sect. = sectional series. Silk = silk, satin or canvas. P/C = playing card.

(4) **Year of issue.** This is approximate only, and should in no way be considered to be binding. Particularly in the case of overseas and pre-1900 issues the date should be treated as merely an indication of the era in which the set was produced.

(5) **Price of odd cards.** Because of high labour costs and overheads it is not an economic proposition to offer odd cards from many post-1945 series. Where shown the price is that of normal cards in the set. End numbers (e.g. numbers 1 and 50 from a set of 50 cards) are DOUBLE the price shown. Known scarce subjects from a series, and also thematic subjects from general series (e.g. cricketers from general interest series) would be more expensive than the price shown here.

Where no cards from a series were actually in stock at the time of compilation the price is shown in *italics*. It must be borne in mind that many of these prices are only approximate, since the discovery of just a few cards from a scarcer series could greatly affect the price.

(6) **Price of complete sets.** Prices shown are for sets in clean, undamaged condition. Where mint sets are required (and available) there will be a premium of 50% extra for sets 1920-1940, and 100% for pre 1920 sets. Where no set price is quoted we had no complete sets in stock at the time of compilation; however, when available these will be sold at prices based on the odds figure. *With each pre 1940 set the appropriate Nostalgia album pages are presented FREE!*

UNLISTED SERIES

Because our stocks are constantly changing we always have in stock a large number of series which are unlisted. In particular we can presently offer an excellent selection of German sets, loose or in their special albums and also a good choice of Australian trade issues. If you require a specific item please send us a stamped addressed envelope for an immediate quotation.

ALIKE SERIES

There are many instances where affiliated companies, or indeed completely independent groups issued identical series, where the pictures are the same, and only the issuer's name is altered. Examples are Fish & Bait issued by Churchman, I.T.C. (Canada) and Wills; British Cavalry Uniforms of the Nineteenth Century issued by Badshah, Brown, Empson, Rington and Willcocks & Willcocks; or even Interesting Animals by Hignett or Church & Dwight. In many instances alphabetical code names have been generally adopted to group similar series of the more prolific subjects, e.g. Actresses FROGA, Boer War Generals CLAM, where the letters of the adopted name indicate some of the leading issuers.

SPECIAL OFFERS

10 different pre 1940 sets, our selection (no pages)	£15.00
35 different post 1945 sets, our selection	£10.00
100 different post 1945 sets, our selection (including the above 35)	£35.00
8 different sets of Trucards	£3.00
10 different Brooke Bond sets (our selection)	£6.00
125 post war type cards from 125 different series	£2.50
Liebig starter pack. Our 1987 Catalogue + 15 sets	£10.00
40 different tobacco advertising inserts	£4.00
12 different cardboard cigarette packets	£2.00
8 different Bassett Sweet Cigarette Packets	£1.00

TERMS OF BUSINESS

All previous lists are cancelled.

Cash with order. Any unsatisfactory items may be returned for credit or refund within seven days of receipt.

Overseas payments can only be accepted by sterling cheque drawn on a British bank, by dollar cheque drawn on a U.S.A. bank (add £2.00 for our bank charges) or by Credit Card.

Credit Cards. We can accept payment by Access, Eurocard, Mastercard and Visa. Just quote your card number and expiry date, and we will complete the amount of items actually sent. This is particularly useful for overseas customers, saving bank and currency conversion problems. Minimum credit card order – £4.00.

Condition. All prices are based on cards in clean, undamaged condition. Where available mint sets 1920-1940 will be at a premium of 50% above the normal price, and mint sets pre 1920 and all mint odd cards will be an extra 100%.

Minimum Order. We are unable to accept orders totalling less than £1.00.

Postage. Inland second class post is included in all prices quoted. Overseas letter post is sent free by surface mail; parcels and (if requested) air mail are charged at cost.

Value Added Tax where applicable is included in all prices shown.

When ordering cards please quote the issuer's name, the name of the set, the date of issue, and the price. This will enable us to identify the precise series.

Odd Lists must be submitted on a separate sheet of paper with the name and address clearly shown; this will be returned with the cards for checking. Remember that end cards are double the normal price. Please write all the numbers required, i.e. NOT "17-20" but 17, 18, 19, 20. If the cards are required to complete an unnumbered set, and you do not know the missing titles, we can supply them provided that you list all the cards that you HAVE in alphabetical order.

Alternatives. Although this catalogue is based upon current stocks, these are bound to fluctuate. Therefore, whenever possible please give alternatives.

Credit Notes. When items are out of stock a credit note is normally sent. This may be utilised or encashed at any time, but MUST be returned when so doing.

Unlisted series. We are always pleased to quote for series unlisted, or unpriced.

Purchasing. We are always pleased to purchase or exchange collectors' unwanted cards. Please write with full details before sending cards.

Enquiries. We are always pleased to offer our advice on all collectors' queries. Please enclose a stamped addressed envelope with all enquiries.

Callers. Our shop is open from 10.00 a.m. to 5.00 p.m. each Monday to Friday, and collectors are always welcome to select from our complete range of cards and accessories. Watford Way is at Hendon Central (Underground, Northern Line), and is served by a number of buses, including Green Line.

Answering machine. For the convenience of customers an answering machine is in operation whenever the shop is closed. Just leave your message, or order with Credit Card number, and it will be dealt with as soon as we re-open. Please note we cannot accept telephone orders for odd cards.

No Hidden Extras. Remember that all prices shown include postage, packing, insurance and (where applicable) V.A.T. And that with every pre 1940 set we include Nostalgia pages *absolutely free!*

CARTOPHILIC SOCIETY REFERENCE BOOKS

A number of the earlier Reference Books have been unavailable for some years. However we are now pleased to be able to offer the following paper backed reprints at exceptionally low cost.

No. 1   Faulkner.
No. 2   Hill.
No. 4   Gallaher.
No. 5   Abdulla, Adkin & Anstie.
No. 6   Ardath.
No. 7   Directory of British Cigarette Card Issuers (16 cards illustrated).
No. 8   Glossary of Cartophilic Terms (27 cards illustrated).
No. 9   Lambert & Butler (25 cards illustrated).
No. 10   Churchman (29 cards illustrated).
No. 12   Taddy (30 cards illustrated).
No. 13   Phillips (225 cards illustrated).
No. 17   Player (26 cards illustrated).

ONLY £2.25 Per Booklet!

The following reprints have been combined in hard covers. The information contained cannot be found elsewhere, and each book represents excellent value. Each contains lists of unnumbered series, illustrations of untitled cards, and background information to most sets.

The Cigarette Card Issues of Wills. Originally 5 parts, now in one volume. 200 pages, 559 cards illustrated. **PRICE £7.00**

The Ogden Reference Book (including Guinea Golds). 244 pages, 536 cards illustrated. **PRICE £12.50**

The Tobacco War and B.A.T. Book, 336 pages, 2,959 cards illustrated! **PRICE £12.50**

A MUST FOR ALL COLLECTORS
THE WORLD TOBACCO ISSUES INDEX

Published by the Cartophilic Society of G.B. Ltd., this work is now in four volumes, which between them list every card issued by tobacco manufacturers that was known at the end of 1980.

Part I. World Index and Handbook reprinted as one volume. 701 pages, 1977 cards illustrated. This is the basic reference work for all serious collectors, including details of nearly every British cigarette card. First published in 1956. **PRICE £15.00**

Part II. 452 pages, with 3,600 cards illustrated. This volume covers additions to Part I, which are mainly overseas cards. In particular it includes most of the information from the American Book of Checklists. **PRICE £12.50**

Part III. 504 pages, 666 cards illustrated. Published in 1978, this latest work updates the information in Parts I and II, and also repeats the lists (amended) which were previously in the Churchman, Lambert & Butler, Taddy, Phillips and Australasian Booklets. Also featured are American non-insert cards, blankets and pins. **PRICE £12.50**

Part IV. 688 pages. Lists of U.S. Baseball, photographic, Maltese etc. as well as additions to three previous parts. **PRICE £20.00**

OTHER LITERATURE

GENERAL WORKS

The Story of Cigarette Cards by Martin Murray. Hardback, 128 pages, including 32 in colour. **£7.25**

Collecting Cigarette Cards by Dorothy Bagnall. 112 pages, illustrated. **£3.95**

Cigarette Cards and Novelties by Frank Doggett. 96 pages, 1291 cards illustrated in colour. Paper back reprint. **£5.00**

Burning Bright. The autobiography of E. C. Wharton-Tigar, President of the Cartophilic Society and editor of its reference books. Well written, very cigarette card orientated. 280 pages. **£15.00**

Operation Red Poppy by Jack Nickle Smith. A spy thriller featuring a cartophilist. Hard cover. 158 pages. **£8.50**

Taking Stock (1985). 75 years of the Oxo Cube. 127 pages, many illustrations. **£8.50**

REFERENCE BOOKS

Handbook Part I. Published by L.C.C.C. Lists and illustrations of pre-1918 unnumbered and alike series (tobacco only). Essential reference. **£6.00**

Handbook Part II. Published by L.C.C.C. Lists of post-1918 series and all silks, with additions to Part I. **£6.00**

Smith Cigarette Cards. 36 pages with illustrations. Lists all known series, including back varieties. **£2.25**

British Trade Index, Part I. Series up to 1940. 216 pages, many illustrations. **£10.00**

British Trade Index, Part II. 232 pages. Additions to Part I and also Issues 1945-1968. **£10.00**

British Trade Index, Part III. 400 pages, many illustrations. Additions to Parts 1 and 2, with new issues to the end of 1985. **£13.50**

Typhoo Tea Cards. 36 pages with illustrations. Lists of back varieties. **£2.25**

A. & B.C. Gum Cards. 40 pages with illustrations. Many lists. **£2.75**

British Silk Issues by Dorothy Sawyer. New Edition, amended, many illustrations. 64 pages with details of all known British Tobacco and Trade silk issues. Essential reading for silk collectors. **£3.00**

Lawn Tennis Cigarette Cards by Derek Hurst. 1986. 37 pages. **£3.00**

The Pinnace Collection. Reproductions of all 2,462 cards. Index. **£7.50**

Half Time (Football and the cigarette card 1890-1940) by David Thompson. 104 pages, listing every tobacco issue. **£9.00**

Errors & Varieties, British Cigarette Cards by W. B. Neilson. 148 pages. Lists all known varieties, corrected or uncorrected. **£7.50**

CRICKET BOOKS

Cricket Cigarette & Trade Cards by Derek Deadman. The definitive work. 254 pages, 16 pages of illustrations. Comprehensive list of all titles known until end of 1984. 'Monumental'. **£6.75**

Classic Cricket Cards. Reproductions of 154 cards in colour — Wills 1896 onwards. Designed to be cut out. **£2.50**

More Classic Cricket Cards. 160 cards, different from above. **£2.50**

Cricket Postcards by Grenville Jennings. 236 cards illustrated **£4.50**

The Old Trafford Story. 1884-1984. 80 page book. Sponsored by Wilson's Brewery. Published at £2.00. **Our price £1.50**

FOREIGN CARDS

Australian & New Zealand Index. Published by Cartophilic Society. Over 300 pages — 600 cards illustrated. Lists all tobacco and trade cards. Published 1983. **£10.50**

Liebig Catalogue in English. See page 193 for full details. **£2.50**

Baseball Card Price Guide. 1st Edition 1987. Published by Sports Collectors Digest. 65,000 cards listed and individually priced. Many illustrations. **£7.50**

Fada Liebig Catalogue. 300 pages, listing all titles from 1863 different sets. Index in three languages (not English), text in Italian. **£6.00**

Sanguinetti Liebig Catalogue. 1986 Edition. 347 pages, listing all titles from 1871 sets and menus, Italian text. Illustrations of 700 series. **£10.00**

Cigarette Cards Australian Issues & Values by Dion H. Skinner. A truly magnificent work. 245 pages, with coloured illustrations of at least one sample front and back(s) of each series. Lists of every card in each series (or illustrations of untitled sets). **Now only £15.00**

MISCELLANEOUS

Sweet Cigarette Packets by Michael Johnston. 36 pages, 127 packets illustrated, Published 1983. **Now only £1.50**

I.P.M. Postcard Catalogue, 14th Edition (1988). 320 pages, completely revised. The one THEY all use! **£6.40**

Postcard Collecting – a beginners guide. 24 pages **65p**

A MAJOR NEW BOOK

The Story of Cigarette Cards by Martin Murray.

The history and development of cigarette and trade cards from their origins in Europe in the mid-Nineteenth Century to 1987. The story is told in words, and more appropriately in pictures. There are no less than 80 pages of illustrations (32 in full colour), with 48 pages of text by a leading authority on the subject. As befits such an important work, the book is hardbound, with an attractive dust cover.

Price – an astonishingly low £7.25 (post paid).

HALF-TIME by David Thompson

Another publication from Murray Cards. A complete list of all known (and some previously unrecorded) soccer tobacco cards issued in Britain to 1940. Every card listed by name (except Pinnace). Amendments to the previously published Pinnace list, with an analysis by team. Illustrations of every specialised soccer set, and many other scarce and interesting cards. Analyses of series, background information on players, teams and managers. An invaluable book for soccer fans.

£9.00 post paid.

COLLECTOR'S AIDS

Cleartex strips, for wrapping standard size sets   **200 for £2.20**

Tweezers, fine quality, with plastic sheath   **£1.00**

Magnifying Glasses, $2\frac{1}{2}''$ diameter   **£3.00**

          $4''$ diameter   **£6.00**

Printed wants lists, numbered 1-50 on thin card   **30 for 75p**

Plastic Wallet. Pocket size with 10 postcard size pages.
     Ideal for carrying odds (and ends)   **£1.60**

Postcard pockets, thin PVC   **100 for £3.00**

THE "HENDON" ALBUM

For Postcards, trade cards, and all printed ephemera.

* Pages in crystal clear material, free of plasticiser.
* 8 different page formats.
* Handsome loose leaf binders, in choice of blue, brown, green or red.
* Matching slip cases.
* Big enough for BIG cards, small enough for small muscles.

Pages available

1. Pocket   Cards size 294 x 214mm.
2. Pockets. Cards size 143 x 214mm.
3. Pockets. Cards size   93 x 214mm.
4. Pockets. Cards size 143 x 105mm. Especially for postcards.
6. Pockets. Cards size   92 x 105mm.
6. Pockets. Cards size 145 x 70mm.   Especially for Medals.
8. Pockets. Cards size   67 x 105mm. Ideal for Gum cards, XL
   cigarette cards.
9. Pockets. Cards size   94 x   68mm. Suitable for playing cards.

Album with 25 pages	**£9.25p** (including postage).
Extra pages	**23p** each.
Matching slip case	**£2.75p** (must be ordered with album).

CIGARETTE CARD AUCTIONS

Our auctions are the largest and most successful in the world!

Every month over 450 interesting lots are sold. These include rare sets and type cards, cheaper sets and mixtures, sets in excellent to mint condition, literature, overseas and trade cards not recorded in our Catalogue and highly specialised collections such as Guinea Golds and silks. Lots are submitted to us from other dealers, collectors disposing of their unwanted cards, estates, overseas sources and antique dealers.

Highlights of recent years have included:-

Sets: Taddy Clowns & Circus Artistes, Actresses with Flowers, V.C. Heroes (125).
Wills Waterloo, The Reign of Edward VIII, Cricketers 1896.
Players Military Series, Old England's Defenders.
Smith Races of Mankind, Boer War Series.
Ogden Guinea Golds 1-1148 complete.
Hudden Soldiers of the Century.
Cope Golfers.

Odds: Player, Wills, Smith Advertisement Cards, Clarke Tobacco Leaf Girls, Kinnear Cricketers, Edwards Ringer & Bigg Eastern Manoeuvres, Taddy Wrestlers etc.

But there is something for everyone each time, from beginner to advanced collector, as the more than 200 participants every month will attest.

You do not have to attend in order to bid. Most of our clients bid by post, knowing that their Instructions will be dealt with fairly and in confidence.

How do you bid? Just assess each lot that interests you. Then tell us the maximum amount that you are prepared to pay for it. We will then obtain it (if there are no higher bids) for the cheapest price possible — if for example your bid is £30 and the next highest received is £20 then you will obtain the lot for just £21. If you wish to put a ceiling on your total spending in any auction then we can accommodate this too.

How do you obtain Auction Catalogues? Send 60p for a sample, or else £6.00 will cover the cost of all 12 Catalogues for 1988, including Prices Realised Lists. Auctions are held on the third Sunday of every month and Catalogues are sent out at least three weeks before sale date.

FRAMING KITS

Best materials — Competitive prices
Easy to do-it-yourself — Cards positioned without damage
— Backs can be read —

MOUNTING BOARDS

A To hold 25 standard sized cards (horizontal or vertical).
E To hold 25 large cards (horizontal or vertical).
F To hold 50 standard size cards (horizontal or vertical).
K To hold 10 standard size cards (horizontal or vertical).
L To hold 6 Liebig cards (horizontal or vertical).

Prices — A £2.50 each   E & F £3.50 each   K & L £1.20 each

COMPLETE KITS

Comprising frame, mounting board, spring clips, rings & screws.

Prices — A £11.00 each   E & F £16.00   K & L £7.50 each

If mounts only are ordered minimum quantity is 6.
(Glass can be supplied only to personal callers).

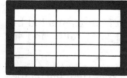

A – 25 Horizontal or Vertical

E – 25 Horizontal or Vertical

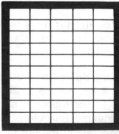

F – 50 Horizontal or Vertical

K – 10 Horizontal or Vertical

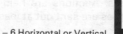

L – 6 Horizontal or Vertical

12

INDEX OF BRANDS (Tobacco)

HERBERT TAREYTON CIGARETTES—See American Tobacco Co. (Part 2)
HOFFMAN HOUSE MAGNUMS—See American Tobacco Co. (Part 2)
HONEST LONG CUT—See Duke or American Tobacco Co. (Part 2)
HUSTLER LITTLE CIGARS—See American Tobacco Co. (Part 2)

ISLANDER, FAGS, SPECIALS, CLUBS—See Bucktrout (Part 1)

JACK ROSE LITTLE CIGARS—See American Tobacco Co. (Part 2)
JERSEY LILY CIGARETTES—See Bradford (Part 1)
JUST MEMBER CIGARETTES—See Pattreiouex (Part 1)

KENSITAS CIGARETTES—See J. Wix (Part 1)

LENOX CIGARETTES—See American Tobacco Co. (Part 2)
LE ROY CIGARS—See Miller (Part 2)
LEVANT FAVOURITES—See B. Morris (Part 1)
LIFEBOAT CIGARETTES—See United Tobacco Co. (Part 2)
LIFE RAY CIGARETTES—See Ray (Part 1)
LITTLE RHODY CUT PLUG—See Geo. F. Young (Part 2)
LOTUS CIGARETTES—See United Tobacco Co. (Part 2)
LUCANA CIGARETTES—See Sandorides (Part 1)
LUCKY STRIKE CIGARETTES—See American Tobacco Co. (Part 2)
LUXURY CIGARETTES—See American Tobacco Co. (Part 2)

MAGPIE CIGARETTES—See Schuh (Part 2)
MANIKIN CIGARS—See Freeman (Part 1)
MATTOSSIANS IMPORTED EGYPTIAN CIGARETTES—See Henly & Watkins (Part 1)
MAX CIGARETTES—See A. & M. Wix (Part 1)
MAYBLOSSOM CIGARETTES—See Lambert & Butler (Part 1)
MECCA CIGARETTES—See American Tobacco Co. (Part 2)
MILLBANK CIGARETTES—See Imperial Tobacco Co. (Canada) (Part 2)
MILLS CIGARETTES—See Amalgamated Tobacco Corporation (Part 1)
MILO CIGARETTES—See Sniders & Abrahams (Part 2)
MINERS EXTRA SMOKING TOBACCO—See American Tobacco Co. (Part 2)
MOGUL CIGARETTES—See American Tobacco Co. (Part 2)
MURAD CIGARETTES—See American Tobacco Co. (Part 2)

NEBO CIGARETTES—See American Tobacco Co. (Part 2)

OK CIGARETTES—See African Tobacco Mfrs. (Part 2)
OBAK CIGARETTES—See American Tobacco Co. (Part 2)
OFFICERS MESS CIGARETTES—See African Tobacco Mfrs. (Part 2)
OLD GOLD CIGARETTES—See American Tobacco Co. (Part 2)
OLD JUDGE CIGARETTES—See Goodwin (Part 2)
ONE OF THE FINEST—See Buchner (Part 2)
ORACLE CIGARETTES—See Tetley (Part 1)
OUR LITTLE BEAUTIES—See Allen & Ginter (Part 2)
OXFORD CIGARETTES—See American Tobacco Co. (Part 2)

PAN HANDLE SCRAP—See American Tobacco Co. (Part 2)
PETER PAN CIGARETTES—See Sniders & Abrahams (Part 2)
PIBROCH VIRGINIA—See Fryer (Part 1)
PICADILLY LITTLE CIGARS—See American Tobacco Co. (Part 2)
PICK-ME-UP CIGARETTES—See Drapkin & Millhoff (Part 1)
PIEDMONT CIGARETTES—See American Tobacco Co. (Part 2)
PINHEAD CIGARETTES—See British American Tobacco Co. (Part 2)
PINNACE—See G. Phillips (Part 1)
PIONEER CIGARETTES—See Richmond Cavendish (Part 1)
PIRATE CIGARETTES—See Wills (Part 1)
POLO MILD CIGARETTES—See Murray (Part 1)
PURITAN LITTLE CIGARS—See American Tobacco Co. (Part 2)

PURPLE MOUNTAIN CIGARETTES—See Wills (Part 1)

R.S.—See R. Sinclair (Part 1)
RECRUIT LITTLE CIGARS—See American Tobacco Co. (Part 2)
RED CROSS—See Lorillard or American Tobacco Co. (Part 2)
REINA REGENTA CIGARS—See B. Morris (Part 1)
RICHMOND GEM CIGARETTES—See Allen & Ginter (Part 2)
RICHMOND STRAIGHT CUT CIGARETTES—See American Tobacco Co. (Part 2)
ROSELAND CIGARETTES—See Glass (Part 1)
ROYAL BENGALS LITTLE CIGARS—See American Tobacco Co. (Part 2)

ST. DUNSTANS CIGARETTES—See Carreras (Part 1)
ST. LEGER LITTLE CIGARS—See American Tobacco Co. (Part 2)
SCOTS CIGARETTES—See African Tobacco Mfrs. (Part 2)
SCRAP IRON SCRAP—See American Tobacco Co. (Part 2)
SENATOR CIGARETTES—See Scerri (Part 2)
SENIOR SERVICE CIGARETTES—See Pattreiouex (Part 1)
SENSATION CUT PLUG—See Lorillard (Part 2)
SHANTUNG CIGARETTES—See British American Tobacco Co. (Part 2)
SILKO CIGARETTES—See American Tobacco Co. (Part 2)
SMILE AWAY TOBACCO—See Carreras (Part 1)
SOVEREIGN CIGARETTES—See American Tobacco Co. (Part 2)
SPANISH PUFFS—See Mandelbaum (Part 2)
SPINET CIGARETTES—See Hill (Part 1)
SPOTLIGHT TOBACCOS—See Hill (Part 1)
SPRINGBOK CIGARETTES—See United Tobacco Co. (Part 2)
STAG TOBACCO—See American Tobacco Co. (Part 2)
STANDARD CIGARETTES—See Carreras (Part 1) or Sniders & Abrahams (Part 2)
STATE EXPRESS CIGARETTES—See Ardath (Part 1)
SUB ROSA CIGARROS—See American Tobacco Co. (Part 2)
SUMMIT—See International Tobacco Co. (Part 1)
SUNRIPE CIGARETTES—See Hill (Part 1)
SUNSPOT CIGARETTES—See Theman (Part 1)
SWEET CAPORAL—See Kinney or American Tobacco Co. (Part 2)
SWEET LAVENDER—See Kimball (Part 2)

TATLEY CIGARETTES—See Walkers (Part 1)
TEAL CIGARETTES—See British American Tobacco Co. (Part 2)
THREE BELLS CIGARETTES—See Bell (Part 1)
THREE CASTLES CIGARETTES—See Wills (Part 1)
TIGER CIGARETTES—See British American Tobacco Co. (Part 1)
TIPSY LOO CIGARETTES—See H. C. Lloyd (Part 1)
TOKIO CIGARETTES—See American Tobacco Co. (Part 2)
TRAWLER CIGARETTES—See Pattreiouex (Part 1)
TRUMPS LONG CUT—See Moore & Calvi (Part 2)
TURF CIGARETTES—See Carreras (Part 1)
TURKEY RED CIGARETTES—See American Tobacco Co. (Part 2)
TURKISH TROPHY CIGARETTES—See American Tobacco Co. (Part 2)
TWELFTH NIGHT CIGARETTES—See American Tobacco Co. (Part 2)

U.S. MARINE—See American Tobacco Co. (Part 2)
UZIT CIGARETTES—See American Tobacco Co. (Part 2)

VANITY FAIR CIGARETTES—See Kimball (Part 2)
VICE REGAL CIGARETTES—See Wills (Part 1)
VIRGINIA BRIGHTS CIGARETTES—See Allen & Ginter (Part 2)

WINGS CIGARETTES—See Brown & Williamson (Part 2)

ZIRA CIGARETTES—See American Tobacco Co. (Part 2)

THE "NOSTALGIA" ALBUM

We believe our album to be the finest on the market — yet this year it is even better. Our pages are now being made from a material which contains no potentially harmful plasticiser and has a crystal-clear appearance. Only available from Murray Cards (International) Ltd. and approved stockists. Note also the following features:—

** Album leaves are made from clear plastic, enabling the entire card to be examined easily without handling!

** Cards easily removed and inserted!

** Wide margin enables pages to be turned in album without removing retention clip!

** A planned range of page formats allows most cards to be housed in one cover. Ten different pages now available!

** Handsome loose leaf PVC binders for easy removal and insertion of pages. Matching slip cases. Four different colours available.

** Black or coloured interleaving to enhance the appearance of your cards.

** Album with 40 pages only £8.00 **

Extra pages	13p each	Matching slip case	£2.00 each
Pastel interleaving	50p per 8	Cover only	£2.80 each
Black interleaving	£1.20 per 40	Tweezers	£1.00 each

Slip cases only supplied with covers. All prices post paid.

Page sizes available:—

- K. holds 15 cards smaller than standard. Size up to 51 x 41 mm.
- A. holds 10 standard size cards. Size up to 80 x 41 mm.
- B. holds 8 cards larger than standard. Size up to 80 x 46 mm.
- M. holds 8 medium size cards. Size up to 80 x 52 mm.
- L. holds 6 large size cards. Size up to 80 x 71 mm.
- T. holds 6 Doncella/Typhoo cards. Size up to 110 x 54 mm.
- X. holds 4 extra large size cards. Size up to 80 x 110 mm.
- C. holds 4 long cards. Size up to 165 x 50 mm.
- P. holds 2 post card size cards. Size up to 165 x 105 mm.
- G. holds 1 card cabinet size. Size up to 223 x 165 mm.

Covers, size 303 x 182 x 60 mm., are available in blue, gold, green or red.

Nostalgia — Collect with Confidence!

NOSTALGIA
ALBUMS

Preserve the best of the past in the best of the present. See opposite page for details.

U.K. Tobacco Issues 1890/1900

Shakespeare Gallery. Copes

Royalty Series. Gallaher

Home & Colonial Regiments.
Gloag. Churchman. Cohen Weenan
Pritchard & Burton

British Birds. Ogdens also Imperial
Tobacco

A Tour Round the World. Smiths, also
Churchman. Edward Ringer & Bigg

Locomotives & Rolling Stock. Wills

Celebrated Gateways. Players, also
Churchman

Part 1

BRITISH TOBACCO MANUFACTURERS

(Including Channel Islands, Eire, and Overseas Issues
by British-based firms)

ABDULLA & CO.

Qty		Date	Odds	Sets
50	Beauties of Today	1938	£2.00	—
25	British Butterflies	1935	25p	£6.25
F52	Cinema Stars, Set 1	1932	£2.00	—
30	Cinema Stars, Set 2	1932	£3.00	—
30	Cinema Stars, Set 3	1933	£2.50	—
32	Cinema Stars, Set 4	1933	£1.00	£30.00
32	Cinema Stars, Set 5	1934	£1.00	£30.00
30	Cinema Stars, Set 6	1934	£1.50	—
25	Feathered Friends	1935	25p	£6.25
50	Film Favourites	1934	£2.00	—
50	Film Stars	1934	*£5.00*	—
P24	Film Stars (Series of Cards)	1934	*£5.00*	—
P24	Film Stars (Series of 24 Cards)	1934	*£5.00*	—
P24	Film Stars, 2nd (25-48)	1934	*£5.00*	—
18	Message Cards	1936	£4.00	—
K18	Message Cards	1936	£5.00	—
L1	Princess Mary Gift Card	1914	—	£8.00
25	Old Favourites	1936	25p	£6.25
40	Screen Stars	1939	50p	£20.00
50	Stage and Cinema Beauties	1935	£2.00	—
30	Stars of The Stage & Screen	1934	£2.50	—

German Issues

Qty		Date	Odds	Sets
M150	Autobilder Serie I	1931	60p	
M150	Autobilder Serie II	1932	60p	
M160	Im Auto Mit Abdulla Durch Die Welt	1930	40p	£65.00
B110	Landerwappen–Sammlung	1932	40p	£44.00
B110	Landerwappen–Sammlung Serie II	1932	40p	—
B150	Landerwappen–Sammlung Serie III	1932	40p	—
B200	Nationale Und Internationale Sport–Rekorde	1931	75p	—
B50	Soldatenbilder Europaischer Armeen Der Gegenwart	1928	£1.00	—
X80	Wappenkarten	1928	40p	£32.00

ADCOCK & SON

Qty		Date	Odds	Sets
11/12	Ancient Norwich	1928	£1.50	£16.50

ADKIN & SONS

Qty		Date	Odds	Sets
25	Actresses–French	1898	*£100.00*	—
12	A Living Picture	1898	£4.00	£48.00
12	A Royal Favourite	1900	£7.50	£90.00
15	Beauties "PAC"	1898	*£100.00*	—
50	Butterflies & Moths	1924	70p	£35.00
12	Character Sketches	1898	£4.00	£48.00
25	Notabilities	1915	£3.00	£75.00
12	Pretty Girl Series (Actresses)	1897	£25.00	£300.00
12	Pretty Girl Series "RASH"	1900	£12.50	—
50	Soldiers of The Queen	1899	£2.50	—
59	Soldiers of The Queen (Series of 60)	1900	£2.50	—
31	Soldiers of The Queen & Portraits	1901	£3.00	—
30	Sporting Cups & Trophies	1914	£8.00	£240.00
25	War Trophies	1917	£3.00	£75.00
50	Wild Animals of the World	1923	70p	£35.00

AIKMAN'S

Qty		Date	Odds	Sets
30	Army Pictures, Cartoons, etc.	1916	£40.00	—

H. J. AINSWORTH

30	Army Pictures, Cartoons, etc.	1916	£40.00	—

ALBERGE & BROMET

25	Boer War & General Interest	1900	£50.00	—
40	Naval & Military Phrases	1904	£50.00	—
30	Proverbs	1903	£50.00	—

PHILLIP ALLMAN & CO. LTD.

50	Coronation Series	1953	20p	£10.00
12	Pin Up Girls, 1st Series (numbered)	1953	75p	£9.00
12	Pin Up Girls, 1st Series (unnumbered)	1953	75p	£9.00
L12	Pin Up Girls, 1st Series	1953	£1.50	£18.00
12	Pin Up Girls, 2nd Series	1953	£1.25	£15.00
L12	Pin Up Girls, 2nd Series	1953	£1.50	£18.00

AMALGAMATED TOBACCO CORPORATION LTD. (Mills)

25	Aircraft of the World	1958	—	£1.50
25	A Nature Series	1958	—	£1.25
25	Animals of the Countryside	1958	—	£1.50
25	Aquarium Fish	1961	—	£1.25
25	Army Badges—Past & Present	1961	—	£3.00
25	British Coins & Costumes	1958	—	£2.50
25	British Locomotives	1961	—	£3.00
25	British Uniforms of the 19th Century	1957	—	£3.00
25	Butterflies & Moths	1957	—	£1.25
25	Cacti	1961	—	£2.50
25	Castles of Britain	1961	—	£8.00
25	Coins of The World	1961	—	£1.50
25	Communications	1961	—	£12.50
25	Dogs	1958	—	£5.00
25	Evolution of The Royal Navy	1957	—	£3.50
M25	Famous British Ships, 1st	1952	—	£1.25
M25	Famous British Ships, 2nd	1952	—	£1.25
25	Football Clubs and Badges	1961	—	£12.50
25	Freshwater Fish	1958	—	£1.25
25	Guerriers a Travers Les Ages (French Text)	1961	—	£8.00
25	Histoire de l'Aviation, Premiere Serie (French)	1961	—	£1.50
25	Histoire de l'Aviation, Seconde Serie (French)	1962	—	£2.50
25	Historical Buildings	1959	—	£8.00
M25/50	History of Aviation	1952	—	£1.00
M50	History of Aviation	1952	—	£25.00
25	Holiday Resorts	1957	—	£1.25
25	Interesting Hobbies	1959	—	£4.00
25	Into Space	1959	—	£2.50
25	Kings of England	1954	80p	£20.00
25	Les Autos Modernes (French Text)	1961	—	£5.00
25	Medals of The World	1959	—	£2.50
25	Merchant Ships of The World	1961	—	£2.00
25	Merveilles Modernes (French Text)	1961	—	£6.00
25	Miniature Cars and Scooters	1958	—	£10.00
25	Naval Battles	1959	—	£2.50

AMALGAMATED TOBACCO CORP. LTD. (Mills)—cont.

Qty		Date	Odds	Sets
25	Ports of The World	1959	—	£1.50
25	Propelled Weapons	1953	—	£2.00
25	Ships of The Royal Navy	1961	—	£4.00
25	Sports and Games	1958	—	£10.00
25	The Wild West	1960	—	£7.50
25	Tropical Birds	1958	—	£12.50
25	Weapons of Defence	1961	—	£4.00
25	Wild Animals	1958	—	£3.00
25	World Locomotives	1959	—	£5.00

THE ANGLO-AMERICAN CIG. MAKING CO. LTD.

20	Russo Japanese War Series	1902	£125.00	—

ANGLO CIGARETTE MFG. CO. LTD.

36	Tariff Reform Series	1909	£15.00	—

ANONYMOUS ISSUES

Printed Backs

41	V.C. Heroes	1916	£3.00	£120.00

Plain Backs

25	Actors & Actresses "FROGA"—C	1900	£5.00	—
?25	Actresses "ANGLO"	1896	£40.00	—
?20	Actresses "ANGOOD"	1898	£6.00	—
20	Actresses "BLARM"	1900	£3.50	£70.00
?50	Actresses "DAVAN"	1902	£20.00	—
26	Actresses "FROGA" A (Brown)	1900	£4.00	£100.00
26	Actresses "FROGA" A (Coloured)	1900	£5.00	—
?25	Actresses "HAGG"	1900	£4.00	—
15	Actresses "RUTAN"	1900	£7.50	—
24	Beauties "BOCCA"	1900	£8.00	—
50	Beauties "CHOAB" (Brown)	1902	£5.00	—
50	Beauties "CHOAB" (Coloured)	1902	£5.00	—
50	Beauties "FECKSA"	1903	£4.00	—
20	Beauties "FENA"	1899	£25.00	—
25	Beauties "GRACC"	1898	£7.50	—
26	Beauties "HOL"	1900	£6.00	—
25	Boer War & General Interest	1901	£12.50	—
20	Boer War Cartoons	1900	£7.50	—
7	Boer War Celebrities "RUTTER"	1901	£6.00	—
20	Boer War Generals "CLAM"	1901	£6.00	—
12	Boer War Generals "FLAC"	1901	£7.50	—
25	Boxer Rebellion—Sketches	1904	£4.00	—
M108	British Naval Crests	1916	£2.00	—
16	British Royal Family	1902	£4.00	—
50	Colonial Troops	1902	£3.00	—
M108	Crests & Badges of the British Army	1916	£1.50	—
20	Cricketers Series	1902	£75.00	—
50	Dogs (as Taddy)	1900	£15.00	—
30	Flags & Flags with Soldiers (Flag Draped)	1902	£2.50	£75.00
15	Flags & Flags with Soldiers (Flag Undraped)	1902	£3.00	—
24	Flags Arms & Types of Nations	1904	£3.00	—
30	Flags of Nations (As Cope)	1903	£3.50	—
40	Home & Colonial Regiments	1900	£3.50	—
2	King Edward & Queen Alexandra	1902	£10.00	£20.00

ANONYMOUS—cont.

Qty		Date	Odds	Sets
40	Naval & Military Phrases	1904	£3.00	—
F30	Photographs (Animal Studies)	1935	75p	—
?50	Pretty Girl Series "BAGG'	1898	£7.50	—
12	Pretty Girl Series "RASH"	1899	£6.00	—
30	Proverbs	1901	£5.00	—
19	Russo Japanese Series	1902	£10.00	—
20	Russo Japanese War Series	1902	£12.50	—
25	Star Girls	1900	£4.00	£100.00
20	The European War Series	1915	£2.50	£50.00
25	Types of British & Colonial Troops	1900	£12.50	—
25	Types of British Soldiers	1914	£3.00	£75.00

E. & W. ANSTIE

Qty		Date	Odds	Sets
25	Aesop's Fables	1934	80p	£20.00
16	British Empire Series	1904	£6.00	£100.00
10	Clifton Suspension Bridge (Sect.)	1938	40p	£4.00
B40	Flags (Silk)	1915	75p	—
X9	Flags (Silk)	1915	£5.00	—
40	Nature Notes	1939	£4.00	—
50	People of Africa	1926	£2.00	£100.00
50	People of Asia	1926	£2.00	£100.00
50	People of Europe	1925	£1.50	£75.00
40	Places of Interest	1939	30p	£12.00
8	Puzzle Series	1900	£50.00	—
25	Racing Series (1-25)	1922	£1.00	£25.00
25	Racing Series (26-50)	1922	£1.20	£30.00
60/83	Regimental Badges (Silk)	1915	60p	—
M5	Royal Mail Series	1900	£120.00	—
X5	Royal Standard & Portraits (Silk)	1915	£10.00	—
50	Scout Series	1923	£1.25	£62.50
10	Stonehenge (Sect.)	1936	40p	£4.00
10	The Victory (Sect.)	1936	50p	£5.00
50	The World's Wonders	1924	80p	£40.00
20	Wells Cathedral (Sect.)	1935	50p	£10.00
40	Wessex	1938	60p	£24.00
20	Wiltshire Downs (Sect.)	1935	40p	£8.00
10	Windsor Castle (Sect.)	1937	40p	£4.00

HENRY ARCHER & CO.

Qty		Date	Odds	Sets
26	Actresses "FROGA"	1900	£35.00	—
50	Beauties "CHOAB" (Brown)	1900	£15.00	—
25	Beauties "CHOAB" (Coloured)	1900	£40.00	—
20	Prince of Wales Series	1912	£15.00	—

ARDATH TOBACCO CO. LTD.

Qty		Date	Odds	Sets
50	Animals at The Zoo	1924	£1.25	—
F54	Beautiful English Women	1930	£1.50	£80.00
25	Big Game Hunting	1930	£2.00	£50.00
L30	Boucher Series	1915	£2.00	£60.00
50	Britain's Defenders	1936	30p	£15.00
50	British Born Film Stars	1934	60p	£30.00
M50	British Born Film Stars	1934	£1.00	—
X1	Calendar 1942	1941	—	£1.00
X1	Calendar 1942-3	1942	—	£1.00

Qty		Date	Odds	Sets
X1	Calendar 1943	1942	—	*£1.50*
X1	Calendar 1943-4	1943	—	60p
X1	Calendar 1944	1943	—	75p
F36	Camera Studies	1939	60p	£21.00
LF45	Camera Studies	1939	50p	£22.50
X25	Champion Dogs	1934	50p	£12.50
X100	Contract Bridge Contest Hands	1930	*£12.50*	—
50	Cricket, Tennis & Golf Celebrities (brown, back—NZ)	1935	70p	£35.00
50	Cricket, Tennis & Golf Celebrities (grey back)	1935	35p	£17.50
X25	Dog Studies (State Express etc.)	1938	£1.20	£30.00
X25	Dog Studies (New Zealand)	1938	*£6.00*	—
25	Eastern Proverbs	1932	60p	£15.00
48	Empire Flying Boat (Sect.)	1938	70p	£35.00
50	Empire Personalities	1937	30p	£15.00
50	Famous Film Stars	1934	35p	£17.50
50	Famous Footballers	1934	35p	£17.50
25	Famous Scots	1935	40p	£10.00
X25	Fighting & Civil Aircraft	1936	60p	£15.00
50	Figures of Speech	1936	30p	£15.00
50	Film, Stage and Radio Stars	1935	35p	£17.50
X25	Film, Stage & Radio Stars (Different)	1935	40p	£10.00
M50	Flags 4th Series (Silk)	1914	*£25.00*	—
M50	Flags 5th Series (Silk)	1914	*£25.00*	—
D50	Flags 6th Series (Silk)	1914	*£35.00*	—
L40	Franz Hals Series	1916	*£10.00*	—
X50	From Screen and Stage	1936	30p	£15.00
L30	Gainsborough Series	1915	£2.00	£60.00
L30	Girls of all Nations	1916	£7.50	—
50	Great War Series	1916	£3.00	£150.00
50	Great War Series "B"	1916	£3.00	—
50	Great War Series "C"	1916	£3.00	—
25	Hand Shadows	1930	*£12.50*	—
X25	Historic Grand Slams	1936	*£12.50*	—
L50	Hollandsche Oude Meesters	1916	*£10.00*	—
X48	How to Recognise The Service Ranks	1940	£2.00	—
X150	Information Slips	1940	£1.50	—
L24	It All Depends On Me	1940	60p	£15.00
50	Life in The Services (adhesive)	1938	30p	£15.00
50	Life in The Services (non-adhesive NZ)	1938	60p	£30.00
96	Modern School Atlas	1936	60p	£60.00
50	National Fitness (adhesive)	1938	20p	£10.00
50	National Fitness (non-adhesive NZ)	1938	50p	£25.00
50	New Zealand Views	1928	£1.50	£75.00
L1	On The Kitchen Front	1942	—	75p
50	Our Empire	1937	60p	£30.00
LF110	Photocards "A" (Lancs. Football Teams)	1936	40p	£45.00
LF110	Photocards "B" (N.E. Football Teams)	1936	50p	£55.00
LF110	Photocards "C" (Yorks. Football Teams)	1936	50p	£55.00
LF165	Photocards "D" (Scots Footballs Teams)	1936	40p	£66.00
LF110	Photocards "E" (Midlands Football Teams)	1936	50p	£55.00
LF110	Photocards "F" (Southern Football Teams)	1936	35p	£37.50
LF99	Photocards "Z" (Sport & General Interest)	1936	15p	£12.50
LF11	Photocards "Supplementary"	1936	£1.50	—

Qty		Date	Odds	Sets
LF22	Photocards Group "A" (Sports)	1937	25p	£5.00
LF21/22	Photocards Group "B" (Coronation, Sports) ...	1937	35p	£7.00
LF21/22	Photocards Group "C" (Lancs. Personalities) ...	1937	50p	—
LF22	Photocards Group "D" (Irish Personalities) ...	1937	50p	—
LF22	Photocards Group "E" (Films, Sports)	1938	50p	£10.00
LF22	Photocards Group "F" (Films, Sports)	1938	60p	—
LF11	Photocards Group "G" (Cricketers)	1938	£10.00	—
LF66	Photocards Group "GS" (Various)	1938	75p	£50.00
LF22	Photocards Group "H" (Films, Sport)	1938	50p	—
LF22	Photocards Group "I" (Films, Various)	1938	75p	£16.50
LF22	Photocards Group "J" (Films, Various)	1939	30p	£6.00
LF22	Photocards Group "K" (Various)	1939	50p	—
LF44	Photocards Group "L" (Various)	1939	35p	£15.00
F45	Photocards Group "M" (Films, Various)	1939	40p	£18.00
LF45	Photocards Group "M" (Films, Various)	1939	30p	£13.50
F45	Photocards Group "N" (Films)	1939	40p	£18.00
LF45	Photocards Group "N" (Films)	1939	35p	£15.00
LF66	Photocards Views of the World	1938	30p	£20.00
25	Proverbs (1-25)	1936	20p	£5.00
25	Proverbs (26-50)	1936	75p	—
L30	Raphael Series	1916	£2.00	£60.00
LF45	Real Photographs Group "O" (Films)	1939	40p	£18.00
F45	Real Photos 1st Series	1939	60p	£27.00
XF18	Real Photos 1st Series (Views)	1937	£1.50	—
F54	Real Photos 2nd Series	1939	60p	£32.50
XF18	Real Photos 2nd Series	1937	£1.50	—
XF18	Real Photos 3rd Series (Views)	1937	£1.50	—
XF18	Real Photos 4th Series	1938	£1.50	—
XF18	Real Photos 5th Series (Views)	1938	£1.50	—
XF18	Real Photos 6th Series	1938	£1.50	—
LF44	Real Photos Series 1—GP1	1939	50p	£22.00
LF44	Real Photos Series 2—GP2	1939	15p	£6.00
LF44	Real Photos Series 3—GP3	1939	£1.50	—
LF44	Real Photos Series 3—CV3 (Views)	1939	40p	—
LF44	Real Photos Series 4—CV4 (Views)	1939	15p	£6.00
XF36	Real Photos Series 7	1938	50p	£18.00
XF54	Real Photos Series 8	1938	35p	£17.50
LF54	Real Photos Series 9	1938	30p	£15.00
XF54	Real Photos Series 9	1938	30p	£15.00
LF54	Real Photos Series 10	1939	30p	£15.00
XF54	Real Photos Series 10	1939	35p	£17.50
LF54	Real Photos Series 11	1939	30p	£15.00
XF54	Real Photos Series 11	1939	50p	£27.00
LF54	Real Photos Series 12	1939	30p	£15.00
LF54	Real Photos Series 13	1939	30p	£15.00
LF36	Real Photographs of Famous Landmarks	1939	£1.50	—
XF36	Real Photographs of Famous Landmarks	1939	60p	£20.00
LF36	Real Photographs of Modern Aircraft	1939	£1.25	—
XF36	Real Photographs of Modern Aircraft	1939	75p	£27.00
L30	Rembrandt Series	1916	£2.00	£75.00
X30	Rembrandt Series	1916	£2.50	—
L30	Rubens Series	1916	£2.00	£60.00
100	Scenes From Big Films	1935	75p	—
M100	Scenes From Big Films	1935	£1.50	—

ARDATH TOBACCO CO. LTD.—cont.

Qty		Date	Odds	Sets
50	Silver Jubilee	1935	30p	£15.00
50	Speed Land Sea & Air (State Express)	1935	50p	£25.00
50	Speed Land Sea & Air ("Ardath"—N.Z.) ...	1935	80p	£40.00
X25	Speed Land Sea & Air (Different)	1938	40p	£10.00
50	Sports Champions (title in 1 line)	1935	30p	£15.00
50	Sports Champions (title in 2 lines—N.Z.) ...	1935	60p	£30.00
6	Sportsmen (Double Ace)	1953	£1.50	—
50	Stamps Rare & Interesting	1939	60p	£30.00
50	Swimming Diving and Life-Saving	1937	60p	£30.00
50	Tennis	1938	60p	£30.00
9	The Office of Chief Whip	1955	£1.50	—
48	Trooping the Colour (Sect.)	1939	80p	£40.00
X?	Types of English Manhood	1935	£10.00	—
L30	Velasquez Series	1916	£2.00	£60.00
X30	Velasquez Series	1916	£3.00	—
50	Who is this? (Film Stars)	1936	30p	£15.00
X?	Wonderful Handcraft	1935	£10.00	—
X24/25	World Views	1937	15p	£3.50
50	Your Birthday Tells Your Fortune	1937	25p	£12.50

ASSOCIATED TOBACCO MANUFACTURERS

25	Cinema Stars	1926	£15.00	—

ATKINSON

30	Army Pictures, Cartoons, etc.	1916	£40.00	—

AVISS BROS. LTD.

40	Naval & Military Phrases	1904	£50.00	—

J. A. BAILEY

40	Naval & Military Phrases	1904	£100.00	—

A. BAKER & CO. LTD.

25	Actresses, 3 Sizes	1901	£15.00	—
L25	Actresses, 3 Sizes (different)	1901	£20.00	—
P?25	Actresses, 3 Sizes (different)	1901	£100.00	—
20	Actresses, "BLARM"	1900	£15.00	—
10	Actresses, "HAGG"	1900	£15.00	£150.00
41	Baker's Tobacconists Shops	1901	£60.00	—
25	Beauties of All Nations (Albert Baker) ...	1898	£8.00	£200.00
25	Beauties of All Nations (A. Baker)	1899	£6.00	£150.00
16	British Royal Family	1902	£25.00	—
20	Cricketers Series	1902	£150.00	—
25	Star Girls	1898	£100.00	—

BAYLEY AND HOLDSWORTH

26	Flag Signalling Code Series	1912	£75.00	—

THOMAS BEAR & SONS LTD.

50	Aeroplanes	1924	£1.50	—
50	Cinema Artistes, Set 2	1936	£2.00	—
50	Cinema Artistes, Set 4	1937	£2.50	—
50	Cinema Stars "BAMT"	1928	£1.00	—
50	Do You Know?	1923	75p	£37.50

THOMAS BEAR & SONS LTD.—cont.

Qty		Date	Odds	Sets
270	Javanese Series (Blue)	1925	60p	£160.00
100	Javanese Series (Yellow)	1925	£5.00	—
50	Stage and Film Stars	1926	£1.50	—

E. C. BEESTON

30	Army Pictures, Cartoons, etc.	1916	£50.00	—

BELFAST SHIPS STORES

?10	Dickens Characters Burlesqued	1900	£150.00	—

J. & F. BELL LTD.

10	Actresses "HAGG"	1900	£40.00	—
25	Beauties (Tobacco Leaf Back)	1897	£60.00	—
25	Colonial Series	1901	£20.00	£500.00
30	Footballers	1902	£20.00	—
60	Rigsvaabner	1925	£15.00	—
25	Scottish Clan Series	1903	£6.00	£150.00
60	Women of All Nations	1925	£15.00	—

R. BELLWOOD

18	Motor Cycle Series	1913	£40.00	—

RICHARD BENSON LTD.

L24	Old Bristol Series	1925	£1.25	£30.00
X24	Old Bristol Series (Reprint)	1946	80p	£20.00

BENSON & HEDGES LTD.

1	Advertisement Card, Original Shop	1973	—	75p
3	Advertisement Cards, Silk Cut	1974	60p	—
48	Ancient & Modern Fire-Fighting Equipment ...	1947	£1.25	£60.00
L10	B.E.A. Aircraft	1958	£2.50	—

FELIX S. BERLYN

25	The Burline Mixture (Golfers Blend) Series ...	1910	£125.00	—

BERRY'S

20	London Views	1904	£85.00	—

BEWLAY & CO.

5	Comic Advertisement Cards	1909	£130.00	—
12	War Series (Portraits)	1915	£8.00	£100.00
25	War Series (Scenes)	1915	£7.00	—

W. O. BIGG & CO.

37	Flags of All Nations	1904	£4.00	—
50	Life on Board a Man Of War	1905	£6.00	—

JAS BIGGS & SON

26	Actresses "FROGA A"	1900	£20.00	—
26	Actresses "FROGA B"	1900	£40.00	—
24	Beauties "BOCCA"	1900	£50.00	—
25	Beauties "CHOAB"	1902	£40.00	—
30	Colonial Troops	1901	£17.50	—
30	Flags & Flags With Soldiers	1903	£15.00	—
25	Star Girls	1900	£100.00	—

J. S. BILLINGHAM

Qty		Date	Odds	Sets
30	Army Pictures, Cartoons, etc.	1916	£45.00	—

R. BINNS

?15	Halifax Town Footballers	1924	£60.00	—

BLANKS CIGARETTES

50	Keystrokes in Break-building	1910	£75.00	—

BOCNAL TOBACCO CO.

25	Luminous Silhouettes of Beauty & Charm	1938	80p	£20.00
25	Proverbs Up To Date	1938	80p	£20.00

ALPHONSE BODE & SON

30	Proverbs	1903	£100.00	—

ALEXANDER BOGUSLAVSKY LTD.

X12	Big Events on the Turf	1924	£7.50	£90.00
25	Conan Doyle Characters (black back)	1923	£2.00	£50.00
25	Conan Doyle Characters (green back)	1923	£2.00	£50.00
25	Mythological Gods and Goddesses	1924	30p	£7.50
25	Sports Records (1-25)	1925	30p	£7.50
25	Sports Records, 2nd Series (26-50)	1925	30p	£7.50
25	Winners on the Turf	1925	£1.00	£25.00
L25	Winners on the Turf	1925	£1.20	£30.00

R. & E. BOYD LTD.

25	Places of Interest	1938	£25.00	—
B25	Places of Interest	1938	£25.00	—
L25	Wild Birds at Home	1938	£25.00	—

WM. BRADFORD

50	Beauties "CHOAB"	1902	£20.00	—
?25	Beauties, Jersey Lily	1900	£125.00	—
20	Boer War Cartoons	1901	£60.00	—

THOS. BRANKSTON & CO. LTD.

30	Colonial Troops	1901	£17.50	—
12	Pretty Girl Series "RASH"	1900	£120.00	—

BRIGHAM & CO.

L16	Down The Thames From Henley to Windsor ...	1912	£50.00	—
16	Reading Football Players	1912	£65.00	—
X3	Tobacco Growing in Hampshire, England	1912	£6.00	£18.00

BRITANNIA ANONYMOUS SOCIETY

?20	Beauties & Couples	1914	£40.00	—

BRITISH & COLONIAL TOBACCO CO.

25	Armies of the World	1900	£75.00	—

BRITISH FASCISTS CIGARETTES

?3	Recruiting Cards	1935	£35.00	—

J. M. BROWN

30	Army Pictures, Cartoons, etc.	1916	£40.00	—

JOHN BRUMFIT

50	The Public Schools Ties Series	1925	£1.60	£80.00

BUCKTROUT & CO. LTD. (Channel Isles)

Qty		Date	Odds	Sets
M416	Around the World/Places of Interest	1924	30p	£125.00
24	Birds of England	1924	£1.75	£42.00
50	Cinema Stars, 1st	1926	80p	£40.00
50	Cinema Stars, 2nd	1927	£1.00	£50.00
M50	Football Teams	1928	80p	£40.00
L22	Football Teams of the Bailiwick	1927	30p	£6.50
123	Guernsey Footballers	1923	£1.25	£150.00
20	Inventors Series	1924	35p	£7.00
25	Marvels of the Universe Series	1919	£1.20	£30.00
M53	Playing Cards	1930	40p	£20.00
25	Sports & Pastimes	1926	£1.60	£40.00

G. A. BULLOGH

30	Army Pictures, Cartoons, etc.	1916	*£40.00*	—

BURSTEIN ISAACS & CO. LTD.

50	Famous Prize Fighters	1923	£1.50	£75.00
F28	London View Series	1922	£2.00	—

BYRT WOOD & CO.

25	Pretty Girl Series "BAGG"	1900	£75.00	—

CABANA CIGAR CO.

B1	Little Manturios Advertisement Card	1904	*£150.00*	—

PERCY E. CADLE & CO.

20	Actresses "BLARM"	1900	£17.50	—
26	Actresses "FROGA" (Chocolate)	1900	£20.00	—
26	Actresses "FROGA" (Coloured)	1900	£25.00	—
?25	Boer War & Boxer Rebellion Sketches	1901	£25.00	—
10	Boer War Generals	1901	*£40.00*	—
20	Footballers	1904	£15.00	—

CARRERAS LTD.

F24	Actresses and Their Pets	1926	£2.00	—
50	A Kodak at the Zoo, A Series	1924	30p	£15.00
50	A Kodak at the Zoo, 2nd Series	1925	30p	£15.00
48	Alice in Wonderland (round corners)	1930	25p	£12.50
48	Alice in Wonderland (square corners)	1930	80p	£40.00
L48	Alice in Wonderland	1930	30p	£15.00
X1	Alice in Wonderland (Instructions)	1930	*£3.00*	—
50	Amusing Tricks & How To Do Them	1937	25p	£12.50
22	Battle of Waterloo	1934	60p	—
L15	Battle of Waterloo	1934	£1.50	—
B1	Battle of Waterloo (Instructions)	1934	—	£2.50
B50	Believe It Or Not	1934	20p	£10.00
50	Birds of the Countryside	1939	20p	£10.00
200	Black Cat Library	1913	£6.00	—
50	Britain's Defences	1938	25p	£12.50
25	British Costumes	1927	50p	£12.50
L25	British Costumes	1927	60p	£15.00
F27	British Prime Ministers	1928	60p	£16.00
1	Calendar	1934	—	*£10.00*

CARRERAS LTD.—cont.

Qty		Date	Odds	Sets
50	Celebrities of British History	1935	15p	£6.50
25	Christie Comedy Girls	1928	£1.00	£25.00
30	Cricketers	1934	£1.25	£37.50
50	Cricketers (A Series of 50)	1934	£1.20	£60.00
F50	Dogs & Friend	1936	15p	£5.00
50	Do You Know?	1939	15p	£4.00
50	Famous Airmen & Airwomen	1936	40p	£20.00
25	Famous Escapes	1926	60p	£15.00
L25	Famous Escapes	1926	60p	£15.00
P10	Famous Escapes	1926	£1.20	£12.00
96	Famous Film Stars	1935	30p	£30.00
48	Famous Footballers	1935	25p	£12.50
25	Famous Men	1927	70p	£17.50
LF24	Famous Naval Men	1929	70p	£17.50
X6	Famous Posters (St. Dunstans)	1923	£12.50	—
LF12	Famous Soldiers	1928	£2.50	£30.00
F27	Famous Women	1929	60p	£16.00
25	Figures of Fiction	1924	70p	£17.50
F54	Film & Stage Beauties	1939	15p	£6.00
LF54	Film and Stage Beauties	1939	16p	£8.50
LF36	Film and Stage Beauties	1939	20p	£7.50
XF36	Film and Stage Beauties	1939	40p	£15.00
50	Film Favourites	1938	30p	£15.00
F54	Film Stars, A Series	1937	20p	£10.00
LF54	Film Stars (as 2nd Series)	1938	35p	£18.00
XF36	Film Stars (Different)	1936	£1.25	£45.00
F54	Film Stars, 2nd Series	1938	15p	£6.50
XF36	Film Stars, 2nd Series (Different)	1936	£1.25	£45.00
XF36	Film Stars, 3rd Series	1937	£1.25	£45.00
XF36	Film Stars, 4th Series	1938	£1.25	£45.00
50	Film Stars (By Desmond)	1936	20p	£10.00
72	Film Stars (Oval)	1934	40p	£30.00
F72	Film Stars (Oval) "Real Photos"	1934	70p	
60	Flags of All Nations (Unissued)	—	—	£7.50
K6	Flags & Arms (Circular)	1915	£40.00	—
K6	Flags of the Allies (Shaped)	1915	£25.00	—
50	Flowers	1936	15p	£7.00
75	Footballers	1934	20p	£15.00
36	Fortune Telling (Card Inset)	1926	20p	£7.50
36	Fortune Telling (Head Inset)	1926	15p	£4.00
L36	Fortune Telling (Card Inset)	1926	15p	£5.00
L36	Fortune Telling (Head Inset)	1926	20p	£7.50
X1	Fortune Telling (Instructions)	1926	*£3.00*	—
F54	Glamour Girls of Stage and Films	1939	15p	£5.00
LF54	Glamour Girls of Stage and Films	1939	15p	£7.00
LF36	Glamour Girls of Stage and Films	1939	20p	£7.50
XF36	Glamour Girls of Stage and Films	1939	30p	£10.00
B50	Gran-Pop	1934	15p	£6.00
L50	Gran-Pop	1934	15p	£7.00
M16	Guards Series (Sectional)	1970	40p	£6.00
M8	Guards Series (Full Length)	1970	50p	£4.00
M4	Guards Series (Mugs)	1971	50p	£2.00
48	Happy Family	1925	15p	£6.00
L48	Happy Family	1925	15p	£6.00

CARRERAS LTD.—cont.

Qty		Date	Odds	Sets
25	Highwaymen	1924	80p	£20.00
50	History of Army Uniforms	1937	50p	£25.00
50	History of Naval Uniforms	1937	35p	£17.50
25	Horses and Hounds	1926	60p	£15.00
L20	Horses and Hounds	1926	50p	£10.00
P10	Horses and Hounds	1926	£1.25	£12.50
50	Kings & Queens of England	1935	40p	£20.00
L50	Kings & Queens of England	1935	£1.00	£50.00
L?84	Lace Motifs	1915	£4.00	—
F27	Malayan Industries	1929	15p	£4.00
F24	Malayan Scenes	1928	60p	£15.00
LF24	Malayan Scenes	1928	15p	£3.50
K53	Miniature Playing Cards	1934	15p	£6.00
50	Notable M.P.s	1929	25p	£12.50
L50	Notable M.P.s	1929	15p	£7.50
F25	Notable Ships Past & Present	1929	60p	£15.00
24	Old Staffordshire Figures	1926	60p	£15.00
L24	Old Staffordshire Figures (Different)	1926	80p	£20.00
P12	Old Staffordshire Figures	1926	£1.50	£18.00
24	Orchids	1925	20p	£5.00
L24	Orchids	1925	20p	£5.00
P24	Orchids	1925	£1.50	—
50	Our Navy	1937	30p	£15.00
50	Palmistry	1933	15p	£6.50
F27	Paramount Stars	1929	40p	£10.00
25	Picture Puzzle Series	1923	60p	£15.00
52	Playing Cards	1926	75p	—
52	Playing Cards & Dominoes (Numbered)	1929	15p	£6.00
52	Playing Cards & Dominoes (Unnumbered)	1929	15p	£7.50
L26	Playing Cards & Dominoes (Numbered)	1929	15p	£4.00
L26	Playing Cards & Dominoes (Unnumbered)	1929	22p	£6.00
48	Popular Footballers	1936	16p	£8.00
72	Popular Personalities (Oval)	1935	30p	£22.50
25	Races Historic & Modern	1927	50p	£12.50
L25	Races Historic & Modern	1927	60p	£15.00
P12	Races Historic & Modern	1927	£1.25	£15.00
50	Radio & T.V. Stars (unissued)	—	£5.00	—
140	Raemaekers War Cartoons (Black Cat)	1916	50p	£70.00
140	Raemaekers War Cartoons (Carreras)	1916	£2.00	—
25	Regalia Series	1925	30p	£7.50
L20	Regalia Series	1925	35p	£7.00
P10	Regalia Series	1925	£1.25	£12.50
L50	Round the World Scenic Models	1925	30p	£15.00
50	School Emblems	1929	25p	£12.50
L40	School Emblems	1929	25p	£10.00
P20	School Emblems	1929	75p	£15.00
L216	Sportsman's Guide—Fly Fishing (Canada)	1950	50p	—
48	Tapestry Reproductions of Famous Paintings (Sect.)	1938	30p	£15.00
52	The Greyhound Racing Game	1926	15p	£6.00
L52	The Greyhound Racing Game	1926	15p	£6.00
X1	The Greyhound Racing Game (Instructions)	1926	*£3.50*	—
B5	The Handy English-French Dictionary	1915	£10.00	—
50	The Nose Game	1927	16p	£8.00

CARRERAS LTD.—cont.

Qty		Date	Odds	Sets
L50	The Nose Game	1927	15p	£6.50
X1	The Nose Game (Instructions)	1927	£3.00	—
50	The Science of Boxing (Black Cat)	1914	80p	£40.00
50	The Science of Boxing (Carreras)	1914	£1.50	—
50	Tools and How To Use Them	1935	35p	£17.50
80	Types of London	1919	75p	£60.00
F27	Views of London	1929	15p	£4.00
F27	Views of the World	1927	40p	£10.00
M15/20	Wild Animals (Canada)	1985	15p	£2.25
25	Wild Flower Art Series	1923	40p	£10.00
50	Women on War Work	1916	£3.00	£150.00

TURF SLIDES

50	British Aircraft	1953	15p	£4.00
50	British Fish	1954	15p	£3.50
50	British Railway Locomotives	1952	25p	£12.50
50	Celebrities of British History	1951	25p	£12.50
50	Famous British Fliers	1956	35p	£17.50
50	Famous Cricketers	1950	£1.00	£50.00
50	Famous Dog Breeds	1952	25p	£12.50
50	Famous Film Stars	1949	30p	£15.00
50	Famous Footballers	1951	35p	£17.50
50	Film Favourites	1948	40p	£20.00
50	Film Stars	1947	30p	£15.00
50	Footballers	1948	35p	£17.50
50	Olympics 1948	1948	40p	£20.00
50	Radio Celebrities	1950	30p	£15.00
50	Sports	1949	30p	£15.00
50	Zoo Animals	1954	15p	£3.50

"BLACK CAT" MODERN ISSUES

50	British Birds	1976	10p	£2.50
50	Flowers All The Year Round	1977	12p	£6.00
50	Kings & Queens of England	1977	12p	£6.00
50	Military Uniforms	1976	10p	£2.50
50	Palmistry	1979	60p	£30.00
50	Sport Fish	1978	10p	£2.50
50	Vintage Cars (with "Filter")	1976	12p	£6.00
50	Vintage Cars (without "Filter")	1976	10p	£2.50

AUSTRALIAN ISSUES

72	Film Stars Series (Smile Away)	1933	£1.00	—
72	Film Stars Series (Standard)	1933	60p	£45.00
72	Football Series	1933	60p	£45.00
24	Personality Series	1933	70p	£17.00
72	Personality Series, Film Stars	1933	60p	£42.50
72	Personality Series, Footballers	1933	70p	£50.00

CARRERAS & MARCIANUS

1	Photo Miniatures Folder	1909	—	£40.00
100	War Series	1915	£35.00	—

CARRICK

12	Military Terms	1900	£35.00	—

P. J. CARROLL & CO.

Qty		Date	Odds	Sets
25	Birds	1939	20p	£5.00
25	British Naval Series	1915	£17.50	—
25	Derby Winners	1914	£40.00	—
24	Jig Saw Puzzles	1935	£7.50	—
20	Louth—All Ireland Champions	1912	£10.00	—
25	Ship Series	1934	£3.00	£75.00

THE CASKET TOBACCO & CIGARETTE CO. LTD.

?	Cricket Fixture Cards	1905	£150.00	—
1	Cyclists Lighting Up Table	1909	£125.00	—
?	Football Fixture Cards	1909	£100.00	—
?	Road Maps	1909	£125.00	

S. CAVANDER & CO.

?25	Beauties "PLUMS"	1898	£100.00	—

CAVANDERS LTD.

25	Ancient Chinese	1926	30p	£7.50
25	Ancient Egypt	1928	30p	£7.50
L25	Ancient Egypt (Different)	1928	40p	£10.00
F36	Animal Studies	1936	16p	£6.00
F50	Beauty Spots of Great Britain	1927	15p	£6.50
MF50	Beauty Spots of Great Britain	1927	15p	£7.50
F54	Camera Studies	1926	15p	£6.00
MF56	Camera Studies	1926	15p	£7.00
30	Cinema Stars	1934	40p	£12.00
MS50	Coloured Stereoscopic	1931	25p	£12.50
25	Feathered Friends	1926	£1.00	£25.00
25	Foreign Birds	1926	50p	£12.50
MS50	Glorious Britain	1930	25p	£12.50
25	Little Friends	1924	50p	£12.50
FS72	Peeps into Many Lands, A Series	1927	15p	£10.00
MFS72	Peeps into Many Lands, A Series	1927	15p	£10.00
XFS36	Peeps into Many Lands, A Series	1927	£1.25	£45.00
FS72	Peeps into Many Lands 2nd Series	1928	15p	£8.50
MFS72	Peeps into Many Lands 2nd Series	1928	15p	£8.50
FS48	Peeps into Many Lands 3rd Series	1929	15p	£6.50
MFS48	Peeps Into Many Lands 3rd Series	1929	15p	£6.50
MFS48	Peeps into Many Lands 3rd (Reprinted)	1929	16p	£8.00
FS48	Peeps into Prehistoric Times 4th Series	1930	16p	£8.00
MFS48	Peeps into Prehistoric Times 4th Series	1930	20p	£10.00
F33	Photographs	1935	£1.00	—
L48	Regimental Standards	1923	£6.00	—
25	Reproductions of Celebrated Oil Paintings	1925	50p	£12.50
F108	River Valleys	1926	20p	£20.00
MF108	River Valleys	1926	25p	£25.00
25	School Badges (Dark Blue Back)	1928	20p	£5.00
25	School Badges (Light Blue Back)	1928	20p	£5.00
MF30	The Colonial Series	1925	25p	£7.50
F54	The Homeland Series (Black Back)	1924	15p	£10.00
F50	The Homeland Series (Blue Back)	1924	40p	£20.00
MF50	The Homeland Series (Coloured)	1924	15p	£6.50
MF56	The Homeland Series (Uncoloured, reprinted)	1924	15p	£8.50
M25	The Nation's Treasures	1925	30p	£7.50
MF30	Wordsworth's Country	1926	30p	£9.00

R. S. CHALLIS & CO. LTD.

Qty		Date	Odds	Sets
50	Comic Animals	1936	25p	£12.50
?30	Flickits (Fresher Cigarettes)	1936	£20.00	—
36	Wild Birds at Home	1935	20p	£7.50
36	Wild Birds at Home (Baldric deleted)	1935	60p	—

CHAPMAN

30	Army Pictures, Cartoons, etc.	1916	£45.00	—

CHARLESWORTH & AUSTIN

50	Beauties "BOCCA"	1900	£15.00	—
16	British Royal Family	1902	£25.00	—
30	Colonial Troops	1901	£17.50	—
20	Cricketers Series	1902	£150.00	—
30	Flags & Flags with Soldiers	1903	£17.50	—

CHESTERFIELD CIGARETTES

M6	Chesterfield Cocktails	1980	20p	£1.25

A. CHEW & CO.

30	Army Pictures, Cartoons, etc.	1916	£45.00	—

CHING & CO. (Channel Isles)

L24	Around & About in Jersey 1st Series	1963	15p	£3.50
L24	Around & About in Jersey 2nd Series	1964	30p	£7.50
25	Do You Know?	1962	—	£1.25
B48	Flowers	1962	50p	£25.00
L24	Jersey Past & Present 1st Series	1960	—	£1.25
L24	Jersey Past & Present 2nd Series	1962	—	£2.00
L24	Jersey Past & Present 3rd Series	1963	—	£1.25
25	Ships and their Workings	1961	—	£1.25
50	Veteran and Vintage Cars	1960	15p	£7.50

W. A. & A. C. CHURCHMAN

?25	Actresses, Unicoloured	1897	£40.00	—
26	Actresses, "FROGA A"	1900	£20.00	—
26	Actresses, "FROGA B"	1900	£25.00	—
M48	Air Raid Precautions	1938	15p	£6.00
25	Army Badges of Rank	1916	£3.00	£75.00
50	Association Footballers, A Series	1938	15p	£7.50
50	Association Footballers, 2nd Series	1939	20p	£10.00
50	A Tour Round The World	1911	£3.50	£175.00
12	Beauties "CERF"	1899	£30.00	—
25	Beauties "CHOAB"	1900	£75.00	—
M?25	Beauties "CHOAB" (Circular)	1900	£250.00	—
25	Beauties "FECKSA"	1903	£50.00	—
25	Beauties "GRACC"	1898	£50.00	—
50	Birds & Eggs	1906	£3.50	£175.00
20	Boer War Cartoons	1901	£60.00	—
41	Boer War Celebrities & Actresses	1901	£12.50	£500.00
20	Boer War Generals "CLAM"	1901	£20.00	—
25	Boxing	1922	£1.50	£37.50
50	Boxing Personalities	1938	20p	£10.00
50	Boy Scouts A Series	1916	£2.50	£125.00
50	Boy Scouts 2nd Series	1916	£2.50	£125.00

U.K. Tobacco 1910s

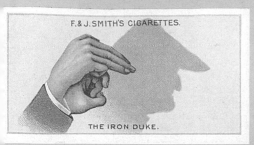

Shadowgraphs. Smiths

Country Seats & Arms. Players

Roses. Wills

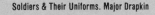

Soldiers & Their Uniforms. Major Drapkin

V.C. Heroes. Gallaher, Machado

World's Locomotives. Lambert & Butler

Boy Scouts. Ogdens also Churhman, Players

U.K. Tobacco 1920s

Feathered Favourites. Scottish CWS

Musical Instruments. Edwards Ringer
& Bigg, also Churchman

Old Inns. Richard Lloyd

Fables & Their Morals. Gallaher

Hunting. Franklyn Davey

Old London. Wills

Sports Records. Alexander
Boguslavsky

Qty		Date	Odds	Sets
50	Boy Scouts 3rd Series (Blue Back)	1916	£5.00	—
50	Boy Scouts 3rd Series (Brown Back)	1916	£2.50	£125.00
25	British Film Stars	1934	80p	£20.00
54/55	Can You Beat Bogey at St. Andrews?	1934	80p	£45.00
54/55	Can You Beat Bogey (Red Overprint)	1934	80p	£45.00
25	Cathedrals & Churches	1924	80p	£20.00
X12	Cathedrals & Churches	1924	£5.00	£60.00
50	Celebrated Gateways	1925	£1.25	£62.50
M1	Christmas Greeting Card	1938	—	75p
25	Civic Insignia and Plate	1926	80p	£20.00
50	Contract Bridge	1935	20p	£10.00
50	Cricketers	1936	£1.25	£62.50
25	Curious Dwellings	1926	80p	£20.00
L12	Curious Dwellings	1926	£2.00	£25.00
25	Curious Signs	1925	80p	£20.00
38	Dogs and Fowls	1908	£3.50	£130.00
25	Eastern Proverbs A Series	1931	25p	£6.25
L12	Eastern Proverbs A Series	1931	£1.60	£20.00
25	Eastern Proverbs 2nd Series	1932	25p	£6.25
L12	Eastern Proverbs 2nd Series	1932	60p	£7.50
L12	Eastern Proverbs 3rd Series	1933	30p	£3.50
L12	Eastern Proverbs 4th Series	1934	25p	£3.00
50	East Suffolk Churches (Black)	1912	£1.20	£60.00
50	East Suffolk Churches (Sepia)	1917	£1.00	£50.00
50	Empire Railways	1931	£1.20	£60.00
25	Famous Cricket Colours	1928	£1.50	£37.50
50	Famous Golfers	1927	£2.00	£100.00
L12	Famous Golfers 1st Series	1927	£4.00	£50.00
L12	Famous Golfers 2nd Series	1928	£4.00	£50.00
25	Famous Railway Trains	1929	£1.20	£30.00
L12	Famous Railway Trains 1st Series	1929	£2.50	£30.00
L12	Famous Railway Trains 2nd Series	1929	£2.50	£30.00
50	Fish & Bait	1914	£3.00	£150.00
30/50	Fishes of the World	1924	£1.20	£36.00
50	Flags & Funnels of Leading Steamship Lines ...	1912	£3.50	£175.00
50	Football Club Colours	1909	£4.00	—
50	Footballers (Brown)	1914	£12.50	£625.00
50	Footballers (Coloured)	1914	£5.00	£250.00
52	Frisky	1925	30p	£15.00
1	Frisky (Instructions)	1925	—	£2.00
50	History & Development of the British Empire ...	1934	40p	£20.00
M48	Holidays in Britain (Views & Maps)	1937	15p	£5.00
M48	Holidays in Britain (Views Only)	1938	15p	£5.00
40	Home & Colonial Regiments	1902	£25.00	—
40	Howlers	1937	15p	£4.00
L16	Howlers	1937	25p	£4.00
50	Interesting Buildings	1905	£3.50	£175.00
25	Interesting Door Knockers	1928	£1.00	£25.00
25	Interesting Experiments	1929	80p	£20.00
50	In Town To-Night	1938	15p	£5.00
L12	Italian Art Exhibition, 1930 1st Series	1930	60p	£7.50
L12	Italian Art Exhibition, 1930 2nd Series	1931	60p	£7.50
50	Kings of Speed	1939	15p	£5.00
50	Landmarks in Railway Progress	1931	£1.20	£60.00

Qty		Date	Odds	Sets
L12	Landmarks in Railway Progress 1st Series ...	1932	£1.75	£20.00
L12	Landmarks in Railway Progress 2nd Series ...	1932	£1.75	£20.00
50	Lawn Tennis	1928	80p	£40.00
L12	Lawn Tennis	1928	£2.50	£30.00
50	Legends of Britain	1936	40p	£20.00
L12	Legends of Britain	1936	75p	£9.00
25	Life in a Liner	1930	50p	£12.50
L12	Life in a Liner	1930	£1.25	£15.00
50	Medals	1910	£4.00	£200.00
50	Men of the Moment in Sport	1928	£1.00	£50.00
L12	Men of the Moment in Sport 1st Series ...	1928	£2.50	£30.00
L12	Men of the Moment in Sport 2nd Series ...	1928	£2.50	£30.00
M48	Modern Wonders	1938	15p	£7.50
25	Musical Instruments	1924	£1.20	£30.00
25	Nature's Architects	1930	50p	£12.50
L12	Nature's Architects	1930	£1.50	£18.00
D55	Olympic Winners Through the Years	1960	60p	—
50	Phil May Sketches (Gold Flake)	1912	£3.50	£175.00
50	Phil May Sketches (no brand)	1912	£5.00	—
25	Pipes of the World	1927	£1.20	£30.00
50	Prominent Golfers	1931	£2.00	£100.00
L12	Prominent Golfers	1931	£4.00	£50.00
50	Racing Greyhounds	1934	70p	£35.00
25	Railway Working A Series	1926	£1.50	£37.50
L12	Railway Working A Series	1926	£4.00	£50.00
25	Railway Working 2nd Series	1927	£1.00	£25.00
L13	Railway Working 2nd Series	1926	£4.00	£52.00
L12	Railway Working 3rd Series	1927	£4.00	£50.00
50	Regimental Colours & Cap Badges	1912	£3.50	£175.00
50	Rivers & Broads	1921	£3.50	—
50	Rivers & Broads of Norfolk & Suffolk	1922	£2.50	£125.00
50	Rugby Internationals	1935	50p	£25.00
50	Sectional Cycling Map	1913	£3.00	£150.00
50	Silhouettes of Warships	1915	£4.00	£200.00
50	Sporting Celebrities	1931	£1.00	£50.00
25	Sporting Trophies	1927	80p	£20.00
L12	Sporting Trophies	1927	£2.50	£30.00
25	Sports & Games in Many Lands	1929	70p	£17.50
25	The Houses of Parliament & Their Story	1931	80p	£20.00
25	The Inns of Court	1922	£1.00	£25.00
50	The King's Coronation	1937	15p	£5.00
L15	The King's Coronation	1937	50p	£7.50
M48	The Navy at Work	1937	15p	£4.50
50	The Queen Mary	1936	40p	£20.00
L16	The Queen Mary	1936	65p	£10.00
M48	The RAF at Work	1937	25p	£12.50
50	The Story of London	1934	50p	£25.00
L12	The Story of London	1934	£1.25	£15.00
50	The Story of Navigation	1937	15p	£5.00
L12	The Story of Navigation	1937	60p	£7.50
D40	The World of Sport	1961	60p	—
36	3 Jovial Golfers in Search of the Perfect Course	1934	80p	£28.00
72	3 Jovial Golfers (Irish Issue)	1934	£2.50	—
50	Treasure Trove	1937	15p	£4.00

W. A. & A. C. CHURCHMAN—cont.

Qty		Date	Odds	Sets
L12	Treasure Trove	1937	50p	£6.00
25	Types of British & Colonial Troops	1899	£30.00	—
25	Warriors of All Nations	1929	£1.20	£30.00
L12	Warriors of All Nations A Series	1929	£2.00	£25.00
L12	Warriors of All Nations 2nd Series	1931	£2.00	£25.00
50	Well Known Ties A Series	1934	30p	£15.00
L12	Well Known Ties A Series	1934	60p	£7.50
50	Well Known Ties 2nd Series	1935	20p	£10.00
L12	Well Known Ties 2nd Series	1935	60p	£7.50
25	Wembley Exhibition	1924	£1.20	£30.00
50	West Suffolk Churches	1919	£1.00	£50.00
50	Wild Animals of the World	1907	£4.00	£200.00
M48	Wings Over The Empire	1939	15p	£7.50
50	Wonderful Railway Travel	1937	15p	£7.50
L12	Wonderful Railway Travel	1937	60p	£7.50
50	World Wonders Old and New (Unissued)	—	—	£10.00

Overseas Issues (No. I.T.C. Clause)

M48	Air Raid Precautions	1938	75p	—
M48	Holidays in Britain (Views & Maps)	1937	75p	—
M48	Holidays in Britain (Views only)	1938	75p	—
M48	Modern Wonders	1938	75p	—
M48	The Navy at Work	1937	£1.00	—
M48	The R.A.F. at Work	1937	75p	—
M48	Wings over the Empire	1939	75p	—

CIGARETTE COMPANY (Channel Isles)

72	Jersey Footballers	1910	£2.50	—

WM. CLARKE & SON

25	Army Life	1915	£6.00	£150.00
16	Boer War Celebrities	1901	£15.00	£240.00
50	Butterflies & Moths	1912	£5.00	£250.00
30	Cricketer Series	1901	£65.00	—
66	Football Series	1902	£7.50	—
25	Marine Series	1907	£7.00	£175.00
50	Royal Mail	1914	£5.00	£250.00
50	Sporting Terms	1900	£20.00	—
20	Tobacco Leaf Girls	1898	£250.00	—
25	Well Known Sayings	1900	£12.00	£300.00

J. H. CLURE & SON

30	Army Pictures, Cartoons, etc.	1916	£40.00	—
50	War Portraits	1916	£40.00	—

J. LOMAX COCKAYNE

50	War Portraits	1916	£40.00	—

COHEN WEENEN & CO.

F40	Actresses, Footballers & Jockeys	1901	£20.00	—
26	Actresses "FROGA"	1900	£40.00	—
24	Beauties "BOCCA"	1899	£50.00	—
25	Beauties "GRACC"	1899	£60.00	—
65	Celebrities (Black & White) ("250" back)	1900	£2.50	—

COHEN WEENEN & CO.—cont.

Qty		Date	Odds	Sets
25	Celebrities (Black & White) ("500" back) ...	1900	£6.00	—
45	Celebrities, Coloured ("100" back)	1901	£2.50	£110.00
121	Celebrities, Coloured ("250" back)	1901	£2.50	—
30	Celebrities, Gainsborough ("400" Back)	1902	£6.00	£180.00
B39	Celebrities, Gainsborough ("250" back)	1902	£25.00	—
BF?150	Celebrities, Gainsborough	1901	£3.50	—
MF?150	Celebrities, Gainsborough (Metal Framed) ...	1901	£10.00	—
25	Cricketers	1926	£4.00	£100.00
20	Cricketers, Footballers & Jockeys	1900	£10.00	£250.00
25	Famous Boxers (black back)	1912	£6.00	—
25	Famous Boxers (green back)	1912	£4.00	£150.00
40	Fiscal Phrases	1902	£6.50	£260.00
60	Football Captains	1908	£6.00	£360.00
100	Heroes of Sport	1897	£30.00	—
40	Home & Colonial Regiments ("100" back) ...	1901	£5.00	£200.00
40	Home & Colonial Regiments ("250" back) ...	1901	£6.00	£240.00
20	Interesting Buildings & Views	1902	£5.00	£100.00
K52	Miniature Playing Cards (Bandmaster) ...	1910	£2.50	—
20	Nations (Non Descriptive)	1902	£8.00	£160.00
20	Nations (Descriptive)	1923	£2.50	£50.00
40	Naval & Military Phrases (Blue Back) ...	1904	£15.00	—
40	Naval & Military Phrases (Red Back) ...	1906	£10.00	£400.00
50	Owners, Jockeys, Footballers, Cricketers Series 2	1906	£5.00	£250.00
20	Owners, Jockeys, Footballers, Cricketers Series 3	1907	£5.00	£100.00
30	Proverbs	1903	£10.00	—
20	Russo Japanese War Series	1902	£8.00	£160.00
25	Silhouettes of Celebrities	1903	£7.00	£175.00
50	Star Artistes	1907	£6.00	£300.00
L16	Victoria Cross Heroes (Silk)	1915	*£25.00*	—
50	Victoria Cross Heroes (51-100)	1916	£4.00	£200.00
50	War Series	1916	£4.00	£200.00
30	Wonders of the World (Green Back) ...	1908	£4.00	£120.00
30	Wonders of the World (Grey Back)	1923	£1.60	£50.00

T. H. COLLINS

Qty		Date	Odds	Sets
25	Homes of England	1924	£3.00	£75.00
25	Sports & Pastimes	1923	£3.00	£75.00

F. COLTON JR.

Qty		Date	Odds	Sets
30	Army Pictures, Cartoons, etc.	1916	*£40.00*	—
50	War Portraits	1916	*£40.00*	—

T. W. CONQUEST

Qty		Date	Odds	Sets
30	Army Pictures, Cartoons, etc.	1916	*£45.00*	—

CONTINENTAL CIGARETTE FACTORY

Qty		Date	Odds	Sets
25	Charming Portraits (Firm's name)	1920	£2.50	—
25	Charming Portraits (Club mixture)	1920	£3.00	—
25	Charming Portraits (Plain back)	1920	£2.50	—

COOPER & CO.

Qty		Date	Odds	Sets
25	Boer War Celebrities "STEW"	1901	*£75.00*	—

CO-OPERATIVE WHOLESALE SOCIETY (C.W.S.)

Qty		Date	Odds	Sets
5	Advertisement Cards	1915	£150.00	—
24	African Types	1936	15p	£3.50
M50	Beauty Spots of Britain	1936	15p	£6.00
50	Boy Scout Badges	1939	25p	£12.50
25	Boy Scout Series	1912	£15.00	
48	British and Foreign Birds	1938	25p	£12.50
50	British Sports Series	1904	£15.00	—
25	Cooking Recipes	1923	£1.60	£40.00
28	Co-operative Buildings & Works	1909	£8.00	£225.00
24	English Roses	1924	£1.60	£40.00
50	Famous Bridges	1937	35p	£17.50
48	Famous Buildings	1935	25p	£12.50
25	How To Do It	1924	£1.20	£30.00
48	Musical Instruments	1934	£1.50	£72.00
25	Parrot Series	1910	£15.00	
48	Poultry	1927	£1.50	£75.00
48	Railway Engines	1936	£1.50	£72.00
24	Sailing Craft	1935	70p	£17.00
18	War Series	1914	£12.50	—
48	Wayside Flowers (Brown Back)	1923	80p	£40.00
48	Wayside Flowers (Green Back) (different)	1928	15p	£7.50
48	Wayside Woodland Trees	1924	£1.25	£60.00
24	Western Stars	1957	—	£1.50

COPE BROS. & CO. LTD.

Qty		Date	Odds	Sets
KF?50	Actors & Actresses	1900	£15.00	—
20	Actresses "BLARM"	1902	£20.00	—
6	Actresses "COPEIS"	1898	*£75.00*	—
26	Actresses "FROGA"	1900	*£60.00*	—
Γ50	Actresses & Beauties	1900	£7.50	£375.00
52	Beauties, P/C Inset	1899	£25.00	—
15	Beauties "PAC"	1898	£40.00	—
50	Boats of the World	1912	£6.00	£300.00
25	Boxers (1-25)	1915	£3.00	£75.00
25	Boxers (26-50)	1915	£3.00	£75.00
25	Boxers (51-75)	1915	£3.00	£75.00
25	Boxers (76-100)	1915	£7.00	£175.00
25	Boxers (101-125)	1915	£4.00	£100.00
1	Boxers (New World Champion)	1915	—	£10.00
25	Boxing Lessons	1935	50p	£12.50
35	Boy Scouts & Girl Guides	1910	£5.00	£175.00
35	Boy Scouts & Girl Guides (Scandinavian)	1910	£15.00	—
X25	Bridge Problems	1924	*£10.00*	—
25	British Admirals	1915	£6.00	£150.00
50	British Warriors	1912	£4.00	£200.00
25	Castles	1939	20p	£5.00
25	Cathedrals	1939	40p	£10.00
50	Characters From Scott	1900	£5.00	£250.00
115	Chinese Series	1903	£7.00	—
50	Copes Golfers	1900	£16.00	£800.00
L25	Dickens Character Series	1939	20p	£5.00
50	Dickens Gallery	1900	£4.00	£200.00
50	Dogs of the World	1912	£4.00	£200.00
50	Dogs of the World (Scandinavian)	1912	£15.00	—
25	Eminent British Regiments Officers Uniforms	1908	£6.00	£150.00
25	Eminent British Regts Uniforms (Scandinavian)	1908	£15.00	—
24	Flags, Arms & Types of All Nations	1904	£4.00	£100.00

COPE BROS & CO. LTD.—cont.

Qty		Date	Odds	Sets
30	Flags of Nations	1903	£6.00	—
30	Flags of all Nations (Indian, blue back)	1903	£25.00	—
B50	General Knowledge	1925	£1.75	—
B32	Golf Strokes	1923	£4.00	£125.00
60	Happy Families	1937	60p	£36.00
B50	Household Hints	1925	80p	£40.00
X20	Kenilworth Phrases	1910	£75.00	—
25	Lawn Tennis Strokes	1924	£1.20	£30.00
5	Lawn Tennis Strokes (26-30)	1925	£5.00	—
L50	Modern Dancing	1926	£8.00	—
50	Music Hall Artistes ("Series of 50")	1913	£20.00	—
50	Music Hall Artistes (no number in series) ...	1913	£4.00	£200.00
472	Noted Footballers (Clips Cigarettes)	1910	£3.50	—
195	Noted Footballers (Solace Cigarettes) ...	1910	£4.00	—
24	Occupations for Women	1897	£40.00	—
T12	Photo Albums for the Million (Buff)	1902	£10.00	£120.00
T12	Photo Albums for the Million (Green)	1902	£10.00	£120.00
25	Pigeons	1926	£1.20	£30.00
52	Playing Cards	1900	£7.50	—
30	Scandinavian Actors & Actresses	1910	£25.00	—
50	Shakespeare Gallery	1900	£5.00	£250.00
25	Song Birds	1926	£1.20	£30.00
25	Sports & Pastimes	1925	£1.20	£30.00
L25	The Game of Poker	1936	15p	£3.75
25	The World's Police	1937	£1.20	£30.00
L25	Toy Models—The Country Fair	1925	15p	£3.75
25	Uniforms of Soldiers & Sailors (circular medal)	1898	£20.00	£500.00
25	Uniforms of Soldiers & Sailors (square medal)	1898	£15.00	£375.00
50	V.C. & D.S.O. Naval & Flying Heroes (Unnumbered)	1916	£3.50	£200.00
25	V.C. & D.S.O. Naval & Flying Heroes (Numbered 51-75)	1916	£4.00	£100.00
20	War Pictures	1915	£6.00	£120.00
25	War Series	1915	£7.50	—
25	Wild Animals & Birds	1907	£10.00	—
25	Wild Animals & Birds (Scandinavian) ...	1907	£15.00	—

E. CORONEL

25	Types of British & Colonial Troops	1900	£40.00	—

DAVID CORRE & CO.

1	Advertisement Card	1903	£200.00	—
40	Naval & Military Phrases	1904	£40.00	—

JOHN COTTON LTD.

L50	Bridge Hands	1934	£3.00	—
50	Golf Strokes A/B	1936	£2.50	—
50	Golf Strokes C/D	1937	£2.50	—
50	Golf Strokes E/F	1938	£3.50	—
50	Golf Strokes G/H	1939	£25.00	—
50	Golf Strokes I/J	1939	£25.00	—

A. & J. COUDENS LTD.

F60	British Beauty Spots	1923	75p	£45.00
F60	Holiday Resorts in East Anglia	1924	60p	£36.00
25	Sports Alphabet	1924	£2.50	£62.50

THE CRAIGMILLAR CREAMERY CO.

Qty		Date	Odds	Sets
M?	Scottish Views	1901	*£200.00*	–

W. R. DANIEL

30	Colonial Troops	1902	£50.00	—
25	National Flags & Flowers—Girls	1901	£75.00	—

W. T. DAVIES & SONS

?50	Actresses	1902	*£40.00*	—
30	Aristocrats of the Turf A Series (1-30)	1924	£1.50	£45.00
12	Aristocrats of the Turf A Series (31-42)	1924	£7.50	—
36	Aristocrats of the Turf 2nd Series	1924	£1.50	£54.00
25	Army Life	1915	£6.00	£150.00
12	Beauties	1903	£25.00	—
25	Boxing	1924	£1.00	£25.00
60	Flags & Funnels of Leading Steamship Lines ...	1913	£5.00	—
?10	Newport Football Club	1904	*£75.00*	—
?5	Royal Welsh Fusiliers	1904	*£100.00*	—

S. H. DAWES

30	Army Pictures, Cartoons, etc.	1916	*£50.00*	—

J. W. DEWHURST

30	Army Pictures, Cartoons, etc.	1916	*£45.00*	—

R. I. DEXTER

30	Borough Arms	1900	40p	£12.00

DIANELLOS & VERGOPOULOS

XF?	Views of Cyprus	1926	*£20.00*	—

GEORGE DOBIE & SON LTD.

M25	Bridge Problems	1933	*£15.00*	—
M32	Four Square Books (1-32)	1959	50p	£16.00
M32	Four Square Books (33-64)	1960	15p	£5.00
M32	Four Square Books (65-96)	1960	15p	£5.00
25	Weapons of All Ages	1924	£3.00	£75.00

DOBSON'S

8	The European War Series	1917	*£20.00*	—

DOMINION TOBACCO CO. (1929) LTD.

25	Old Ships 1st Series	1934	80p	£20.00
25	Old Ships 2nd Series	1935	30p	£7.50
25	Old Ships 3rd Series	1936	30p	£7.50
25	Old Ships 4th Series	1936	50p	£12.50

JOSEPH W. DOYLE LTD.

F12	Beauties (Series CC.D)	1928	£20.00	—
F12	Beauties (Series CC.E)	1928	£20.00	—
XF18	Children	1928	£7.50	—
F12	Dirt Track Riders (Series CC.A)	1928	*£30.00*	—
F12	Views (Series CC.B)	1928	£20.00	—
F12	Views (Series CC.C)	1928	£20.00	—

MAJOR DRAPKIN & CO.

Qty		Date	Odds	Sets
12	Actresses	1910	£4.00	—
8	Advertisement Cards	1926	£3.00	£24.00
50	Around Britain	1929	75p	£37.50
L50	Around Britain	1929	£1.50	—
50	Around the Mediterranean	1926	75p	—
L50	Around the Mediterranean	1926	£1.50	—
F40	Australian and English Test Cricketers	1928	65p	£26.00
?100	Bandmaster Conundrums	1907	£4.00	—
25	British Beauties	1930	£1.20	£30.00
F36	Celebrities of the Great War	1916	35p	£12.50
F34	Celebrities of the Great War (Plain Backs)	1916	35p	£12.00
B96	Cinematograph Actors	1913	£4.00	—
15	Dogs and Their Treatment	1924	£1.60	£24.00
L15	Dogs and Their Treatment	1924	£2.00	£30.00
50	Girls of Many Lands	1929	£1.50	—
M50	Girls of Many Lands	1929	15p	£7.00
25	How to Keep Fit	1912	£6.00	£150.00
54	Life at Whipsnade Zoo	1934	25p	£12.50
50	Limericks	1929	35p	£17.50
F36	National Types of Beauty	1928	35p	£12.50
25	Optical Illusions	1926	£1.00	£25.00
L25	Optical Illusions	1926	£1.50	£37.50
25	Palmistry	1927	80p	£20.00
L25	Palmistry	1927	£1.00	£25.00
48	Photogravure Masterpieces	1915	£4.00	—
25	Puzzle Pictures	1926	£1.20	£30.00
L25	Puzzle Pictures	1926	£1.50	£37.50
M40	Regimental Colours & Badges of the Indian Army (Silk)	1915	£2.50	—
T22/25	Soldiers & Their Uniforms (cut-outs)	1914	45p	£10.00
T25	Soldiers & Their Uniforms (cut-outs)	1914	—	£35.00
F35/36	Sporting Celebrities in Action	1930	60p	£21.00
40	The Game of Sporting Snap	1928	75p	£30.00
1	The Greys Advertisement Card	1935	—	£1.25
12	Views of the World	1910	£3.00	—
6	Warships	1912	£6.00	£36.00

DRAPKIN & MILLHOFF

Qty		Date	Odds	Sets
?40	Beauties "KEWA"	1899	£75.00	—
25	Boer War Celebrities "PAM"	1901	£15.00	—
30	Colonial Troops	1902	£25.00	—
?25	Pretty Girl Series "BAGG"	1898	£75.00	—

DU MAURIER CIGARETTES

Qty		Date	Odds	Sets
X?50	Advertising Inserts	1931	£3.50	—

J. DUNCAN & CO. LTD.

Qty		Date	Odds	Sets
47/50	Evolution of the Steamship	1925	25p	£12.00
48	Flags, Arms & Types of Nations	1911	£17.50	—
20	Inventors & Their Inventions	1915	£30.00	—
30	Scottish Clans, Arms of Chiefs & Tartans	1912	£10.00	£300.00
L72	Scottish Gems (Coloured)	1912	£7.50	—
L50	Scottish Gems 2nd Series	1913	£7.50	—

J. DUNCAN & CO. LTD.—cont.

Qty		Date	Odds	Sets
L50	Scottish Gems 3rd Series	1914	£7.50	—
L50	Scottish Gems (Reprint, Black & White)	1925	30p	£15.00
25	Types of British Soldiers	1910	£30.00	—

GEO. DUNCOMBE

| 30 | Army Pictures, Cartoons, etc. ... ... | 1916 | £45.00 | — |

EDWARD VII CIGARETTES

| 40 | Home & Colonial Regiments ... ... | 1901 | £150.00 | — |

EDWARDS, RINGER & CO.

| X50 | How To Count Cribbage Hands ... ... | 1908 | £50.00 | — |

EDWARDS RINGER & BIGG

Qty		Date	Odds	Sets
25	Abbeys & Castles	1912	£5.00	£125.00
25	Alpine Views	1912	£5.00	£125.00
50	A Tour Round the World	1909	£5.00	—
12	Beauties "CERF"	1905	£35.00	—
25	Beauties "FECKSA"	1900	£20.00	—
50	Birds & Eggs	1906	£7.50	—
?25	Boer War Sketches	1901	£75.00	—
25	Boer War Celebrities "STEW"	1901	£25.00	—
25	British Trees & Their Uses	1933	£1.50	£37.50
1	Calendar & Lighting up Table	1899	£150.00	—
1	Calendar	1905	£150.00	—
1	Calendar	1910	£150.00	—
50	Celebrated Bridges	1924	£1.20	£60.00
50	Cinema Stars	1923	35p	£17.50
L25	Cinema Stars	1923	50p	£12.50
25	Coast and Country	1911	£5.00	£125.00
23	Dogs Series (Exmoor Hunt)	1908	£4.00	—
23	Dogs Series (Klondyke)	1908	£1.50	£35.00
3	Easter Manoeuvres of our Volunteers	1897	£200.00	—
37	Flags of All Nations (various printings)	1907	£4.00	—
25	Garden Life	1934	£1.60	—
25	How to Tell Fortunes	1929	£2.50	£62.50
50	Life on Board a Man Of War	1905	£5.00	—
1	Miners Bound for Klondyke	1897	£250.00	—
50	Mining	1925	£1.20	£60.00
25	Musical Instruments	1924	£1.50	£37.50
25	Optical Illusions	1936	£1.20	£30.00
25	Our Pets A series	1926	£1.20	£30.00
25	Our Pets 2nd Series	1926	£1.50	£37.50
25	Past & Present	1928	£2.00	£50.00
10	Portraits of His Majesty the King	1902	£25.00	£250.00
25	Prehistoric Animals	1924	£1.50	£37.50
25	Sports & Games in Many Lands	1935	£1.20	£30.00
56	War Map, Western Front	1916	£5.00	£280.00
54	War Map of the Western Front, Series 2	1917	£5.00	£260.00

S. EISISKI

?20	Actresses "ANGOOD"	1900	£100.00	—
?20	Beauties "FENA"	1899	£100.00	—
?40	Beauties "KEWA"	1900	£100.00	—

EMPIRE TOBACCO CO.

Qty		Date	Odds	Sets
6	Franco British Exhibition	1907	*£100.00*	—

ENCHANTERESSE EGYPTIAN CIG. CO.

| 20 | Actresses "ANGOOD" ... ... | 1898 | *£100.00* | — |

THE EXPRESS TOBACCO CO. LTD

| M50 | How It Is Made (Motor Cars) ... ... | 1939 | £1.50 | £75.00 |

L. & J. FABIAN

| F24 | The Elite Series ... ... | 1932 | *£25.00* | — |

FAIRWEATHER & SONS

| 50 | Historic Buildings of Scotland ... ... | 1914 | £30.00 | £1500.00 |

W. & F. FAULKNER

26	Actresses "FROGA"	1900	£25.00	—
25	Angling	1929	£1.60	£40.00
12	'Ation Series	1901	£10.00	£120.00
25	Beauties (Coloured)	1898	£40.00	—
49	Beauties "FECKSA"	1901	£10.00	—
16	British Royal Family	1901	£20.00	—
50	Celebrated Bridges	1925	£1.20	£60.00
12	Coster Series	1900	£10.00	£120.00
20	Cricketers Series	1902	£100.00	—
12	Cricket Terms	1899	£20.00	£240.00
12	Football Terms 1st Series	1900	£10.00	£120.00
12	Football Terms 2nd Series	1900	£10.00	£120.00
12	Golf Terms	1901	£30.00	£360.00
12	Grenadier Guards	1899	£12.50	£150.00
40	Kings & Queens	1902	£15.00	—
12	Kipling Series	1900	£10.00	£120.00
12	Military Terms 1st Series	1899	£10.00	£120.00
12	Military Terms 2nd Series	1899	£10.00	£120.00
12	Nautical Terms 1st Series	1900	£10.00	£120.00
12	Nautical Terms 2nd Series	1900	£10.00	£120.00
25	Old Sporting Prints	1930	£1.20	£30.00
25	Optical Illusions	1935	£1.20	£30.00
90	Our Colonial Troops	1900	£7.00	£630.00
20	Our Gallant Grenadiers	1902	£10.00	£200.00
40	Our Gallant Grenadiers (With I.T.C. Clause) ...	1903	£15.00	£600.00
25	Our Pets	1926	£1.50	£37.50
25	Our Pets 2nd Series	1926	£1.20	£30.00
12	Policemen of the World	1899	£20.00	—
12	Police Terms	1899	£10.00	£120.00
25	Prominent Racehorses of the Present Day ...	1923	£1.00	£25.00
25	Prominent Racehorses of the Present Day 2nd Series	1924	£1.60	£40.00
12	Puzzle Series	1898	£30.00	—
25	South African War Series	1901	£8.00	£200.00
12	Sporting Terms	1900	£12.50	—
12	Street Cries	1902	£10.00	£120.00
12	The Language of Flowers	1900	£17.50	£210.00

FIELD FAVORITES CIGARETTES

| F? | Footballers ... ... | 1893 | *£150.00* | — |

FINLAY & CO. LTD.

Qty		Date	Odds	Sets
?10	Our Girls	1910	£75.00	—
30	World's Aircraft	1912	£25.00	—

FLYNN

26	Beauties "HOL"	1899	£100.00	—

FRAENKEL BROS.

?20	Beauties—Don Jorge	1897	£125.00	—
?20	Beauties—"FENA"	1899	£60.00	—
25	Beauties—"GRACC"	1898	£75.00	—
24	Beauties—"HUMPS"	1899	£75.00	—
26	Music Hall Artistes	1900	£50.00	—
25	Types of British & Colonial Troops	1900	£40.00	—

FRANKLYN DAVEY & CO.

12	Beauties "CERF"	1905	£35.00	—
50	Birds	1896	£35.00	—
10	Boer War Generals	1901	£50.00	—
25	Boxing	1924	70p	£17.50
25	Ceremonial and Court Dress	1915	£5.00	£125.00
50	Children of All Nations	1934	30p	£15.00
50	Football Club Colours	1909	£6.00	—
50	Historic Events	1924	£1.25	£62.50
25	Hunting	1925	40p	£10.00
50	Modern Dance Steps	1930	£2.50	—
50	Modern Dance Steps 2nd Series	1931	30p	£15.00
50	Naval Dress & Badges	1916	£6.00	—
50	Overseas Dominions (Australia)	1923	£2.00	—
25	Star Girls	1901	£100.00	—
10	Types of Smokers	1898	£35.00	£350.00
50	Wild Animals of the World	1902	£6.00	—

A. H. FRANKS & SONS

56	Beauties	1901	£30.00	—
24	Nautical Expressions	1902	£40.00	—
25	Types of British & Colonial Troops	1900	£40.00	—

J. J. FREEMAN & CO.

12	Actresses "FRAN"	1915	£25.00	—
33	Football Challenge	1969	£1.50	—
B12	Manikin Cards	1915	£50.00	—
12	Views of the World	1910	£25.00	—

C. FRYER & SONS LTD.

25	Boer War & General Interest	1900	£75.00	—
X50	Clan Sketches	1930	£5.00	£250.00
40	Naval & Military Phrases	1904	£30.00	—
?25	Vita Berlin Series	1901	£100.00	—

FRYER & COULTMAN

X12	Almanack	1893	£125.00	—

J. GABRIEL

10	Actresses "HAGG"	1900	£35.00	—
25	Beauties "GRACC"	1898	£80.00	—
20	Cricketers Series	1902	£175.00	—

43

J. GABRIEL—cont.

Qty		Date	Odds	Sets
40	Home & Colonial Regiments	1902	£50.00	—
?50	Pretty Girl Series "BAGG"	1898	£50.00	—
25	Types of British & Colonial Troops	1899	£40.00	—

GALA CIGARETTES

1	Stamp Cards	1910	—	£75.00

GALLAHER LTD.

Qty		Date	Odds	Sets
F110	Actors & Actresses	1901	£3.00	—
48	Aeroplanes	1939	16p	£8.00
25	Aesop's Fables (Series of 25)	1931	24p	£6.00
25	Aesop's Fables (Series of 50)	1931	30p	£7.50
100	Animals & Birds of Commercial Value	1921	30p	£30.00
48	Army Badges	1939	25p	£12.00
L24	Art Treasures of the World	1930	20p	£5.00
100	Association Football Club Colours	1910	£2.00	£200.00
52	Beauties (P/C Inset)	1905	£8.00	£400.00
52	Beauties (No Inset)	1905	£8.00	£400.00
MF48	Beautiful Scotland	1939	30p	£15.00
50	Birds & Eggs	1905	£5.00	—
100	Birds Nests & Eggs	1919	75p	£75.00
100	Boy Scout Series (Green back)	1911	80p	£80.00
100	Boy Scout Series (Brown back)	1922	70p	£70.00
48	British Birds	1937	15p	£6.00
100	British Birds by George Rankin	1923	35p	£35.00
75	British Champions of 1923	1924	60p	£45.00
50	British Naval Series	1914	£2.50	£125.00
48	Butterflies & Moths	1938	15p	£5.00
25	Champion Animals & Birds of 1923	1924	60p	£15.00
48	Champions A Series	1934	15p	£7.50
48	Champions 2nd Series	1935	15p	£6.00
48	Champions of Screen & Stage (Red back)	1934	15p	£6.00
48	Champions of Screen & Stage (Blue back)	1934	40p	£20.00
100	Cinema Stars	1926	75p	£75.00
MF48	Coastwise	1938	30p	—
24	Dogs (Caption in block)	1934	20p	£5.00
24	Dogs (Caption in script)	1934	60p	£15.00
L24	Dogs (Caption in block)	1934	20p	£5.00
L24	Dogs (Caption in script)	1934	60p	
48	Dogs A Series	1936	16p	£8.00
48	Dogs 2nd Series	1938	15p	£6.50
F100	English & Scotch Views	1910	£2.00	£200.00
100	Fables & Their Morals (No. by caption)	1912	£1.00	£100.00
100	Fables & Their Morals (Thick numerals)	1922	35p	£35.00
100	Fables & Their Morals (Thin numerals)	1922	40p	£40.00
100	Famous Cricketers	1926	£1.20	£120.00
48	Famous Film Scenes	1935	15p	£6.00
50	Famous Footballers (Brown back)	1926	80p	£40.00
100	Famous Footballers (Green back)	1925	60p	£60.00
48	Famous Jockeys	1936	20p	£10.00
48	Film Episodes	1936	15p	£7.50
48	Film Partners	1935	15p	£7.00
M24	Flags (Silk)	1915	£5.00	£120.00
MF48	Flying	1938	50p	—
50	Footballers (1-50)	1925	80p	£40.00
50	Footballers (51-100)	1925	£1.00	£50.00

GALLAHER LTD.—cont.

Qty		Date	Odds	Sets
50	Footballers in Action	1928	75p	£37.50
48	Garden Flowers	1938	15p	£5.00
100	How To Do It	1916	£1.50	£150.00
F100	Interesting Views (Black & White)	1923	75p	£75.00
F100	Interesting Views (Coloured)	1923	£1.25	—
400	Irish Views Scenery (Numbered on back)	1908	£1.25	—
F400	Irish View Scenery	1910	60p	£240.00
F200	Irish View Scenery (401-600)	1910	£1.25	—
LF48	Island Sporting Celebrities	1938	40p	£20.00
100	Kute Kiddies	1916	£1.50	£150.00
F50	Latest Actresses	1909	£7.50	—
50	Lawn Tennis Celebrities	1928	£1.25	£62.50
24	Motor Cars	1934	£1.50	£36.00
48	My Favourite Part	1939	15p	£6.00
MF48	Our Countryside	1938	40p	—
100	Plants of Commercial Value	1917	40p	£40.00
48	Portraits of Famous Stars	1935	15p	£6.00
48	Racing Scenes	1938	15p	£4.50
50	Regimental Colours & Standards	1899	£3.00	£150.00
100	Robinson Crusoe	1928	80p	£80.00
50	Royalty Series	1902	£3.50	£175.00
LF48	Scenes from the Empire	1939	15p	£6.50
48	Shots from Famous Films	1935	15p	£6.50
MF24	Shots from the Films	1936	*£1.00*	—
48	Signed Portraits of Famous Stars	1935	60p	£30.00
48	Sporting Personalities	1936	15p	£5.00
100	Sports Series	1912	£2.00	£200.00
100	Stage & Variety Celebrities	1899	£35.00	—
48	Stars of Screen & Stage (Brown back)	1935	60p	£30.00
48	Stars of Screen & Stage (Green back)	1935	15p	£5.00
25	The Allies Flags	1914	£3.00	£75.00
100	The Great War Series	1915	£1.25	£125.00
100	The Great War Second Series	1915	£1.25	£125.00
25	The Great War V.C. Heroes 1st Series	1915	£2.00	£50.00
25	The Great War V.C. Heroes 2nd Series	1915	£1.60	£40.00
25	The Great War V.C. Heroes 3rd Series	1915	£1.60	£40.00
25	The Great War V.C. Heroes 4th Series	1916	£1.60	£40.00
25	The Great War V.C. Heroes 5th Series	1916	£1.60	£40.00
25	The Great War V.C. Heroes 6th Series	1917	£1.60	£40.00
25	The Great War V.C. Heroes 7th Series	1917	£1.60	£40.00
25	The Great War V.C. Heroes 8th Series	1918	£1.60	£40.00
48	The Navy (Gallaher)	1937	16p	£8.00
48	The Navy (Park Drive)	1937	15p	£4.00
100	The Reason Why	1924	35p	£35.00
111	The South African Series	1901	£3.50	£400.00
100	The Zoo Aquarium	1924	60p	£60.00
48	Trains of the World	1937	25p	£12.00
100	Tricks & Puzzles Series (Green back)	1913	£1.75	£175.00
100	Tricks & Puzzles Series (Black back)	1933	30p	£30.00
50	Types of the British Army (Battle Honours)	1897	£6.00	£300.00
50	Types of the British Army (Green back)	1898	£5.00	£250.00
50	Types of the British Army (numbered 1-50)	1898	£5.00	£250.00
50	Types of the British Army (numbered 51-100)	1898	£4.00	£200.00
100	Useful Hints Series	1915	£1.50	£150.00

GALLAHER LTD.—cont.

Qty		Date	Odds	Sets
25	Views in North of Ireland	1912	£30.00	—
50	Votaries of the Weed	1916	£3.00	£150.00
100	Why Is It? (Brown back)	1915	£1.50	£150.00
100	Why Is It? (Green back)	1915	£1.50	£150.00
48	Wild Animals	1937	15p	£5.00
48	Wild Flowers	1939	15p	£5.00
100	Woodland Trees Series	1912	£1.50	£150.00
50	Zoo Tropical Birds 1st Series	1928	70p	£35.00
50	Zoo Tropical Birds 2nd Series	1929	70p	£35.00

GASPA

Qty		Date	Odds	Sets
?20	Our Great Novelists	1930	£20.00	—

SAMUEL GAWITH

Qty		Date	Odds	Sets
X25	The English Lakeland	1926	£12.50	—

F. GENNARI

Qty		Date	Odds	Sets
50	War Portraits	1916	£40.00	—

LOUIS GERARD LTD.

Qty		Date	Odds	Sets
50	Modern Armaments (Numbered)	1938	16p	£8.00
50	Modern Armaments (Unnumbered)	1938	25p	£12.50
24	Screen Favourites	1937	£1.50	—
48	Screen Favourites & Dancers	1937	80p	£40.00

GLASS & CO. LTD.

Qty		Date	Odds	Sets
20	Actresses "BLARM"	1900	£40.00	—
10	Actresses "HAGG"	1900	£40.00	—
25	Beauties "FECKSA"	1903	£50.00	—
20	Boer War Cartoons	1901	£60.00	—
25	Boer War Celebrities "STEW"	1901	£40.00	—
16	British Royal Family	1901	£40.00	—
20	Cricketers Series	1902	£175.00	—
40	Naval & Military Phrases	1902	£50.00	—
19	Russo Japanese Series	1903	£35.00	—

R. P. GLOAG & CO.

Qty		Date	Odds	Sets
?25	Actresses "ANGLO"	1896	£120.00	—
?50	Beauties "PLUMS" (Black & White)	1896	£65.00	—
?50	Beauties "PLUMS" (Brown)	1896	£100.00	—
40	Home & Colonial Regiments	1900	£35.00	—
30	Proverbs	1901	£60.00	—
25	Types of British & Colonial Troops	1900	£35.00	—

THE GLOBE CIGARETTE CO.

Qty		Date	Odds	Sets
25	Actresses—French	1898	£100.00	—

GOLDS LTD.

Qty		Date	Odds	Sets
1	Advertisement Card	1905	£200.00	—
18	Motor Cycle Series	1914	£25.00	—
L?15	Prints from Noted Pictures	1908	£80.00	—

T. P. & R. GOODBODY

Qty		Date	Odds	Sets
20	Actresses "ANGOOD"	1898	£80.00	—
?50	Beauties "KEWA"	1898	£75.00	—

T. P. & R. GOODBODY—cont.

Qty		Date	Odds	Sets
25	Boer War Celebrities	1901	£17.50	—
16	Boer War Celebrities	1900	£17.50	—
?50	Colonial Forces	1900	£45.00	—
B?50	Colonial Forces	1900	*£80.00*	—
?50	Dogs	1903	*£40.00*	—
26	Eminent Actresses	1900	£25.00	—
20	Irish Scenery	1905	£30.00	—
?25	Pretty Girl Series "BAGG"	1898	*£75.00*	—
50	Questions & Answers in Natural History	1924	£1.50	£75.00
25	Sports & Pastimes	1925	£3.00	£75.00
25	Types of Soldiers	1914	£35.00	—
20	War Pictures	1915	£12.50	£250.00
12	With the Flag to Pretoria	1901	£65.00	—

GORDON'S

?4	Billiards	1912	*£120.00*	—

GRAVESON

30	Army Pictures, Cartoons, etc.	1916	*£40.00*	—

FRED GRAY

25	Types of British Soldiers	1914	*£60.00*	—

GRIFFITHS BROS.

XF18	Children	1928	*£40.00*	—

GUERNSEY TOBACCO CO. (Channel Isles)

49	And When Did You Last See Your Father? (Sect)	1936	75p	£37.50
K52	Miniature Playing Cards	1933	60p	—
48	The Laughing Cavalier (Sect)	1935	75p	£37.50
48	The Toast (Sect)	1935	75p	£37.50

HARRIS & SONS

26	Beauties "HOL"	1900	£15.00	—
30	Colonial Troops	1901	*£50.00*	—
25	Star Girls	1899	*£100.00*	—

JAS. H. HARRISON

18	Motor Cycle Series	1914	*£40.00*	—

HARVEY & DAVEY

50	Birds & Eggs	1905	£2.50	£125.00
35	Chinese & South African Series	1901	*£75.00*	—
30	Colonial Troops	1902	50.00	—
25	Types of British & Colonial Troops	1901	*£60.00*	—

W. HEATON

?6	Birkby Views	1912	*£80.00*	—

HENLY & WATKINS LTD.

25	Ancient Egyptian Gods (Plain back)	1924	£1.60	£40.00
25	Ancient Egyptian Gods (Printed back)	1924	£1.60	£40.00

HIGNETT BROS & CO.

Qty		Date	Odds	Sets
50	Actors Natural & Character Studies	1938	16p	£8.00
26	Actresses "FROGA"	1900	£35.00	—
25	Actresses, Photogravure	1900	£15.00	—
28	Actresses, PILPI I	1901	£12.50	£350.00
F50	Actresses, PILPI II	1901	£8.00	£400.00
50	A.F.C. Nicknames	1933	£1.40	—
50	Air Raid Precautions	1939	30p	£15.00
60	Animal Pictures	1899	£17.50	—
50	Arms & Armour	1924	£1.50	£75.50
25	Beauties "CHOAB"	1900	£75.00	—
50	Beauties, Gravure	1898	£40.00	—
BF50	Beauties (Chess Cigarettes) (Set 1)	1927	50p	£25.00
BF50	Beauties (Chess Cigarettes) (Set 2)	1927	50p	£25.00
BF50	Beauties (No brand)	1927	60p	£30.00
50	British Birds & Their Eggs	1938	75p	£37.50
50	Broadcasting	1935	80p	—
20	Cabinet 1900	1900	£50.00	—
25	Cathedrals & Churches	1909	£2.00	£50.00
50	Celebrated Old Inns	1925	£1.60	£80.00
50	Champions of 1936	1936	80p	£40.00
25	Common Objects of the Sea-Shore	1924	£1.20	£30.00
25	Company Drill	1915	£2.50	£62.50
50	Coronation Procession	1937	£1.00	
50	Dogs	1936	50p	£25.00
50	Football Caricatures	1935	80p	—
50	Football Club Captains	1936	£1.00	—
25	Greetings of the World	1907	£1.40	£35.00
25	Historical London	1926	£1.50	£37.50
50	How to Swim	1935	30p	£15.00
50	Interesting Buildings	1905	£3.00	£150.00
25	International Caps and Badges	1924	£1.60	£40.00
25	Life In Pond & Stream	1925	£1.50	£37.50
40	Medals	1900	£15.00	—
25	Military Portraits	1914	£3.00	£75.00
50	Modern Railways	1936	£1.00	—
25	Modern Statesmen	1906	£3.00	£75.00
20	Music Hall Artistes	1898	£30.00	—
50	Ocean Greyhounds	1938	60p	
25	Panama Canal	1914	£4.00	£100.00
12	Pretty Girl Series "RASH"	1900	£30.00	—
50	Prominent Cricketers of 1938	1938	£1.20	£60.00
50	Prominent Racehorses of 1933	1933	50p	£25.00
50	Sea Adventure	1939	15p	£7.50
25	Ships, Flags & Cap Badges A Series	1926	£1.50	£37.50
25	Ships, Flags & Cap Badges 2nd Series	1927	£2.00	£50.00
50	Shots from the Films	1936	75p	£37.50
25	The Prince of Wales Empire Tour	1924	£1.40	£35.00
50	Trick Billiards	1934	£1.50	—
25	Turnpikes	1927	£1.20	£30.00
25	V.C. Heroes	1901	£30.00	£750.00
20	Yachts (Black back)	1898	£40.00	—
20	Yachts (White back)	1898	£40.00	—
50	Zoo Studies	1937	40p	£20.00

INSURANCE

With the spiralling value of cards it has become increasingly necessary to provide for the possibility of one's cards being lost, damaged or stolen. For many collectors monetary value is of little importance, but the prudent householder insures all his valuable possessions, so that there is either some monetary compensation for the loss, or the means to start again.

Insurance for a card collection can often be effected as an addition to a normal household policy, but some insurance companies may not be sufficiently aware of the peculiar circumstances of a cigarette card collection, and therefore ask for perhaps the same precautions as a stamp collection, which might prove to be impracticable. It might therefore be worthwhile to obtain a quotation from a specialist in this field.

One hint which may prove to be particularly convenient is to use our Catalogue as the basis for settlement, at an agreed proportion of our selling prices. Most collectors mark each year the sets that they possess in the current edition, and it would be quite easy to keep the previous year's Catalogue in a safe place as a permanent record of your collection, changing it every year without too much effort.

ILLUSTD SWEET CAPORAL
PARIS FIREMAN, FRENCH ARMY 1886.

WILLIAM MURRAY.
SUPT. OF POLICE, NEW YORK.

Metropolitan Fire Brigade
Steamer Drill

OGDEN'S CIGARETTES

Apart from insuring, a few simple precautions can help to remove the need ever to claim. The use of good quality albums will, for example, preserve cards from damage caused by handling, or the accidental spillage of coffee (or beer).

On several occasions we have been asked to replace items previously sent by us 'because the puppy got to the post before I did'. Care in packing cards before sending them through the post can also avoid having to make a claim. Valuable cards should in any case always be registered or insured under one of the Post Office schemes when being posted.

Always keep cards away from damp conditions, or potential leaks. And remember that cigarette cards are just as susceptible to cigarette burns and fire as any other household item!

REPRINTS & FORGERIES

Until recently the prices of cigarette cards have been so modest that it has hardly been worthwhile for anyone to forge cards. However the recent appearance of colour reproductions of cards in various books has made the task easier and the temptation greater. The best example of this is the series of Clowns & Circus Artistes by Taddy, which is a plain backed set, and has been reproduced in colour in both 'Cigarette Cards & Novelties' and the special album of Jacob's 'Famous Picture Cards from History'. Some keen collectors have cut out the reproductions and stuck them on to white card, since this is the nearest they are likely to come to actually owning a set; others have then tried to pass these off as originals.

Because of the demand for some series, and their comparative scarcity, a number of reprints have been produced on both sides of the Atlantic, even including a postwar set (Mars Attacks). Jacob's, as mentioned above, issued a set of 32 Famous Picture Cards from History, which included reproductions of cards from 32 different sets. Cricket card reproductions are available in the form of two books which are designed to be torn out; Classic Cricket Cards is in fact based on an American idea which was first used for Baseball cards. And 'Nostalgia Reprints' so far encompass four different sets of classic issues such as Wills 1896 Cricketers and Cope's Golfers. All these series, mostly produced with the cooperation of Murray Cards (International) Ltd., are marked on the backs to indicate that they are reprints. So if you are offered a set of Player's Military Series with slightly damaged backs and at a bargain price BEWARE!

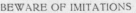

R. & J. HILL LTD.

Qty		Date	Odds	Sets
25	Actresses—Belle of New York Series	1899	£12.50	—
20	Actresses—Chocolate	1917	£10.00	—
30	Actresses—Continental	1906	£8.00	£240.00
26	Actresses "FROGA"	1900	£30.00	—
?25	Actresses "HAGG"	1900	£20.00	—
20	Animal Series (Crowfoot Cigarettes)	1909	£15.00	—
20	Animal Series (Hill's)	1909	£15.00	—
20	Animal Series (Anonymous)	1909	£12.50	—
F25	Artistas Teatrais Portuguesos	1924	£25.00	—
25	Aviation Series	1934	70p	£17.50
?15	Battleships	1908	£100.00	—
25	Battleships & Crests	1901	£8.00	£200.00
12	Boer War Generals	1901	£20.00	£240.00
20	Breeds of Dogs	1914	£8.00	£160.00
L30	Britain's Stately Homes (Silk)	1917	£2.50	—
?50	British Navy Series	1902	£17.50	—
L40	Canvas Masterpieces Series 1 (Silk)	1916	£1.00	£40.00
L40	Canvas Masterpieces Series 2 (Silk)	1916	£1.50	£60.00
X10	Canvas Masterpieces Series 2 (Silk)	1916	£1.50	—
50	Caricatures of Famous Cricketers	1926	£1.25	£62.50
L50	Caricatures of Famous Cricketers	1926	80p	£40.00
?	Celebrated Pictures	1905	£100.00	—
50	Celebrities of Sport	1939	40p	£20.00
P4/5	Chinese Pottery & Porcelain (Silk)	1915	25p	£1.00
X11	Chinese Pottery & Porcelain Series 2 (Silk) ...	1915	£3.00	—
10	Chinese Series	1912	£35.00	—
35	Cinema Celebrities	1936	25p	£9.00
50	Colonial Troops	1901	£15.00	£750.00
40	Crystal Palace Souvenir Cards	1937	50p	£20.00
48	Decorations & Medals	1940	80p	£40.00
F48	Famous Cinema Celebrities	1931	£1.50	—
LF48	Famous Cinema Celebrities, Series A	1931	£2.50	—
F50	Famous Cinema Celebrities, Series C	1932	£1.50	—
LF50	Famous Cinema Celebrities, Series D	1932	£1.50	—
28	Famous Cricketers Series (Blue back)	1912	£35.00	—
28	Famous Cricketers Series (Red back)	1912	£35.00	—
40	Famous Cricketers	1923	£2.00	£80.00
50	Famous Cricketers, including the S. Africa Test Team	1925	£2.00	£100.00
L50	Famous Cricketers, including the S. Africa Test Team	1925	£2.50	£125.00
50	Famous Dog Breeds	1952	£3.50	—
L30	Famous Engravings, Series XI	1910	£2.50	£75.00
40	Famous Film Stars	1938	40p	£16.00
40	Famous Film Stars (Arabic Text)	1938	50p	£20.00
20	Famous Footballers Series	1912	£7.00	£140.00
50	Famous Footballers (Brown)	1923	80p	£40.00
50	Famous Footballers (Coloured)	1939	70p	£35.00
25	Famous Footballers (51-75)	1939	80p	£20.00
25	Famous Pictures	1913	£2.50	£62.50
50	Famous Ships	1940	16p	£8.00
48	Film Stars and Celebrity Dancers	1935	80p	£40.00
30	Flags & Flags with Soldiers	1901	£15.00	—
24	Flags, Arms & Types of Nations	1910	£6.00	£150.00

R. & J. HILL LTD.—cont.

Qty		Date	Odds	Sets
20	Football Captain Series	1906	£12.50	—
20	Fragments From France (Coloured)	1916	£10.00	£200.00
10	Fragments From France (Buff)	1916	£12.50	£125.00
10	Fragments From France (Black & White)	1916	£35.00	—
L23	Great War Leaders, Series 10 (Silk)	1917	£3.00	—
50	Historic Places From Dickens' Classics	1926	30p	£15.00
L50	Historic Places From Dickens' Classics	1926	25p	£12.50
50	Holiday Resorts	1925	40p	£20.00
L50	Holiday Resorts	1925	40p	£20.00
20	Inventors and Their Inventions Series (1-20) ...	1907	£3.00	£60.00
20	Inventors & Their Inventions (Plain Back) ...	1934	60p	£12.00
20	Inventors and Their Inventions Series (21-40)	1908	£5.00	£100.00
15	Japanese Series (Black & White)	1904	£25.00	—
15	Japanese Series (Coloured)	1904	£35.00	—
30	Lighthouse Series	1903	£25.00	£750.00
50	Magical Puzzles	1938	50p	£25.00
50	Modern Beauties	1939	35p	£17.50
30	Music Hall Celebrities—Past & Present	1930	70p	£21.00
L30	Music Hall Celebrities—Past & Present	1930	80p	£24.00
20	National Flag Series	1914	£4.00	£80.00
30	Nature Pictures	1930	80p	£24.00
30	Nautical Songs	1937	30p	£9.00
B25	Naval Series (Unnumbered)	1901	£30.00	—
30	Naval Series (Numbered)	1902	£8.00	—
30	Our Empire Series	1929	15p	£4.50
L30	Our Empire Series	1929	16p	£5.00
M30	Popular Footballers Series A	1935	80p	£24.00
M20	Popular Footballers Series B	1935	80p	£16.00
20	Prince of Wales Series	1911	£8.00	£160.00
L?15	Prints From Noted Pictures	1908	*£75.00*	—
50	Public Schools and Colleges	1923	35p	£17.50
L50	Public Schools and Colleges	1923	40p	£20.00
75	Public Schools and Colleges	1923	40p	£30.00
L75	Public Schools and Colleges	1923	50p	£37.50
50	Puzzle Series	1937	30p	£15
42	Real Photographs Set 1	1930	£1.25	—
F42	Real Photographs Set 2	1930	£1.25	—
20	Rhymes	1904	£16.00	—
F50	Scenes from the Films	1934	£1.25	£62.50
40	Scenes from the Films	1938	15p	£6.00
35	Scientific Inventions and Discoveries (Black) ...	1929	50p	£17.50
35	Scientific Inventions and Discoveries (Coloured)	1929	50p	£17.50
L35	Scientific Inventions and Discoveries (Coloured)	1929	50p	£17.50
F50	Sports	1934	£1.75	—
28	Statuary Set 1	1898	£8.00	—
30	Statuary Set 2	1899	£5.00	£150.00
25	Statuary Set 3	1898	£15.00	—
X1	Sunripe Twins Bookmark	1925	—	£6.00
30	The All Blacks	1924	£2.00	£60.00
50	The Railway Centenary	1925	60p	£30.00
L50	The Railway Centenary	1925	70p	£35.00
25	The Railway Centenary 2nd Series	1925	80p	£20.00
L25	The Railway Centenary 2nd Series	1925	80p	£20.00

R. & J. HILL LTD.—cont.

Qty		Date	Odds	Sets
25	The River Thames (1-25)	1924	£1.00	£25.00
25	The River Thames (26-50)	1924	60p	£15.00
L50	The River Thames	1924	60p	£30.00
100	Transfers	1935	£3.00	—
20	Types of the British Army	1914	£20.00	£400.00
LF48	Views of Interest 1st Series (Spinet)	1938	15p	£6.50
LF48	Views of Interest 1st Series (Sunripe)	1938	15p	£5.00
LF48	Views of Interest 2nd Series	1938	15p	£5.00
LF48	Views of Interest 3rd Series	1939	15p	£5.00
LF48	Views of Interest 4th Series	1939	16p	£8.00
LF48	Views of Interest 5th Series	1939	16p	£8.00
LF48	Views of Interest—Canada	1940	15p	£7.50
LF48	Views of Interest—India	1940	£2.00	£96.00
50	Views of London	1925	50p	£25.00
L50	Views of London	1925	60p	£30.00
L50	Views of the River Thames	1924	60p	£30.00
25	War Series	1915	£7.00	£175.00
50	Who's Who in British Films	1927	50p	£25.00
L50	Who's Who in British Films	1927	60p	£30.00
84	Wireless Telephony	1923	70p	£60.00
L20	Wireless Telephony—Broadcasting Series ...	1923	£1.50	£30.00
25	World's Masterpieces 2nd Series	1914	£1.40	£35.00
50	Zoological Series	1924	50p	£25.00
L50	Zoological Series	1924	60p	£30.00

J. W. HOBSON

Qty		Date	Odds	Sets
18	Motor Cycle Series	1914	£40.00	—

HOCKINGS BAZAAR, PORTHCAWL

Qty		Date	Odds	Sets
30	Army Pictures, Cartoons, etc.	1916	£50.00	—

J. & T. HODGE

Qty		Date	Odds	Sets
?5	Britain's Naval Crests	1896	£150.00	—
16	British Royal Family	1901	£100.00	—
?20	Scottish Views	1898	£80.00	—

HOOK OF HOLLAND CIGARETTES

Qty		Date	Odds	Sets
?15	Footballers	1900	£125.00	—

HUDDEN & CO.

Qty		Date	Odds	Sets
26	Actresses "FROGA"	1900	£30.00	—
25	Beauties "CHOAB"	1901	£30.00	—
20	Beauties, Crown Seal	1898	£80.00	—
24	Beauties "HUMPS" (blue back)	1899	£40.00	—
24	Beauties "HUMPS" (orange back)	1899	£35.00	—
24	Beauties "HUMPS" (type set back)	1899	£150.00	—
?12	Comic Phrases	1900	£65.00	—
25	Famous Boxers	1927	£16.00	—
25	Flags of All Nations	1904	£8.00	£200.00
48	Japanese Playing Cards	1900	£60.00	—
18	Pretty Girl Series "RASH"	1900	£50.00	—
50	Public Schools & Colleges	1924	£1.25	£62.50
25	Soldiers of the Century	1903	£30.00	£750.00
25	Sports & Pastimes	1926	£35.00	—
25	Star Girls	1900	£50.00	—
25	Types of Smokers	1903	£25.00	£625.00

HUDSON'S

Qty		Date	Odds	Sets
24	Beauties "BOCCA"	1900	£150.00	—

HUNTER

?12	Footballers	1910	£150.00	—

JAMES ILLINGWORTH LTD.

MF48	Beautiful Scotland	1939	50p	—
M25	Cavalry	1924	£3.00	£75.00
MF48	Coastwise	1938	50p	£25.00
25	Comicartoons of Sport	1927	£3.00	£75.00
MF48	Flying	1938	60p	—
25	Motor Car Bonnets	1925	£3.50	£87.50
25	Old Hostels	1926	£3.50	£87.50
MF48	Our Countryside	1938	50p	£25.00
MF24	Shots from the Films	1937	£1.50	—
?10	Views from the English Lakes	1895	£100.00	—

IMPERIAL TOBACCO CO. LTD.

50	British Birds	1909	£2.50	£125.00
X1	Coronation Folder	1902	—	£40.00

INGRAMS (Eastleigh)

30	Army Pictures, Cartoons etc.	1916	£60.00	—

INTERNATIONAL TOBACCO CO. LTD.

28	Domino Cards	1938	15p	£4.00
D50	Famous Buildings & Monuments (Metal) Series A	1934	40p	£20.00
D50	Famous Buildings & Monuments (Metal) Series B	1934	80p	—
100	Film Favourites	1937	75p	—
D100	Gentlemen! The King! (black back)	1938	15p	£9.00
D100	Gentlemen! The King! (blue back)	1938	20p	—
50	International Code of Signals	1934	15p	£6.50
48	Screen Lovers (Summit)	Unissued	£1.25	—

PETER JACKSON

F28	Beautiful Scotland	1939	50p	£14.00
MF48	Beautiful Scotland	1939	50p	£25.00
F28	Coastwise	1938	50p	£14.00
MF48	Coastwise	1938	60p	—
F28	Famous Film Stars	1935	£1.30	£37.00
F27	Famous Films	1934	£1.30	£36.50
F28	Film Scenes	1936	75p	£21.00
LF28	Film Scenes (Different)	1936	£1.50	£42.00
F28	Flying	1938	80p	£22.50
MF28	Flying	1938	60p	—
D100	Gentlemen! The King (Mixed Size)	1938	40p	—
F28	Life in the Navy	1937	75p	£21.00
LF28	Life in the Navy (Different)	1937	£1.00	£28.00
F28	Our Countryside	1938	50p	£14.00
MF48	Our Countryside	1938	50p	—
F28	Shots from the Films	1937	65p	£18.50
MF24	Shots from the Films	1937	£1.00	—
D250	Speed Through the Ages (Mixed Sizes)	1937	15p	£35.00
F28	Stars in Famous Films	1934	£1.25	£35.00
D150	The Pageant of Kingship (Mixed Size)	1937	20p	£30.00

JACOBI BROS. & CO. LTD.

Qty		Date	Odds	Sets
?50	Boer War Celebrities "JASAS"	1901	£75.00	—

JAMES & CO. (B'HAM) LTD.

M20	Arms of Countries	1915	£75.00	—

JAMES'S

?50	Pretty Girl Series "BAGG"	1898	£100.00	—

JERSEY TOBACCO CO. LTD. (Channel Isles)

K53	Miniature Playing Cards	1933	50p	—

SOCIETE JOB

25	British Lighthouses	1925	£2.00	£50.00
B48	Cinema Stars (numbered)	1926	£5.00	—
B48	Cinema Stars (unnumbered)	1926	25p	£20.00
48	Cinema Stars (numbered)	1926	£2.00	—
48	Cinema Stars (unnumbered)	1926	£2.00	—
25	Dogs	1911	£8.00	£200.00
25	Liners	1912	£17.50	—
K53	Miniature Playing Cards	1926	£5.00	—
25	Orders of Chivalry	1924	£1.40	£35.00
25	Orders of Chivalry 2nd Series	1927	£1.40	£35.00
3	Orders of Chivalry (Unnumbered)	1927	£3.00	£9.00
25	Racehorses	1909	£8.00	£200.00

J. B. JOHNSON & CO.

25	National Flags, Flowers & Girls	1901	£80.00	—

JOHNSTON'S

?	Views	1910	£75.00	—

JONES BROS.

14/18	Spurs Footballers	1912	£2.50	—

A. I. JONES & CO. LTD.

B1	Advertisement Card	1901	£250.00	—
12	Nautical Terms	1905	£25.00	£300.00

ALEX JONES & CO.

20	Actresses "ANGOOD"	1898	£100.00	—
1	Diamond Jubilee 1897	1897	—	£80.00

A. S. JONES

30	Army Pictures, Cartoons, etc.	1916	£45.00	—

T. E. JONES & CO.

12	Conundrums	1900	£100.00	—
50	Flags of All Nations	1899	£60.00	—
?50	Footballers	1900	£85.00	—
16	Well-known Proverbs	1900	£100.00	—

C. H. JORDEN LTD.

F12	Celebrities of the Great War	1915	£40.00	—

J. & E. KENNEDY

Qty		Date	Odds	Sets
25	Beauties "FECKSA"	1902	£20.00	—

RICHARD KENNEDY

Qty		Date	Odds	Sets
P?25	Army & Navy Cartoons	1906	*£75.00*	—
50	War Portraits	1916	*£50.00*	—

KINNEAR LTD.

Qty		Date	Odds	Sets
13	Actresses	1899	£65.00	£850.00
B1	A Gentleman in Kharki	1900	—	£35.00
15	Australian Cricket Team	1897	£100.00	—
?25	Cricketers	1898	*£200.00*	—
X1	Cricket Fixture Folder	1903	*£300.00*	—
25	Footballers & Club Colours	1898	£60.00	—
12	Jockeys, Set 1	1898	£20.00	£240.00
26	Jockeys (Different)	1898	£40.00	—
2	Prominent Personages	1902	*£150.00*	—
13	Royalty	1897	£30.00	£400.00
L1	The Four Generations	1900	*£125.00*	—
K?25	Views	1898	*£150.00*	—

B. KRIEGSFELD & CO.

Qty		Date	Odds	Sets
1	Advertisement Card	1900	*£250.00*	—
50	Beauties "KEWA"	1898	£50.00	—
?10	Celebrities	1901	*£100.00*	—
50	Flags of All Nations	1899	£35.00	—
50	Phrases & Advertisements	1900	£40.00	—

A. KUIT LTD.

Qty		Date	Odds	Sets
K?12	Arms of Cambridge Colleges	1914	*£50.00*	—
K?12	Arms of Companies	1914	*£50.00*	—
F30	British Beauties (Oval)	1914	£30.00	—
F?10	Crosmedo Bijou Cards	1915	*£80.00*	—
25	Principal Streets of British Cities & Towns ...	1915	£75.00	—
F50	Types of Beauty	1914	*£75.00*	—

L. & Y. TOB. MFG. CO.

Qty		Date	Odds	Sets
26	Actresses "FROGA"	1900	*£125.00*	—

LAMBERT & BUTLER

Qty		Date	Odds	Sets
10	Actresses & their Autographs (narrow)	1898	£60.00	—
10	Actresses & their Autographs (wide)	1898	£70.00	—
20	Actresses "BLARM"	1900	£12.50	£250.00
50	Admirals	1900	£10.00	—
1	Advertisement Card	1898	—	£225.00
50	Aeroplane Markings	1937	40p	£20.00
25	A History of Aviation (Brown Front)	1933	60p	£15.00
25	A History of Aviation (Green Front)	1932	40p	£10.00
40	Arms of Kings & Queens of England	1906	£2.50	£100.00
25	Aviation	1915	£1.40	£35.00
26	Beauties "HOL"	1899	£20.00	—
50	Birds & Eggs	1906	£1.75	£87.50

54

LAMBERT & BUTLER—cont.

Qty		Date	Odds	Sets
?25	Boer War & Boxer Rebellion—Sketches	1901	£17.50	—
20	Boer War Generals "CLAM"	1901	£17.50	—
10	Boer War Generals "FLAC"	1901	£20.00	—
25	British Trees & Their Uses	1937	80p	£20.00
1	Colonel R.S.S. Baden-Powell, King of Scouts ...	1901	—	£200.00
25	Common Fallacies	1928	80p	£20.00
50	Conundrums (Blue Back)	1901	£12.50	—
50	Conundrums (Green Back)	1901	£8.00	£400.00
12	Coronation Robes	1902	£10.00	£120.00
25	Dance Band Leaders	1936	£1.50	£37.50
28	Dominoes (Packets)	1955	75p	—
50	Empire Air Routes	1936	50p	£25.00
25	Famous British Airmen & Airwomen	1935	30p	£7.50
25	Fauna of Rhodesia	1929	50p	£12.50
50	Find Your Way	1932	50p	£25.00
50	Footballers 1930-1	1931	£1.25	£62.50
25	Garden Life	1930	50p	£12.50
25	Hints & Tips for Motorists	1929	£1.20	£30.00
50	Horsemanship	1938	50p	£25.00
25	How Motor Cars Work	1931	80p	£20.00
50	Interesting Customs & Traditions of the Navy, Army & Air Force	1939	40p	£20.00
25	Interesting Musical Instruments	1929	£1.20	£30.00
50	Interesting Sidelights on the Work of the G.P.O.	1939	40p	£20.00
20	International Yachts	1902	£30.00	—
25	Japanese Series	1904	£4.00	£100.00
4	Jockeys (no Frame)	1902	£15.00	£60.00
10	Jockeys (with Frame)	1902	£15.00	£150.00
50	Keep Fit	1937	25p	£12.50
25	London Characters	1934	70p	£17.50
25	Motor Car Radiators	1928	£1.60	£40.00
25	Motor Cars A Series (Green Back)	1922	£1.20	£30.00
25	Motor Cars 2nd Series (26-50)	1923	£1.20	£30.00
50	Motor Cars 3rd Series	1926	£1.60	£80.00
25	Motor Cars (Grey Back)	1934	£1.00	£25.00
50	Motor Cycles	1923	£1.25	£62.50
50	Motor Index Marks	1926	£1.00	£50.00
25	Motors	1908	£12.00	£300.00
25	Naval Portraits (Series of 25)	1914	£2.00	£50.00
50	Naval Portraits (Series of 50)	1915	£2.00	£100.00
25	Pirates & Highwaymen	1926	30p	£7.50
25	Rhodesian Series	1928	60p	£15.00
50	The Thames From Lechlade to London	1907	£3.00	£150.00
25	Third Rhodesian Series	1930	30p	£7.50
4	Types of the British Army & Navy (Specialities)	1897	£35.00	£140.00
4	Types of the British Army & Navy (Viking) ...	1897	£40.00	—
25	Waverley Series	1904	£6.00	£150.00
25	Winter Sports	1914	£1.40	£35.00
25	Wireless Telegraphy	1909	£3.00	£75.00
25	Wonders of Nature	1924	30p	£7.50
25	World's Locomotives (Series of 25)	1912	£2.00	£50.00
50	World's Locomotives (Series of 50)	1912	£2.50	£125.00
25	World's Locomotives (Additional)	1913	£2.50	£62.50

LAMBERT & BUTLER—cont.

Qty		Date	Odds	Sets
Overseas Issues				
50	Actors & Actresses "WALP"	1908	£1.50	—
250	Actresses "ALWICS"	1908	£1.50	—
50	Beauties "LAWHA"	1908	£1.50	—
83	Danske Byvaabner	1912	*£7.50*	—
26	Etchings (Dogs)	1928	*£15.00*	—
L26	Etchings (Dogs)	1928	*£20.00*	—
25	Flag Girls of All Nations	1910	£6.00	£150.00
F50	Homeland Events	1925	80p	£40.00
?2	Indian Women	1910	*£30.00*	—
25	London Characters	1934	*£7.50*	—
F50	London Zoo	1924	70p	£35.00
50	Merchant Ships of the World	1924	£1.20	£60.00
50	Music Hall Celebrities	1906	£1.75	—
F50	Popular Film Stars (Title in 1 Line)	1925	70p	£35.00
F50	Popular Film Stars (Title in 2 Lines)	1925	60p	£30.00
F50	Popular Film Stars (Varsity Cigarettes)	1925	£1.20	—
100	Royalty Notabilities & Events 1900-2	1902	£7.50	—
100	Russo Japanese Series	1903	£2.50	—
F50	The Royal Family at Home and Abroad ...	1928	50p	£25.00
F50	The World of Sport	1926	60p	£30.00
F50	Types of Modern Beauty	1927	50p	£25.00
F50	Who's Who in Sport (1926)	1926	60p	£30.00

LAMBKIN BROS.

36	Country Scenes (Ser. 1-6)	1924	£3.00	—
L36	Country Scenes (Ser. 7-12)	1926	£3.50	—
L?6	Lily of Killarney Views	1925	*£50.00*	—

C. & J. LAW

25	Types of British Soldiers	1914	£16.00	£400.00
50	War Portraits	1915	*£40.00*	—

R. J. LEA LTD.

2	Advertisement Cards	1923	*£100.00*	—
B12	Butterflies & Moths (Silk)	1924	60p	£7.50
L12	Butterflies & Moths (Silk)	1924	60p	£7.50
P6	Butterflies & Moths (Silk)	1924	£1.00	£6.00
12	Chairman Puzzles	1910	*£100.00*	—
70	Cigarette Transfers (Locomotives)	1916	£3.00	£210.00
25	Civilians of Countries Fighting with the Allies ...	1914	£6.00	£150.00
F48	Coronation Souvenir (Glossy)	1937	15p	£7.00
48	Coronation Souvenir (Matt)	1937	25p	£12.50
LF48	Coronation Souvenir	1937	30p	£15.00
25	Dogs (1-25)	1923	£2.00	£50.00
25	Dogs (26-50)	1923	£3.00	£75.00
25	English Birds	1922	£1.50	£37.50
F54	Famous Film Stars	1939	60p	£30.00
F48	Famous Racehorses of 1926	1927	£1.00	£50.00
MF48	Famous Racehorses of 1926	1927	£1.40	£70.00
F48	Famous Views (glossy)	1936	15p	£7.50
48	Famous Views (matt)	1936	30p	£15.00

R. J. LEA LTD.—cont.

Qty		Date	Odds	Sets
MF48	Famous Views	1936	30p	£15.00
F36	Film Stars 1st Series	1934	£1.25	F45.00
F36	Film Stars 2nd Series	1934	£1.00	£36.00
25	Fish	1926	70p	£17.50
50	Flowers to Grow The Best Perennials	1913	£2.00	£100.00
F48	Girls from the Shows (glossy)	1935	80p	£40.00
48	Girls from the Shows (matt)	1935	£1.00	—
50	Miniatures (No Border)	1912	£1.60	£80.00
50	Miniatures (Gold Border)	1912	£1.60	£80.00
50	Miniatures (51-100)	1912	£1.50	£75.00
46/50	Modern Miniatures	1913	70p	£32.50
12	More Lea's Smokers (green border)	1906	£40.00	—
12	More Lea's Smokers (red frame)	1906	£50.00	—
P24	Old English Pottery & Porcelain	1912	£4.00	£100.00
50	Old English Pottery & Porcelain	1912	£1.00	£50.00
50	Old Pottery & Porcelain 2nd Series (Chairman)	1912	80p	£40.00
50	Old Pottery & Porcelain 2nd Series (Recorder)	1912	£3.00	—
50	Old Pottery & Porcelain 3rd Series (Chairman) ...	1912	80p	£40.00
50	Old Pottery & Porcelain 3rd Series (Recorder)	1912	£3.00	—
50	Old Pottery & Porcelain 4th Series	1913	80p	£40.00
50	Old Pottery & Porcelain 5th Series	1913	80p	£40.00
54	Old Pottery (Silk)	1914	60p	£40.00
72	Old Pottery (Silk Different)	1914	60p	£45.00
F54	Radio Stars (glossy)	1935	£1.00	£50.00
54	Radio Stars (matt)	1935	£1.00	—
100	Regimental Crests & Badges (Silk)	1923	75p	£75.00
50	Roses	1924	60p	£30.00
50	Ships of the World	1925	£1.00	£50.00
25	The Evolution of the Royal Navy	1925	£1.00	F25.00
25	War Pictures	1915	£2.50	£62.50
25	War Portraits	1915	£3.00	£75.00
F48	Wonders of the World (glossy)	1938	20p	£10.00
48	Wonders of the World (matt)	1938	30p	£15.00
MF48	Wonders of the World	1938	30p	£15.00

J. LEES

20	Northampton Town Football Club (301-320) ...	1915	£35.00	—

ALFRED L. LEAVER

B12	Manikin Cards	1915	£40.00	—

LEON DE CUBA CIGARS

30	Colonial Troops	1902	£65.00	—

A. LEWIS & CO. (WESTMINSTER) LTD.

52	Horoscopes	1938	50p	£26.00

H. C. LLOYD & SONS LTD.

28	Academy Gems	1902	£35.00	—
26	Actresses & Boer War Celebrities	1901	£30.00	—
B18	Devon Footballers (with Frame line)	1902	£80.00	—
B40	Devon Footballers & Boer War Celebrities	1902	£35.00	—

H. C. LLOYD & SONS LTD.—cont.

Qty		Date	Odds	Sets
25	Star Girls	1899	£125.00	—
L36	War Pictures	1914	£75.00	—

RICHARD LLOYD & SONS

Qty		Date	Odds	Sets
20	Actresses, Celebrities & Yachts	1900	£65.00	—
25	Atlantic Records	1936	80p	£20.00
25	Boer War Celebrities	1899	£20.00	£500.00
F27	Cinema Stars (1-27)	1935	£2.50	—
F27	Cinema Stars (28-54)	1935	30p	£8.00
F27	Cinema Stars, 3rd Series (55-81)	1936	£2.50	—
25	Cinema Stars (Matt)	1937	40p	£10.00
25	Famous Cricketers Puzzle Series	1930	£2.50	£62.50
96	National Types, Costumes & Flags	1900	£20.00	
25	Old English Inns	1923	60p	£15.00
25	Old Inns, Series 2	1924	£1.20	£30.00
50	Old Inns	1925	40p	£20.00
10	Scenes From San Toy	1905	£5.00	£50.00
25	Tricks & Puzzles	1935	25p	£6.25
25	Types of Horses	1926	£1.20	£30.00
25	Zoo Series	1926	50p	£12.50

LUSBY LTD.

Qty		Date	Odds	Sets
25	Scenes from Circus Life	1902	£75.00	

HUGH McCALL

Qty		Date	Odds	Sets
1	RAF Recruiting Card	1924	£75.00	

D. & J. MACDONALD

Qty		Date	Odds	Sets
10	Actresses "MUTA"	1901	£75.00	—
L?	Cricket & Football Teams	1902	£100.00	—
25	Cricketers	1902	£160.00	—
L1	Yorkshire County Team	1900	—	£350.00

MACKENZIE & CO.

Qty		Date	Odds	Sets
F50	Music Hall Artistes	1902	£10.00	£500.00
50	The Zoo	1910	£12.50	—
50	Victorian Art Pictures	1910	£10.00	—

WM. McKINNELL

Qty		Date	Odds	Sets
20	The European War Series	1915	£40.00	—
50	War Portraits	1916	£40.00	—

MACNAUGHTON JENKINS & CO. LTD.

Qty		Date	Odds	Sets
B50	Castles of Ireland—Ancient & Modern	1924	£1.60	£80.00
50	Various Uses of Rubber	1924	£1.40	£70.00

A. McTAVISH

Qty		Date	Odds	Sets
30	Army Pictures, Cartoons, etc.	1916	£40.00	—

McWATTIE & SONS

Qty		Date	Odds	Sets
30	Army Pictures, Cartoons, etc.	1916	£40.00	—

THE MANXLAND TOB. CO.

Qty		Date	Odds	Sets
?	Views in the Isle of Man	1900	*£125.00*	—

MARCOVITCH & CO.

| F18 | Beauties (Plain Back) ... ... | 1932 | 15p | £2.75 |
| L7 | The Story in Red and White ... ... | 1955 | £1.00 | — |

MARCUS'S

?25	Cricketers	1897	*£200.00*	—
25	Footballers & Club Colours	1898	£60.00	—
L1	The Four Generations	1900	—	*£150.00*

MARKHAM

| M?25 | Views of Bridgwater ... ... | 1906 | *£60.00* | — |

MARSUMA CO.

| 50 | Famous Golfers & Their Strokes ... ... | 1914 | £10.00 | £500.00 |

C. MARTIN

| 30 | Army Pictures, Cartoons etc. ... ... | 1916 | *£50.00* | — |

MARTINS LTD.

1	Arf A Mo Kaiser!	1915		£35.00
D?12	Carlyle Series	1923	*£60.00*	—
P?750	The Performer Tobacco Fund Photographs ...	1916	£3.00	—
25	V.C. Heroes	1916	£12.00	£300.00

R. MASON & CO.

| 30 | Colonial Troops ... ... | 1902 | £40.00 | — |
| 40 | Naval & Military Phrases ... ... | 1904 | £35.00 | — |

MASCOT CIGARETTES

| ?20 | British Views ... ... | 1925 | *£35.00* | — |

JUSTUS VAN MAURIK

| X12 | Views of Holland ... ... | 1915 | *£75.00* | — |

MAY QUEEN VIRGINIA CIGARETTES

| M10/12 | Interesting Pictures ... ... | — | 25p | £2.50 |

MENTORS LTD.

| 32 | Views of Ireland ... ... | 1912 | £5.00 | — |

J. MILLHOFF & CO. LTD.

F54	Antique Pottery	1927	40p	£20.00
MF56	Antique Pottery	1927	50p	£28.00
30	Art Treasures	1927	35p	£10.50
L50	Art Treasures	1926	25p	£12.50
L25	Art Treasures 2nd Series (51-75)	1928	60p	£15.00
M74	De Reszke Pictures (several printings) ...	1925	75p	—
L25	England Historic & Picturesque (1-25) ...	1928	40p	£10.00
L25	England Historic & Picturesque 2nd Series (26-50)	1928	40p	£10.00
F27	Famous Golfers	1928	£2.50	£70.00
F27	Famous Test Cricketers	1928	£2.00	£55.00
MF27	Famous Test Cricketers	1928	£2.50	£55.00
M25	Gallery Pictures	1929	60p	£15.00

J. MILLHOFF & CO. LTD.—cont.

Qty		Date	Odds	Sets
50	Geographia Map Series (Sect.)	1931	70p	£35.00
F36	In the Public Eye	1930	50p	£18.00
25	Men of Genius	1924	£2.00	£50.00
L25	Picturesque Old England	1931	50p	£12.50
F27	Real Photographs A Series (glossy)	1931	15p	£3.50
F27	Real Photographs A Series (matt)	1931	15p	£4.00
F27	Real Photographs 2nd Series	1931	15p	£3.50
F27	Real Photographs 3rd Series	1932	15p	£3.50
F27	Real Photographs 4th Series	1932	15p	£3.50
F27	Real Photographs 5th Series	1933	15p	£3.50
F27	Real Photographs 6th Series	1933	15p	£3.50
25	Reproductions of Celebrated Oil Paintings ...	1928	60p	£15.00
L25	Roses	1927	80p	£20.00
M?6	Theatre Advertisement Cards	1905	£50.00	—
X?6	Theatre Advertisement Cards	1905	£75.00	—
F54	The Homeland Series	1933	15p	£7.00
MF56	The Homeland Series	1933	15p	£7.50
50	Things to Make	1935	20p	£10.00
50	What the Stars Say	1934	25p	£12.50
F36	Zoological Studies	1929	15p	£5.00

Dutch Issues

Qty		Date	Odds	Sets
L40	Film Series 1	1924	£5.00	—
L60	Film Series 1	1924	£5.00	—
L60	Film Series 2	1925	£5.00	—
L25	Film Series 3	1925	£5.00	—
MF105	Film Series 4	1926	£4.00	—
MF206	Film Series 4	1926	£4.00	—
F?70	Sports Series	1925	£12.50	—

MIRANDA LTD.

Qty		Date	Odds	Sets
20	Dogs	1925	£2.50	—
25	Sports and Pastimes	1925	£2.50	—

STEPHEN MITCHELL

Qty		Date	Odds	Sets
51	Actors & Actresses "FROGA" (Coloured)	1899	£10.00	—
26	Actors & Actresses "FROGA B" (Brown)	1899	£10.00	—
26	Actors & Actresses "FROGA C" (Coloured) ...	1899	£10.00	—
50	Actors & Actresses "FROGA D" (Brown)	1899	£10.00	—
1	Advertisement Card	1900	£200.00	—
50	A Gallery of 1934	1935	60p	£30.00
50	A Gallery of 1935	1935	40p	£20.00
50	Air Raid Precautions	1938	40p	£20.00
30	A Model Army	1932	50p	£15.00
25	Angling	1928	£1.60	£40.00
50	Arms & Armour	1916	£2.00	£100.00
25	Army Ribbons & Buttons	1916	£2.50	£62.50
50	A Road Map of Scotland	1933	80p	—
25	Boxer Rebellion—Sketches	1901	£15.00	—
25	British Warships (1-25)	1915	£3.00	£75.00
25	British Warships, 2nd Series (26-50)	1915	£3.00	£75.00
50	Clan Tartans A Series	1927	80p	£40.00
25	Clan Tartans 2nd Series	1927	30p	£7.50
25	Empire Exhibition, Scotland 1938	1938	20p	£5.00

STEPHEN MITCHELL—cont.

Qty		Date	Odds	Sets
25	Famous Crosses	1923	24p	£6.00
50	Famous Scots	1933	30p	£15.00
50	First Aid	1938	30p	£15.00
P3	Glasgow International Exhibition 1901	1901	£30.00	—
50	Humorous Drawings	1924	£1.00	£50.00
50	Interesting Buildings	1905	£3.00	£150.00
40	London Ceremonials	1928	65p	£26.00
25	Medals	1916	£3.00	£75.00
25	Money	1913	£2.50	£62.50
25	Old Sporting Prints	1930	30p	£7.50
50	Our Empire	1937	16p	£8.00
25	Regimental Crests & Collar Badges	1900	£6.00	£150.00
70	River & Coastal Steamers	1925	£1.25	£90.00
50	Scotland's Story	1929	£1.20	£60.00
25	Scottish Clan Series	1903	£6.00	£150.00
50	Scottish Footballers	1934	60p	£30.00
50	Scottish Football Snaps	1935	60p	£30.00
25	Seals	1911	£3.00	£75.00
25	Sports	1907	£4.00	£100.00
25	Stars of Screen & History	1939	40p	£10.00
25	Statues & Monuments	1914	£2.50	£62.50
50	The World of Tomorrow	1936	35p	£17.50
25	Village Models	1925	80p	£20.00
25	Village Models 2nd Series	1925	£1.00	£25.00
L25	Village Models	1925	£2.00	£50.00
L25	Village Models 2nd Series	1925	£2.00	£50.00
50	Wonderful Century	1937	20p	£10.00

MOORGATE TOBACCO CO. LTD.

Qty		Date	Odds	Sets
D30	The New Elizabethan Age	1953	£1.20	£36.00

B. MORRIS & SONS LTD.

Qty		Date	Odds	Sets
30	Actresses (Black & White)	1898	70p	£30.00
26	Actresses "FROGA A"	1899	£17.50	—
L26	Actresses "FROGA B"	1899	£150.00	—
50	Animals at the Zoo (Blue Back)	1924	35p	£17.50
50	Animals at the Zoo (Grey Back)	1924	30p	£15.00
35	At the London Zoo Aquarium	1928	20p	£7.00
25	Australian Cricketers	1925	£1.40	£35.00
M24	Battleship Crests (Silk)	1915	£15.00	—
50	Beauties "CHOAB"	1900	£25.00	—
50	Beauties Collotype	1897	£75.00	—
21	Beauties "MOM"	1899	£17.50	—
20	Boer War 1900	1900	£20.00	£400.00
25	Boer War Celebrities "PAM"	1901	£15.00	—
25	Captain Blood	1937	30p	£7.50
L25	English & Foreign Birds (Silk)	1915	£1.60	£40.00
L25	English Flowers (Silk)	1915	£1.60	£40.00
L50	English Flowers (Silk)	1915	£2.00	£100.00
50	Film Star Series	1923	£1.25	£62.50
30	General Interest	1910	£3.50	£100.00
25	Golf Strokes Series	1923	£1.40	£35.00
12	Horoscopes	1936	16p	£2.00
25	How Films are Made	1934	30p	£7.50

B. MORRIS & SONS LTD.—cont.

Qty		Date	Odds	Sets
50	How to Sketch	1929	50p	£25.00
20	London Views	1904	£17.50	—
25	Marvels of the Universe Series	1912	£2.00	£50.00
25	Measurement of Time	1924	50p	£12.50
25	Motor Series	1922	£1.50	£37.50
50	National & Colonial Arms	1917	£3.50	£175.00
25	Racing Greyhounds	1939	30p	£7.50
L25	Regimental Colours (Silk)	1916	£1.50	—
24	Shadowgraphs	1925	£1.00	£24.00
25	The Queen's Dolls House	1925	£1.40	£35.00
13	Treasure Island	1924	30p	£4.00
50	Victory Signs Series	1928	16p	£8.00
25	War Celebrities	1916	£3.00	£75.00
25	War Pictures	1915	£4.00	£100.00
25	Wax Art Series	1931	20p	£5.00
25	Whipsnade Zoo	1932	20p	£5.00
25	Wireless Series	1923	£1.40	£35.00

PHILIP MORRIS & CO. LTD.

50	British Views	1924	£1.50	£75.00
L50	British Views	1924	£1.75	—

P. MOUAT & CO.

30	Colonial Troops	1902	£75.00	—

MOUSTAFA LTD.

F50	Camera Studies	1923	£1.75	—
25	Cinema Stars	1924	£2.00	—
40	Leo Chambers Dogs Heads	1924	£1.20	£50.00
25	Pictures of World Interest	1923	£1.60	£40.00
F25	Real Photos	1925	20p	£5.00

MUNRO

30	Colonial Troops	1902	£100.00	—

B. MURATTI SONS & CO. LTD.

P?25	Actresses, Collotype	1899	£80.00	—
26	Actresses "FROGA" (Cigarette Connoisseur) ...	1899	£12.00	£300.00
26	Actresses "FROGA" (Zinnia)	1899	£15.00	—
P?50	Actresses & Beauties, Fancy Frames	1899	£80.00	—
X?30	Advertisement Cards	1900	£200.00	—
F24	Australian Racehorses	1931	30p	£7.00
25	Beauties "CHOAB"	1900	£25.00	—
L50	Beautiful Women	1900	£40.00	—
20	Boer War Generals "CLAM"	1900	£20.00	—
B15	Caricatures (Specialities)	1903	£15.00	£225.00
B15	Caricatures (Vassos)	1903	£30.00	—
B15	Caricatures (Zinnia)	1903	£15.00	£225.00
L35	Crowned Heads	1912	£8.00	—
53	Japanese Series (P/C Inset) (printed back) ...	1904	£8.00	—
53	Japanese Series (P/C Inset) (plain back) ...	1904	£7.00	—
XF?	Post Card Series	1902	£5.00	—
19	Russo Japanese Series	1904	£7.00	£135.00

B. MURATTI SONS & CO. LTD.—cont.

Qty		Date	Odds	Sets
25	Star Girls	1899	*£80.00*	—
50	Views of Jersey (printed back)	1913	£10.00	—
50	Views of Jersey (plain back)	1913	£8.00	—
25	War Series I	1916	£12.50	—
25	War Series II	1917	£7.00	£175.00

Silk Issues

Qty		Date	Odds	Sets
L40	Canvas Masterpieces Series M (small globe) ...	1916	£1.60	£65.00
L40	Canvas Masterpieces Series M (large globe) ...	1916	£4.00	—
P16	Canvas Masterpieces Series P	1916	£6.00	—
M24	Flags, Series A (26-49)	1914	£2.50	£60.00
P3	Flags, Series A (1-3)	1914	£6.00	—
L1	Flags, Series B (No. 19)	1914	—	£4.00
M25	Flags, Series C (20-44)	1914	£2.00	£50.00
P18	Flags, Series C (1-18)	1914	£6.00	—
P3	Flags, Series D (45-47)	1914	£6.00	—
M25	Flags, Series E (48-72)	1914	£2.00	£50.00
P6	Flags, Series F (73-78)	1914	£4.00	—
P18	Great War Leaders, Series P	1916	£7.50	—
M25	Regimental Badges, Series A	1915	£3.00	£75.00
L48	Regimental Badges, Series B	1915	£3.50	—
L18	Regimental Badges, Series B (Different) (4-18) ...	1915	£3.50	—
L16	Regimental Badges, Series G (79-94) ...	1915	£5.00	—
L25	Regimental Colours, Series CB	1915	£6.00	—
M72	Regimental Colours, Series RB	1915	£3.50	—

German Issues

Qty		Date	Odds	Sets
X216	Brennpunkte des Deutschen Sports Band 1 ...	1935	50p	£100.00
X288	Brennpunkte des Deutschen Sports Band 2 ...	1936	50p	£140.00
X216	Brennpunkte des Deutschen Sports Band 3 ...	1936	50p	£100.00

MURRAY, SONS & CO.

Qty		Date	Odds	Sets
20	Actresses "BLARM"	1902	*£40.00*	—
F22	Bathing Beauties	1929	£3.00	—
40	Bathing Belles	1939	15p	£4.00
15	Chess & Draughts Problems	1910	£35.00	—
F22	Cinema Scenes	1929	£3.00	—
20	Cricketers (black front)	1912	£35.00	—
20	Cricketers (brown front)	1912	£60.00	—
25	Crossword Puzzles	1923	*£35.00*	—
F26	Dancers	1929	£3.00	—
F25	Dancing Girls	1929	£1.40	£35.00
F26	Dancing Girls (As Above)	1930	£1.60	—
25	Famous Works of Art	1910	£12.50	—
B16	Flags (Silk)	1910	£12.50	—
X3	Flags & Arms (Silk)	1910	*£50.00*	—
34	Footballers, Series H	1912	£10.00	—
104	Footballers, Series J	1913	£10.00	—
?25	Football Colours (Shaped)	1905	*£30.00*	—
25	Football Rules	1911	£15.00	—
25	High Class Works of Art	1909	£15.00	—
20	Holidays by the L.M.S.	1927	£5.00	£100.00
20	Inventors Series	1924	£1.75	£35.00
25	Irish Scenery	1905	£15.00	—

MURRAY, SONS & CO.—cont.

Qty		Date	Odds	Sets
31	Orders of Chivalry (Silk)	1925	£10.00	—
25	Polo Pictures	1910	£12.00	£300.00
50	Prominent Politicians (two strengths back) ...	1909	£1.50	£75.00
50	Prominent Politicians (without "in two strengths")	1909	£12.50	—
50	Puzzle Series	1929	£1.75	—
B25	Regimental Badges (Silk)	1910	£12.50	—
50	Stage and Film Stars	1926	£1.50	£75.00
25	Steamships	1939	40p	£10.00
50	The Story of Ships	1940	15p	£4.50
25	Types of Aeroplanes	1929	40p	£10.00
20	Types of Dogs	1924	£2.50	£50.00
35	War Series K	1915	£16.00	£560.00
25	War Series L	1916	£1.50	£50.00

H. J. NATHAN

Qty		Date	Odds	Sets
40	Comic Military & Naval Pictures	1904	£40.00	—

JAMES NELSON

Qty		Date	Odds	Sets
?20	Beauties "FENA"	1899	£125.00	—

EDWD. J. NEWBEGIN

Qty		Date	Odds	Sets
F50	Actors & Actresses	1901	£35.00	—
10	Actresses "HAGG"	1900	£100.00	—
20	Cricketers Series	1902	£175.00	—
1	Mabel Love Advertisement Card	1900	£250.00	—
19	Russo Japanese Series	1904	£75.00	—
16	Well-known Proverbs	1900	£65.00	—
24	Well-known Songs	1900	£65.00	—

W. H. NEWMAN LTD.

Qty		Date	Odds	Sets
18	Motor Cycle Series	1914	£50.00	—

THE NEW MOSLEM CIG. CO. LTD.

Qty		Date	Odds	Sets
30	Proverbs	1903	£50.00	—

THOS. NICHOLLS & CO.

Qty		Date	Odds	Sets
50	Orders of Chivalry	1916	£3.00	£150.00

THE NILMA TOBACCO COY.

Qty		Date	Odds	Sets
40	Home & Colonial Regiments	1903	£40.00	—
30	Proverbs	1903	£40.00	—

M. E. NOTARAS LTD.

Qty		Date	Odds	Sets
B24	Chinese Scenes	1925	15p	£3.50
F36	National Types of Beauty	1925	30p	£10.00

OGDENS LTD.

Qty		Date	Odds	Sets
25	ABC of Sport	1927	£1.20	£30.00
50	Actors, Natural & Character Studies	1938	15p	£6.50
25	Actresses (No Glycerine back)	1895	£60.00	—
?200	Actresses, Collotype	1894	£30.00	—
50	Actresses, Green Gravure	1898	£5.00	£250.00

This Catalogue concentrates on British tobacco and trade issues, and English language issues overseas. This does cover a fairly large part of the globe, including North America, South Africa, Malta and Australasia, in all of which areas there were many attractive issues of cards. The last of these is the subject of a separate reference book published by the Cartophilic Society, which includes all known tobacco and trade series. Many of the sets issued in the British Empire by subsidiaries of the British American Tobacco Co. are similar to G.B. sets, such as Merchant Ships of the World and Picturesque People of the Empire. B.A.T. even used a Gallaher set in Canada, The Reason Why, and Ardath 'borrowed' Player's Tennis for New Zealand.

There are three main areas excluded from this book. Firstly the Continent of Europe. Here one can find many non-insert cards, particularly from France, Belgium and Germany; these are mainly from the 19th Century, and of very high quality. There are also many later issues, very frequently associated with special albums, from Switzerland, Belgium and Holland. In particular Germany is a fruitful area; many of their sets complete in the special albums can still be purchased reasonably today.

The second area is Central and South America, where many attractive and original ideas were put on to cards, particularly in Cuba and Peru, but extending back to the Canary Islands and Spain. Thirdly there is the Far East, notably China, where small firms abounded, and each seemed to produce one or two sets, normally on a Chinese theme, and usually with a Chinese text, although quite often the firm's name also appeared in English. Other parts of the world such as North Africa have also produced cards in the past, and we hope will again in the future.

THEMATIC COLLECTING

HORNET MOTH

PLAYER'S CIGARETTES

SINGER 12 H.P. SALOON

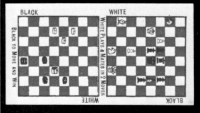

BLACK   WHITE

COPE'S CIGARETTES.
6.—George Robey.

Billiards

Many people come into the hobby not because of an interest in cards themselves, but as an extension of an already existing interest. For there cannot be one subject that is not covered by at least one set of cards, in every case with an illustration and often with informative text.

One of the most popular themes to be collected is sport, and particularly cricket, golf and soccer. The value to the enthusiast can be shown by series such as the Taddy County Cricketers and Prominent Footballers, which depicted almost every first class player of the time, and the series of 2,462 different Footballers issued in the 1920s by Godfrey Phillips with their Pinnace Cigarettes. In the U.S.A. of course Baseball is the main cartophilic interest, while in Canada it is hockey. Other games sought by collectors are tennis, billiards, chess and archery.

Militaria, shipping and cinema are other themes that were issued in large numbers and have many devotees. Subjects such as aviation, opera, motoring, music hall and railways are also extensively covered, as are modern subjects like space exploration and television. The significance of most of these is that they are contemporary records, and one can trace the development of the subject through a period of nearly a century.

COUNTY CRICKETERS.

MR R. H. T. TURNER,
NOTTINGHAMSHIRE.

ROYAL ARTILLERY

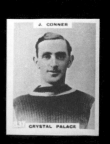

J. CONNER

CRYSTAL PALACE

NORMA SHEARER

OGDENS LTD.—cont.

Qty		Date	Odds	Sets
?1	Actresses, Green, green border	1898	*£120.00*	—
200	Actresses, Woodburytype	1894	£20.00	—
F?573	Actresses, Guinea Gold Type	1900	£1.40	—
50	A.F.C. Nicknames	1933	£1.25	£62.50
50	Air Raid Precautions	1938	15p	£7.00
50	Applied Electricity	1928	50p	£25.00
192	Army Crests and Mottoes	1902	£2.50	£475.00
36	Australian Test Cricketers	1928	£1.50	£54.00
28	Beauties "BOCCA"	1899	£15.00	—
50	Beauties "CHOAB"	1899	£15.00	—
26	Beauties "HOL"	1899	£10.00	£260.00
66	Beauties, Green Net Back (black & white)	1901	£6.50	£450.00
100	Beauties, Green Net Back (coloured)	1901	£12.50	
52	Beauties, P/C Inset	1899	£16.00	£825.00
26	Beauties, As P/C Inset	1899	£22.50	—
52	Beauties & Military, P/C Inset	1898	£16.00	£825.00
F50	Beauty Series (Unnumbered)	1900	£35.00	—
F50	Beauty Series (Numbered)	1900	£1.25	£62.50
50	Billiards by Tom Newman	1928	80p	£40.00
50	Birds Eggs	1908	80p	£40.00
50	Birds Eggs (Cut-Outs)	1923	40p	£20.00
F?141	Boer War & General Interest	1901	£1.75	—
LF?50	Boer War & General Interest	1901	*£15.00*	—
50	Boxers	1915	£3.00	£150.00
25	Boxing	1914	£2.50	£62.50
50	Boy Scouts (Blue Back)	1911	£1.20	£60.00
50	Boy Scouts (Green Back)	1911	£2.00	£100.00
50	Boy Scouts, 2nd Series (Blue Back)	1912	£1.25	£62.50
50	Boy Scouts, 2nd Series (Green Back)	1912	£2.00	£100.00
50	Boy Scouts, 3rd Series (Blue Back)	1912	£1.25	£62.50
50	Boy Scouts, 3rd Series (Green Back)	1912	£2.00	£100.00
50	Boy Scouts, 4th Series	1913	£1.50	£75.00
25	Boy Scouts, 5th Series	1914	£1.60	£40.00
50	Boy Scouts (Different)	1929	60p	£30.00
50	British Birds	1905	80p	£40.00
50	British Birds, 2nd Series	1909	£1.00	£50.00
50	British Birds (Cut-Outs)	1923	30p	£15.00
50	British Birds & Their Eggs	1939	50p	£25.00
50	British Costumes From 100 B.C. to 1904	1905	£3.00	£150.00
50	Broadcasting	1935	50p	£25.00
50	By the Roadside	1932	50p	£25.00
44	Captains of Association Football Clubs & Colours	1926	£1.00	£44.00
50	Cathedrals & Abbeys	1936	40p	£20.00
50	Champions of 1936	1937	40p	£20.00
50	Children of All Nations	1924	30p	£15.00
50	Club Badges	1914	£2.50	£125.00
50	Colour in Nature	1932	50p	£25.00
25	Comic Pictures	1897	*£175.00*	—
50	Construction of Railway Trains	1930	£1.00	£50.00
50	Coronation Procession (Sect.)	1937	50p	£25.00
12	Cricketers & Footballers—Women	1896	*£125.00*	—
50	Cricketers & Sportsmen	1898	£35.00	—
50	Cricket 1926	1926	£1.20	£60.00

OGDENS LTD.—cont.

Qty		Date	Odds	Sets
25	Derby Entrants 1926	1926	70p	£17.50
50	Derby Entrants 1928	1928	70p	£35.00
50	Derby Entrants 1929	1929	80p	£40.00
50	Dogs	1936	60p	£30.00
55	Dominoes	1909	80p	£44.00
112	Dominoes—Actress & Beauty Backs	1900	£15.00	—
25	Famous Dirt Track Riders	1929	£1.60	£40.00
50	Famous Footballers	1908	£1.40	£70.00
50	Famous Rugby Players	1926	80p	£40.00
50	Flags & Funnels of Leading Steamship Lines ...	1906	£2.00	£100.00
50	Football Caricatures	1935	80p	£40.00
43	Football Club Badges (Shaped)	1910	£3.00	—
50	Football Club Captains	1936	50p	£25.00
51	Football Club Colours	1906	£1.00	£50.00
50	Foreign Birds	1924	35p	£17.50
50	Fowls Pigeons & Dogs	1904	£1.60	£80.00
25	Greyhound Racing 1st Series	1927	£1.60	£40.00
25	Greyhound Racing 2nd Series	1928	£1.60	£40.00
1	History of the Union Jack (Folder)	1900	—	£120.00
50	How to Swim	1935	16p	£8.00
50	Infantry Training	1915	£1.20	£60.00
50	Jockey and Owners Colours	1927	£1.00	£50.00
50	Jockeys 1930	1930	£1.00	£50.00
50	Leaders of Men	1924	80p	£40.00
MF3	Liners (Guinea Gold Type)	1901	£75.00	—
25	Marvels of Motion	1928	80p	£20.00
K154	Miniature Playing Cards (Actress/Beauty Back)	1900	£2.00	—
K52	Miniature Playing Cards (Coolie)	1904	£1.50	£80.00
K52	Miniature Playing Cards (Tabs)	1909	£1.75	—
50	Modern British Pottery	1925	30p	£15.00
50	Modern Railways	1936	60p	£30.00
50	Modern War Weapons	1915	£1.50	£75.00
25	Modes of Conveyance	1927	£1.20	£30.00
50	Motor Races 1931	1931	£1.20	£60.00
50	Ocean Greyhounds	1938	40p	£20.00
25	Optical Illusions	1923	£1.00	£25.00
50	Orders of Chivalry	1907	£1.60	£80.00
25	Owners Racing Colours & Jockeys (Green Back)	1914	£1.60	£40.00
50	Owners Racing Colours & Jockeys (Blue Back)	1906	£1.40	£70.00
25	Picturesque People of the Empire	1927	60p	£15.00
50	Picturesque Villages	1936	40p	£20.00
25	Poultry (Ogdens On Front) (1-25)	1915	£1.40	£35.00
25	Poultry (No Ogdens On Front) (1-25)	1915	£1.60	£40.00
25	Poultry 2nd Series (26-50)	1916	£1.40	£35.00
25	Poultry Alphabet	1924	£1.00	£25.00
25	Poultry Rearing & Management 1st Series	1922	80p	£20.00
25	Poultry Rearing & Management 2nd Series ...	1923	80p	£20.00
50	Prominent Cricketers of 1938	1938	70p	£35.00
50	Prominent Racehorses of 1933	1934	60p	£30.00
50	Pugilists & Wrestlers A Series (1-50)	1908	£1.50	£75.00
25	Pugilists & Wrestlers 2nd Series (51-75)	1909	£2.00	£50.00
50	Pugilists in Action	1928	70p	£35.00
50	Racehorses	1907	£1.50	£75.00
50	Racing Pigeons	1931	70p	£35.00

OGDENS LTD.—cont.

Qty		Date	Odds	Sets
25	Records of the World	1908	£1.60	£40.00
50	Royal Mail	1909	£2.50	£125.00
50	Sea Adventure	1939	15p	£5.00
50	Sectional Cycling Map	1910	£1.60	£80.00
50	Shakespeare Series (numbered)	1905	£8.00	£400.00
50	Shakespeare Series (unnumbered)	1905	£7.50	£375.00
50	Shots from the Films	1936	50p	£25.00
25	Sights of London	1923	70p	£17.50
50	Smugglers and Smuggling	1932	60p	£30.00
50	Soldiers of the King	1909	£3.00	£150.00
P36	Sporting & Other Girls	1898	*£250.00*	—
50	Steeplechase Celebrities	1931	70p	£35.00
50	Steeplechase Trainers and Owners Colours ...	1927	70p	£35.00
50	Swimming Diving and Life Saving	1931	35p	£17.50
25	Swiss Views 1-25	1910	£1.60	£40.00
25	Swiss Views 26-50	1910	£3.00	£75.00
50	The Blue Riband of the Atlantic	1929	£1.00	£50.00
50	The Story of Sand	1935	40p	£20.00
25	Trainers and Owners Colours 1st Series ...	1925	70p	£17.50
25	Trainers and Owners Colours 2nd Series ...	1926	£1.00	£25.00
50	Trick Billiards	1934	50p	£25.00
50	Turf Personalities	1929	£1.00	£50.00
48	Victoria Cross Heroes	1901	£8.00	£400.00
25	Whaling	1927	£1.40	£35.00
50	Yachts & Motor Boats	1930	£1.20	£60.00
50	Zoo Studies	1937	25p	£12.50

Guinea Gold Issues

Qty		Date	Odds	Sets
LF1	Actresses Base C	1899	—	£17.50
F374	Actresses Base D	1900	65p	—
LF423	Actresses Base D	1900	80p	—
F40	Actresses Base E	1900	£1.75	£70.00
F662	Actresses Base I	1899	60p	—
LF21	Actresses Base I	1899	£30.00	—
F30	Actresses Base J	1899	£2.50	—
F238	Actresses Base K	1899	£1.25	—
F215	Actresses Base L	1899	£1.25	—
F113	Actresses & Miscellaneous Base I	1900	60p	—
F2974	Actresses & Miscellaneous Base M	1900	60p	—
LF403	Actresses & Miscellaneous Base M	1900	80p	—
F58	Boer War & Actresses Base F	1901	60p	£35.00
F186	Boer War & Miscellaneous Base D	1901	50p	—
LF153	Boer War & Miscellaneous Base D	1900	70p	—
F312	Continental Actresses Base B	1899	£1.25	—
LF71	Continental Actresses Base B	1899	£8.00	—
F11	Cricketers Base I	1901	£6.50	£72.50
F77	Cricketers Base M	1899	£8.00	—
F57	Cyclists Base M	1899	£3.00	—
F58	Denumbered Group Base D	1900	£1.25	—
LF50	Denumbered Group Base D	1900	£1.50	—
F176	Footballers Base M	1899	£4.00	—
F320	General Interest (White Panel) Base D	1900	60p	£200.00
F200	General Interest Numbered 1-200	1899	25p	£50.00
F300	General Interest Numbered 201-500	1900	60p	—
F395/397	General Interest Numbered 501-898	1900	50p	£200.00

Qty		Date	Odds	Sets
F180/200	General Interest Numbered 899-1098	1901	80p	—
F50	General Interest Numbered 1099-1148	1901	70p	—
F18	Golf Base I	1901	£7.50	£135.00
F14	London Street Scenes Base I	1901	£1.50	£21.00
F400	New Series 1	1902	60p	£240.00
F400	New Series B	1902	70p	£280.00
F300	New Series C	1902	50p	£150.00
F46	Pantomime & Theatre Artistes Base D	1899	£2.00	—
LF45	Pantomime & Theatre Artistes Base D	1899	£2.50	—
F50	Pantomime & Theatre Artistes Base M	1899	£2.00	—
F60/62	Politicians, Base D	1900	50p	£30.00
F3	Royalty Base M	1899	£1.25	£3.75
F32	Turner Paintings Base I	1901	80p	£25.00
F10	Views & Scenes Abroad Base I	1901	60p	£6.00

Tabs Type Issues

Qty		Date	Odds	Sets
75	Actresses (numbered 126-200)	1900	£6.00	—
?200	Actresses (Plain Back)	1900	£1.50	—
200	Actresses & Foreign Views	1900	£1.25	—
1	General de Wet	1901	—	£1.50
1	General Interest (Unnumbered)	1901	—	£3.00
?33	General Interest (no Labour clause)	1900	£15.00	—
150	General Interest A Series	1901	35p	£70.00
200	General Interest B Series	1901	35p	£80.00
200	General Interest C Series (1-200)	1902	35p	£70.00
100	General Interest C Series (201-300)	1902	£1.50	—
50	General Interest C Series (301-350)	1902	40p	£20.00
200	General Interest D Series	1902	35p	£70.00
120	General Interest E Series	1902	60p	£72.00
320	General Interest F Series (1-320)	1902	60p	£180.00
100	General Interest F Series (321-420)	1902	£1.50	—
120	General Interest (1-120)	1902	60p	£72.00
196	General Interest (Item 95)	1902	50p	£100.00
100	General Interest (Item 96)	1902	50p	£50.00
100	General Interest (Item 97-1)	1902	80p	£80.00
200	General Interest (Item 97-2)	1902	50p	£100.00
?107	General Interest (Oblong back)	1902	£7.50	—
17	Heroes of the Ring	1901	£2.50	£42.50
1	H.M. The Queen	1901	—	£2.00
2	H.R.H. The Prince of Wales	1901	£2.00	£4.00
14	Imperial Interest	1901	50p	£7.00
106	Imperial or International Interest	1901	40p	£40.00
3	International Interest	1901	60p	£1.80
14	International Interest or a Prominent British Officer	1901	50p	£7.00
71	Leading Artistes of the Day	1901	60p	£42.50
?24	Leading Artistes of the Day (no Labour clause)	1901	£15.00	—
?82	Leading Artistes of the Day (non descriptive)	1901	£7.50	—
22	Leading Athletes	1901	£1.00	£22.00
15	Leading Favourites of the Turf	1901	£1.50	£22.50
54	Leading Generals at the War	1901	50p	—
25	Leading Generals at the War (Different)	1901	60p	—
47	Leading Generals at the War (Non-Descriptive)	1901	60p	—
25	Leading Generals at the War (Lucky Star)	1901	£2.50	—

OGDENS LTD.—cont.

Qty		Date	Odds	Sets
2	Members of Parliament	1901	£1.50	£3.00
11	Notable Coursing Dogs	1901	£2.00	£22.00
12	Our Leading Cricketers	1901	£6.50	£78.00
17	Our Leading Footballers	1901	£1.60	£27.00
37	Prominent British Officers	1901	50p	£18.50
50	Stage Artistes & Celebrities	1900	£1.25	£62.50
1	The Yacht "Columbia"	1901	—	£2.50
1	The Yacht "Shamrock"	1901	—	£2.50

Australian Issues (Tabs Type, Guinea Gold Brand)

Qty		Date	Odds	Sets
1	Christian de Wet	1901	*£4.00*	—
1	Corporal G. E. Nurse, V.C.	1901	*£4.00*	—
14	English Cricketer Series	1901	£25.00	—
400	General Interest (Numbered)	1901	£1.75	—
?84	General Interest (Unnumbered)	1901	£3.00	—
1	Imperial Interest	1901	*£4.00*	—
21	Imperial or International Interest	1901	*£4.00*	—
4	International Interest	1901	*£4.00*	—
1	Lady Sarah Wilson	1901	*£4.00*	—
29	Leading Generals at the War	1901	*£4.00*	—
8	Prominent British Officers	1901	*£4.00*	—

Other Overseas Issues

Qty		Date	Odds	Sets
51	Actresses, Black & White (Polo)	1906	£1.75	—
30	Actresses, Brown (Polo)	1908	£1.50	£45.00
17	Animals (Polo)	1916	£8.00	—
60	Animals (Ruler)	1912	£1.60	£100.00
60	Animals (Tabs)	1912	£1.60	£100.00
50	Aviation Series (Tabs)	1912	£3.00	—
45	Beauties—Picture Hats (Polo)	1911	£4.00	—
50	Best Dogs of Their Breed (Polo blue)	1916	£5.00	—
50	Best Dogs of Their Breed (Polo pink)	1916	£5.00	—
52	Birds of Brilliant Plumage, P/C Inset (Ruler) ...	1914	£1.75	£90.00
25	British Trees & Their Uses (Guinea Gold) ...	1927	80p	£20.00
25	China's Ancient Warriors (Ruler)	1913	£2.50	£62.50
25	Famous Railway Trains (Guinea Gold)	1928	£1.20	£30.00
20	Flowers (Polo)	1915	£3.50	—
25	Indian Women (Polo)	1919	£3.00	£75.00
30	Music Hall Celebrities (Polo)	1911	£3.00	£90.00
50	Music Hall Celebrities (Tabs)	1911	£3.00	—
52	Playing Cards (Polo)	1922	*£7.50*	—
50	Riders of the World (Polo)	1911	£2.50	£125.00
50	Russo Japanese Series	1904	*£15.00*	—
36	Ships & Their Pennants (Polo)	1911	£3.50	—
32	Transport of the World (Polo)	1917	£3.50	—

THE ORLANDO CIGARETTE & CIGAR CO.

Qty		Date	Odds	Sets
40	Home & Colonial Regiments	1901	*£150.00*	—

W. T. OSBORNE & CO.

Qty		Date	Odds	Sets
40	Naval & Military Phrases	1904	£30.00	—

OSBORNE TOBACCO CO.

Qty		Date	Odds	Sets
50	Modern Aircraft (Blue Front)	1952	—	£3.00
50	Modern Aircraft (Brown Front)	1952	—	£6.00

J. A. PATTREIOUEX LTD.

Early Photographic Sets, Mainly with Serial Letters

Qty		Date	Odds	Sets
F96	Animals (CA1-96)	1926	50p	—
LF50	Animals & Scenes (Unnumbered)	1924	60p	—
LF50	Animals & Scenes (1-50)	1925	60p	—
F192	Animals & Scenes (250-441)	1925	50p	—
F96	Animals & Scenes (CC1-96)	1926	50p	—
LF50	Animals & Scenes (I1-50)	1927	60p	—
F96	Animals & Scenes (JS1-96A)	1928	50p	—
LF100	Animal Studies (A42-141)	1925	50p	—
LF50	Animal Studies (A151-200)	1925	50p	—
LF30	Beauties (JM1-30)	1928	£1.25	—
LF50	British & Egyptian Scenes (CM1-50A)	1927	60p	—
LF50	British Empire Exhibition (JM1-50B)	1928	80p	£40.00
XF100	Cathedrals, Abbeys & Castles (SJ1-100) ...	1928	£1.25	—
LF30	Child Studies (JM No. 1-30)	1928	£2.00	—
F96	Famous Cricketers (C1-96, plain back)	1926	£20.00	—
F96	Famous Cricketers (C1-96, printed back)	1926	£20.00	—
F191	Famous Footballers (F1-191)	1927	£2.50	—
LF50	Famous Statues (JCM1-50C)	1928	80p	£40.00
F96	Footballers (FA1-96)	1927	£1.50	£150.00
F96	Footballers (FB1-96)	1928	£1.50	£150.00
F96	Footballers (FC1-96)	1928	£1.50	£150.00
LF48	Football Teams (F192-239)	1927	£4.00	—
F96	Natives & Scenes (1-96B)	1926	50p	—
F36	Natives & Scenes (1-36B) (As Above)	1926	50p	—
F96	Natives & Scenes (CB1-96)	1926	50p	—
F96	Natives & Scenes (JS1-96) (As Above)	1926	50p	—
F96	Overseas Scenes (1-96C)	1926	50p	—
LF50	Overseas Scenes (CM1-50B)	1926	60p	—
LF50	Overseas Scenes (JM1-50) (As Above)	1928	60p	£30.00
LF50	Overseas Scenes (CM1-50S)	1927	60p	—
LF50	Overseas Scenes (S101-150) (As Above)	1929	60p	—
F96	Overseas Scenes (1-96D)	1927	50p	—
LF50	Overseas Scenes (1-50E)	1928	60p	—
LF50	Overseas Scenes (1-50F)	1928	60p	—
LF50	Overseas Scenes (JM1-50A)	1928	60p	£30.00
LF50	Scenes (201-250)	1925	60p	£30.00
LF50	Scenes (G1-50)	1927	75p	—
LF50	Scenes (1-50H)	1927	60p	—
LF50	Scenes (JCM1-50D)	1927	60p	—
LF100	Scenes (S1-100)	1928	60p	—
LF4	Scenes (V1-4)	1928	£2.50	—

Other Series

Qty		Date	Odds	Sets
F28	Beautiful Scotland	1939	35p	£10.00
MF48	Beautiful Scotland	1939	15p	£5.00
MF48	Britain from the Air	1939	15p	£5.00
50	British Empire Exhibition Series	1929	£1.20	£60.00
MF48	British Railways	1938	15p	£7.50
50	Builders of the British Empire	1929	£1.60	£80.00

J. A. PATTREIOUEX LTD.—cont.

Qty		Date	Odds	Sets
50	Celebrities in Sport	1930	£1.60	£80.00
F28	Coastwise	1939	35p	£10.00
MF48	Coastwise	1939	15p	£6.00
75	Cricketers Series	1928	£4.00	£300.00
50	Dirt Track Riders	1929	£4.00	£200.00
F54	Dirt Track Riders	1935	£5.00	—
MF48	Dogs	1939	15p	£6.00
30	Drawing Made Easy	1930	£1.40	£42.00
F28	Flying	1938	80p	£22.50
MF48	Flying	1938	16p	£8.00
F78	Footballers in Action	1934	£1.25	£100.00
100	Footballers Series	1927	£3.00	£300.00
MF48	Holiday Haunts by the Sea	1938	15p	£7.50
X24	Jackpot Jigsaws	1969	50p	—
25	King Lud Problems	1936	£8.00	—
26	Maritime Flags	1931	£5.00	£130.00
F28	Our Countryside	1938	35p	£10.00
MF48	Our Countryside	1938	15p	£5.00
25	Photos of Football Stars	1929	£12.50	—
50	Railway Posters by Famous Artists	1930	£3.50	£175.00
F54	Real Photographs of London	1936	£1.20	£65.00
F28	Shots from the Films	1938	60p	£16.50
MF48	Sights of Britain	1936	15p	£6.00
MF48	Sights of Britain 2nd Series	1936	15p	£4.00
MF48	Sights of Britain 3rd Series	1937	15p	£5.00
MF48	Sights of London 1st Series	1935	25p	£12.50
MF12	Sights of London—Supplementary Series ...	1935	40p	£5.00
F54	Sporting Celebrities	1935	£1.40	£75.00
MF96	Sporting Events and Stars	1935	30p	£30.00
50	Sports Trophies	1931	£1.25	£62.50
MF48	The Bridges of Britain	1938	15p	£5.00
52	The English & Welsh Counties	1928	£1.00	£52.00
MF48	The Navy	1937	15p	£6.00
B24	Treasure Isle	1968	50p	—
F51	Views	1933	70p	£35.00
F54	Views of Britain	1937	£1.00	£55.00
MF48	Winter Scenes	1937	15p	£5.00

W. PEPPERDY

Qty		Date	Odds	Sets
30	Army Pictures, Cartoons, etc.	1916	£50.00	—

M. PEZARO & SON

Qty		Date	Odds	Sets
25	Armies of the World	1900	£60.00	—
?25	Song Titles Illustrated	1900	£90.00	—

GODFREY PHILLIPS LTD.

Qty		Date	Odds	Sets
50	Actresses (Oval)	1916	£4.00	£200.00
50	Actresses (Oval, Anonymous)	1916	£2.50	£125.00
25	Actresses, C Series (Ball of Beauty)	1900	£60.00	—
25	Actresses, C Series (Carriage)	1900	£17.50	—
25	Actresses, C Series (Derby)	1900	£50.00	—
25	Actresses, C Series (Horseshoe)	1900	£15.00	—
25	Actresses, C Series (Teapot)	1900	£60.00	—
25	Actresses, C Series (Volunteer)	1900	£50.00	—

GODFREY PHILLIPS LTD.—cont.

Qty		Date	Odds	Sets
2	Advertisement Cards	1934	£6.50	£13.00
50	Aircraft	1938	60p	£30.00
54	Aircraft Series No. 1 (matt)	1938	20p	£10.00
54	Aircraft Series No. 1 (varnished)	1938	£2.00	—
40	Animal Series	1903	£3.50	£140.00
M30	Animal Studies	1936	15p	£4.00
50	Annuals	1939	15p	£5.00
L25	Arms of the English Sees	1924	£3.00	£75.00
48	A Selection of BDV Wonderful Gifts	1930	50p	£24.00
48	A Selection of BDV Wonderful Gifts	1931	50p	£24.00
48	A Selection of BDV Wonderful Gifts	1932	50p	£24.00
24	Beauties "HUMPS"	1898	£40.00	—
24	Beauties "HUMPS" (Plums front)	1898	*£150.00*	—
30	Beauties, Nymphs	1896	£40.00	—
?50	Beauties, Plums (black & white)	1897	*£80.00*	—
50	Beauties, Plums (green front)	1897	£30.00	—
50	Beauties, Plums (plum front)	1897	£30.00	—
25	Beauties (Numbered 801-825)	1902	£6.00	£150.00
30	Beauties, Oval (Plain Backs)	1914	£1.20	£36.00
44	Beauties of To-day	1937	60p	£26.00
50	Beauties of To-day	1938	30p	£15.00
36	Beauties of To-day 2nd Series	1940	20p	£7.00
F54	Beauties of To-day	1939	50p	£27.00
LF36	Beauties of To-day	1938	£1.50	£54.00
XF36	Beauties of To-day (Unnumbered)	1937	70p	£25.00
XF36	Beauties of To-day 2nd Series	1938	50p	£18.00
XF36	Beauties of To-day 3rd Series	1938	40p	£15.00
XF36	Beauties of To-day 4th Series	1938	40p	£15.00
XF36	Beauties of To-day 5th Series	1938	20p	£7.00
XF36	Beauties of To-day 6th Series	1939	20p	£7.00
XF36	Beauties of To-day 7th Series	1939	20p	£7.00
XF36	Beauties of To-day (B.D.V. Back)	1939	15p	£5.00
36	Beauties of the World	1931	75p	£27.00
36	Beauties of the World Series No. 2	1933	75p	£27.00
50	Beautiful Women (I.F. Series)	1908	£6.00	£300.00
50	Beautiful Women (W.I. Series)	1908	£6.00	£300.00
L50	Beautiful Women	1908	£12.00	—
P30	Beauty Spots of the Homeland	1938	16p	£5.00
50	Bird Painting	1938	15p	£6.00
25	Boxer Rebellion	1904	£15.00	—
50	British Beauties (Photogravure)	1916	£3.50	£175.00
K76	British Beauties	1916	£1.75	£135.00
F54	British Beauties (1-54)	1914	£1.50	£80.00
F54	British Beauties (55-108)	1915	£1.50	£80.00
108	British Beauties (Plain Back)	1914	£2.00	—
50	British Birds and Their Eggs	1936	40p	£20.00
30	British Butterflies, No. 1 Issue	1911	£3.00	£90.00
25	British Butterflies	1927	30p	£7.50
25	British Butterflies (Transfers)	1936	30p	£7.50
25	British Orders of Chivalry & Valour (De Reszke)	1939	80p	£20.00
25	British Orders of Chivalry & Valour (Phillips) ...	1939	80p	£20.00
25	British Warships	1915	£3.00	£75.00
L25	British Warships	1915	£25.00	—

Qty		Date	Odds	Sets
F80	British Warships	1916	£7.50	—
50	Busts of Famous People (brown back)	1907	*£15.00*	—
50	Busts of Famous People (green back)	1907	£3.50	£175.00
M36	Characters Come to Life	1938	15p	£5.00
25	Chinese Series (English text)	1910	£3.50	£87.50
25	Chinese Series (Volunteer Cigarettes)	1910	£4.00	—
M25	Cinema Stars (Circular)	1924	£1.00	£25.00
F52	Cinema Stars (Set 1)	1923	£1.50	£80.00
30	Cinema Stars (Brown)	1924	£1.20	£36.00
30	Cinema Stars (Black & White)	1925	70p	£21.00
32	Cinema Stars (Black & White)	1930	60p	£19.00
32	Cinema Stars (Brown, Hand Coloured)	1934	70p	£21.00
30	Cinema Stars (Plain Back)	1935	25p	£7.50
50	Colonial Troops	1902	£15.00	—
50	Coronation of Their Majesties	1937	15p	£5.00
M36	Coronation of Their Majesties	1937	15p	£4.00
P24	Coronation of Their Majesties	1937	70p	£17.00
KF198	Cricketers (Pinnace)	1924	£4.00	—
F192	Cricketers (Brown Back)	1924	£4.00	—
LF25	Cricketers (Brown Back)	1924	£8.00	—
LF?75	Cricketers (Pinnace)	1924	£20.00	—
1	Cricket Fixture Card	1936	—	£2.50
25	Derby Winners & Jockeys	1923	£1.40	£35.00
30	Eggs, Nests & Birds (Numbered)	1912	£3.50	£105.00
30	Eggs, Nests & Birds (Unnumbered)	1912	£3.50	£105.00
25	Empire Industries	1927	50p	£12.50
49/50	Evolution of the British Navy	1930	50p	£25.00
25	Famous Boys	1924	£1.20	£30.00
32	Famous Cricketers	1926	£2.50	f80.00
25	Famous Crowns	1938	16p	£4.00
50	Famous Footballers	1936	50p	£25.00
M36	Famous Love Scenes	1939	15p	£5.00
50	Famous Minors	1936	15p	£5.00
P26	Famous Paintings	1936	80p	£21.00
25	Feathered Friends	1928	70p	£17.50
50	Film Favourites	1934	15p	£6.50
50	Film Stars	1934	15p	£7.50
P24	Film Stars (Series of Cards) (Vivid Fronts)	1934	40p	£10.00
P24	Film Stars (Series of 24 Cards)	1934	80p	£20.00
P24	Film Stars, 2nd (25-48)	1934	£1.50	£36.00
50	First Aid	1923	60p	£30.00
25	First Aid Series	1914	£3.50	£87.50
25	Fish	1924	£1.20	£30.00
M30	Flower Studies	1937	15p	£3.50
P30	Flower Studies	1937	25p	£7.50
KF940	Footballers (Pinnace 1-940)	1922	50p	—
KF1522	Footballers (Pinnace 941-2462)	1923	£1.00	—
LF2462	Footballers (Pinnace)	1923	£1.75	—
P30	Garden Studies	1938	15p	£4.50
13	General Interest	1896	£30.00	£390.00
90	Guinea Gold Series (Numbered)	1902	£2.50	£225.00
100	Guinea Gold Series	1902	£3.00	£300.00
160	Guinea Gold Series	1902	£2.50	£400.00
100	Guinea Gold Series (Brown)	1902	£6.00	—

GODFREY PHILLIPS LTD.—cont.

Qty		Date	Odds	Sets
25	Home Pets	1924	£1.00	£25.00
25	How to Build a Two Valve Set	1929	80p	£20.00
25	How To Do It Series	1913	£5.00	£125.00
25	How to Make a Valve Amplifier	1924	£1.20	£30.00
25	How to Make Your Own Wireless Set	1923	80p	£20.00
25	Indian Series	1908	£10.00	£250.00
54	In the Public Eye	1935	15p	£6.00
50	International Caps	1936	35p	£17.50
35/37	Kings & Queens of England	1925	£1.00	£35.00
25	Lawn Tennis	1930	80p	£20.00
K52	Miniature Playing Cards (Red back)	1906	*£60.00*	—
K53	Miniature Playing Cards (Blue Design)	1934	30p	£16.00
K53	Miniature Playing Cards (Buff)	1932	30p	£16.00
K53	Miniature Playing Cards (White)	1933	35p	—
K53	Miniature Playing Cards (Yellow)	1933	35p	—
25	Model Railways	1927	£1.20	£30.00
30	Morse Signalling	1916	£4.00	£120.00
50	Motor Cars at a Glance	1924	£1.60	£80.00
20	Novelty Series	1924	£5.00	£100.00
25	Old Favourites	1924	60p	£15.00
M36	Old Masters	1939	16p	£6.00
36	Olympic Champions, Amsterdam 1928	1928	70p	£25.00
25	Optical Illusions	1927	80p	£20.00
36	Our Dogs	1939	50p	£18.00
M30	Our Dogs	1939	16p	£5.00
P30	Our Dogs	1939	£1.60	£50.00
M48	Our Favourites	1935	15p	£5.00
P30	Our Glorious Empire	1939	25p	£7.50
M30	Our Puppies	1936	15p	£4.50
P30	Our Puppies	1936	40p	£12.00
25	Personalities of To-day	1932	70p	£17.50
25	Popular Superstitions	1930	60p	£15.00
25	Prizes for Needlework	1925	£1.20	£30.00
25	Railway Engines	1934	£1.20	£30.00
KF27	Real Photo Series (War Leaders)	1916	£5.00	£135.00
1	Real Stamp Card	1928	—	50p
25	Red Indians	1927	£1.00	£25.00
20	Russo Japanese War Series	1905	*£100.00*	—
25	School Badges	1927	40p	£10.00
48	Screen Stars A	1936	20p	£10.00
48	Screen Stars B (different)	1936	25p	£12.50
48	Screen Stars (not embossed)	1936	30p	£15.00
30	Semaphore Signalling	1916	£4.00	£120.00
25	Ships and their Flags	1924	£1.40	£35.00
M36	Ships that have Made History	1938	15p	£4.00
M48	Shots from the Films	1934	15p	£6.00
50	Soccer Stars	1936	35p	£17.50
36	Soldiers of The King	1939	25p	£9.00
M20	Special Jubilee Year Series	1935	15p	£3.00
P12	Special Jubilee Year Series	1935	£1.00	£12.00
30	Speed Champions	1930	75p	£22.50
36	Sporting Champions	1929	75p	£27.00
25	Sporting Series	1910	£10.00	—
25	Sports	1923	£1.50	£37.50

Qty		Date	Odds	Sets
50	Sportsmen—Spot the Winner	1937	15p	£6.00
35	Stage & Cinema Beauties A	1933	50p	£17.50
35	Stage & Cinema Beauties B (Different)	1933	30p	£10.50
50	Stage & Cinema Beauties (Different)	1935	50p	£25.00
54	Stars of the Screen	1934	50p	£27.00
48	Stars of the Screen (Different)	1936	20p	£10.00
25	Statues & Monuments (brown back)	1907	*£30.00*	—
25	Statues & Monuments (green back)	1907	£5.00	£125.00
25	Territorial Series (Motors Back)	1908	£14.00	£350.00
25	The 1924 Cabinet	1924	£1.00	£25.00
48	The "Old Country"	1935	30p	£15.00
50	This Mechanized Age 1st Series (adhesive)	1936	15p	£6.00
50	This Mechanized Age 1st Series (non-adhesive)	1936	15p	£7.50
50	This Mechanized Age 2nd Series	1937	15p	£7.50
25	Types of British & Colonial Troops	1899	£30.00	—
25	Types of British Soldiers (M651-MG75)	1900	f10.00	£250.00
F63	War Photos	1916	£5.00	£315.00
X20	Wrestling Holds	1930	*£15.00*	—
XS30	Zoo Studies—Come to Life Series	1939	60p	£18.00
X1	Zoo Studies Viewer	1939	—	£1.50

BDV Package Issues

Qty		Date	Odds	Sets
17	Boxers	1932	£1.25	—
53	Cricketers	1932	£3.50	—
67	Film Stars	1932	75p	—
132	Footballers	1932	£1.25	—
19	Jockeys	1932	75p	—
21	Speedway Riders	1932	£3.00	—
38	Sportsmen	1932	£1.50	—

"Sports" Package Issues

Qty		Date	Odds	Sets
50	All Sports 1st	1948	£1.50	—
25	All Sports 2nd	1949	£1.50	—
25	All Sports 3rd	1953	£1.50	—
25	All Sports 4th	1954	£1.50	—
25	Cricketers 1st	1948	£3.50	—
25	Cricketers 2nd	1951	£3.50	—
25	Footballers 1st	1948	£1.50	—
50	Footballers 2nd	1950	£1.50	—
25	Footballers 3rd	1951	£1.50	—
25	Jockeys	1952	£1.25	—
25	Radio Stars	1949	£1.25	—
25	Rugby & Association Footballers	1952	£1.50	—

Overseas Issues

Qty		Date	Odds	Sets
50	Animal Studies	1930	£1.00	£50.00
50	Annuals	1939	60p	£30.00
X32	Australian Birds (Cartons)	1968	—	£3.50
X24	Australian Scenes (Cartons)	1965	—	*£6.00*
50	Australian Sporting Celebrities	1932	£1.20	£60.00
X32	Australian Wild Flowers (Cartons)	1967	—	*£6.00*
50	Film Stars	1934	80p	£40.00
E16	Gemstones (Cartons)	1970	—	£3.00
50	Stars of British Films	1934	80p	£40.00
38	Test Cricketers	1932	£1.20	£45.00

Qty		Date	Odds	Sets
X32	The Barrier Reef (Cartons)	1968	—	£3.00
50	Victorian Footballers	1933	£1.00	—
75	Victorian Footballers	1933	£1.00	—
50	Victorian League and Association Footballers	1934	£1.25	—
100	Who's Who in Australian Sport	1933	£1.00	£100.00

Silk Issues

M62	Arms of Countries & Territories	1912	£2.00	—
B32	Beauties—Modern Paintings	1910	£6.00	—
P32	Beauties—Modern Paintings	1910	£25.00	—
B100	Birds	1920	£1.50	—
M12	Birds of the Tropics	1913	£6.00	—
L12	Birds of the Tropics	1913	£7.50	—
P12	Birds of the Tropics	1913	£12.50	—
X24	British Admirals	1916	£3.00	£72.00
D50	British Butterflies & Moths	1922	£2.00	—
M108	British Naval Crests (Anon)	1915	60p	—
M108	British Naval Crests (B.D.V.)	1915	75p	—
B23	Butterflies	1911	£6.00	—
B47	Ceramic Art	1925	60p	£28.00
M47	Ceramic Art	1925	50p	£23.50
L47	Ceramic Art	1925	£1.00	—
B65	Clan Tartans	1922	65p	—
M65	Clan Tartans (B.D.V.)	1922	50p	£32.50
M49	Clan Tartans (Anon)	1922	70p	£35.00
L56	Clan Tartans	1922	£2.00	—
P12	Clan Tartans	1922	£2.50	£30.00
M108	Colonial Army Badges	1913	75p	£75.00
M17	County Cricket Badges (Anon)	1921	£7.50	—
M17	County Cricket Badges (BDV)	1921	£7.50	—
M108	Crests & Badges of the British Army (Anon, Numbered)	1914	50p	£54.00
M108	Crests & Badges of the British Army (Anon, Unnumbered)	1914	60p	£65.00
M108	Crests & Badges of the British Army (BDV)	1914	50p	£54.00
L108	Crests & Badges of the British Army (Anon)	1914	75p	—
L108	Crests & Badges of the British Army (BDV)	1914	£1.00	—
M143	Flags, Set 4 (Short)	1913	50p	—
L142	Flags, Set 4 (Long)	1913	£1.25	—
M24	Flags, Set 5 (With Caption)	1913	60p	£15.00
M12	Flags, Set 5 (No Caption)	1913	75p	£9.00
G8	Flags, Set 5	1913	£10.00	—
M18	Flags, Set 6	1913	50p	£9.00
M20	Flags, Set 7	1913	60p	£12.00
M50	Flags, 5th Series	1914	80p	£40.00
M120	Flags, 7th Series	1914	50p	£60.00
L120	Flags, 10th Series	1915	60p	—
M120	Flags, 12th Series	1915	50p	—
L65	Flags, 15th Series	1916	75p	—
L64	Flags, 16th Series	1916	75p	£48.00
M132	Flags, 20th Series	1917	50p	—
M126	Flags, 25th Series	1917	50p	£60.00
L62	Flags, 25th Series	1917	£2.00	—
M112	Flags, 26th Series	1918	50p	£55.00

GODFREY PHILLIPS LTD.—cont.

Qty		Date	Odds	Sets
M70	Flags, 28th Series	1918	50p	£35.00
P18	Flags, Set 13	1914	£1.00	£18.00
G23	Flags, Set 13 (Anon)	1914	£1.00	£23.00
G27	Flags, Set 13 (BDV)	1914	£1.00	£27.00
M21	Football Colours (Anon)	1920	£2.50	—
M86	Football Colours (BDV)	1920	£1.75	—
P78	Football Colours	1920	£1.75	—
M126	G.P. Territorial Badges	1913	80p	£100.00
L25	Great War Leaders (Sepia)	1915	£2.50	£62.50
M3	Great War Leaders & Celebrities (Anon)	1916	£3.00	£9.00
M4	Great War Leaders & Celebrities (BDV)	1916	£3.00	£12.00
L3	Great War Leaders & Celebrities (Anon)	1916	£3.00	£9.00
L2	Great War Leaders & Celebrities (BDV)	1916	£3.00	£6.00
P18	Great War Leaders & Celebrities (BDV)	1916	£2.50	—
G29	Great War Leaders & Celebrities (Anon)	1916	£2.00	—
G45	Great War Leaders & Celebrities (BDV)	1916	£2.00	—
M51	Great War Leaders & Warships	1914	£4.00	—
B25	Heraldic Series	1924	60p	—
M25	Heraldic Series	1924	60p	£15.00
L25	Heraldic Series	1924	£2.00	—
P12	Heraldic Series	1924	£2.50	£30.00
M26	House Flags	1915	£4.00	—
M10	Irish Patriots	1919	£7.50	—
X10	Irish Patriots	1919	£7.50	—
P10	Irish Patriots	1919	£10.00	—
M1	Irish Republican Stamp	1925	—	75p
M1	Let 'Em All Come	1920	—	£6.00
M54	Naval Badges of Rank & Military Headdress	1917	£3.50	—
G1	Nelson's Signal at Trafalgar	1921	—	*£25.00*
G40	Old Masters, Set 1	1911	£17.50	—
G20	Old Masters, Set 2 (Anon)	1912	£3.00	£60.00
G20	Old Masters, Set 2 (BDV)	1912	£2.50	£50.00
M85	Old Masters, Set 3 (Anon)	1912	£1.50	—
M40	Old Masters, Set 3 (BDV)	1912	£1.75	—
M120	Old Masters, Set 4	1913	£1.00	£120.00
M20	Old Masters, Set 5 (Anon, Unnumbered)	1915	£1.50	—
M20	Old Masters, Set 5 (Anon, 101–120)	1915	60p	£12.00
M60	Old Masters, Set 5 (BDV 1–60)	1915	50p	—
M20	Old Masters, Set 5 (BDV 101–120)	1915	60p	£12.00
B50	Old Masters, Set 6	1924	50p	—
M50	Old Masters, Set 7 (301–350)	1916	£1.50	—
M50	Orders of Chivalry (Anon)	1920	£1.00	—
M24	Orders of Chivalry (BDV, 1–24)	1914	75p	£18.00
M24	Orders of Chivalry (GP401–424)	1914	£1.00	—
M25	Pilot & Signal Flags (Anon)	1921	£1.00	—
M25	Pilot & Signal Flags (BDV)	1921	80p	£20.00
L72	Regimental Colours	1914	£2.00	—
M50	Regimental Colours, Series 12	1918	£1.00	£50.00
M120	Regimental Colours & Crests (Anon)	1915	60p	—
M120	Regimental Colours & Crests (BDV)	1915	60p	—
G120	Regimental Colours & Crests (Anon)	1915	£3.50	—
G120	Regimental Colours & Crests (BDV)	1915	£3.00	—
M10	Religious Pictures	1911	£10.00	—
X10	Religious Pictures	1911	£10.00	—

GODFREY PHILLIPS LTD.—cont.

Qty		Date	Odds	Sets
G10	Religious Pictures	1911	£20.00	—
B1	The Allies Flags	1915	—	£5.00
G2	The Allies Flags (Anon)	1915	£4.00	—
G2	The Allies Flags (BDV)	1915	£4.00	—
M75	Town & City Arms	1918	£1.00	—
L75	Town & City Arms	1918	£1.00	—
M25	Victoria Cross Heroes I	1915	£6.00	—
M25	Victoria Cross Heroes II (With Flags)	1915	£7.50	—
M90	War Pictures	1915	£4.00	—

JOHN PLAYER & SONS

Qty		Date	Odds	Sets
25	Actors & Actresses	1898	£16.00	£400.00
50	Actresses	1897	£16.00	£800.00
8	Advertisement Cards	1894	£200.00	—
1	Advertisement Card—Sailor	1929	—	£2.00
L1	Advertisement Card—Sailor	1929	—	£7.50
L1	Advertisement Card—Wants List	1936	—	60p
50	Aeroplanes (Eire)	1935	60p	£30.00
50	Aeroplanes (Civil)	1935	15p	£7.50
50	Aircraft of the Royal Air Force	1938	15p	£6.50
X10	Allied Cavalry	1914	£5.00	£50.00
L24	A Nature Calendar	1930	£1.50	£36.00
50	Animals of the Countryside	1939	15p	£5.00
50	Animals of the Countryside (Eire)	1939	40p	—
L25	Aquarium Studies	1932	£1.00	£25.00
L25	Architectural Beauties	1927	£1.00	£25.00
50	Arms & Armour (blue back)	1909	£1.40	£70.00
50	Army Corps & Divisional Signs (1-50)	1924	15p	£5.50
100	Army Corps & Divisional Signs 2nd (51-150) ...	1925	16p	£16.00
25	Army Life	1910	50p	£12.50
X12	Artillery in Action	1917	£2.00	£24.00
50	A Sectional Map of Ireland	1932	£1.00	£50.00
50	Association Cup Winners	1930	40p	£20.00
50	Aviary and Cage Birds	1933	30p	£15.00
50	Aviary and Cage Birds (Transfers)	1933	15p	£7.50
L25	Aviary & Cage Birds	1935	£1.00	£25.00
50	Badges & Flags of British Regiments (Green) ...	1903	£1.25	£62.50
50	Badges & Flags of British Regiments (Brown back, Numbered)	1904	£1.25	£62.50
50	Badges & Flags of British Regiments (Brown back, Unnumbered)	1904	£1.50	£75.00
50	Birds & Their Young	1937	15p	£5.00
50	Birds & Their Young (Eire) (adhesive)	1937	40p	—
50	Birds & Their Young (Eire) (non-adhesive) ...	1937	50p	—
25	Birds & Their Young (non-adhesive)	Unissued	15p	£2.00
25	Birds & Their Young 2nd (non-adhesive) ...	Unissued	15p	£2.00
CF10	Bookmarks (Authors)	1900	£35.00	£350.00
25	Boxing (Eire)	1934	£1.20	£30.00
50	Boy Scouts & Girl Guide	1933	15p	£7.00
50	Boy Scouts & Girl Guide (Transfers)	1933	15p	£7.00
L25	British Butterflies	1934	£1.00	£25.00
50	British Empire Series	1904	70p	£35.00
25	British Live Stock	1915	50p	£12.50

78

Qty		Date	Odds	Sets
X25	British Live Stock (Blue Back)	1923	80p	£20.00
X25	British Live Stock (Brown Back)	1916	£1.50	£37.50
L25	British Naval Craft	1939	20p	£5.00
X20	British Pedigree Stock	1925	£1.00	£20.00
L25	British Regalia	1937	60p	£15.00
50	Butterflies	1932	35p	£17.50
50	Butterflies (Transfers)	1932	15p	£7.50
50	Butterflies & Moths	1904	£1.00	£50.00
25	Bygone Beauties	1914	60p	£15.00
X10	Bygone Beauties	1916	£2.50	£25.00
G?30	Cabinet Size Pictures	1896	£50.00	—
20	Castles & Abbeys (no border)	1895	£17.50	£350.00
20	Castles & Abbeys (white border)	1895	£16.00	£320.00
L24	Cats	1936	£2.50	£60.00
50	Celebrated Bridges	1903	£1.25	£62.50
50	Celebrated Gateways	1909	60p	£30.00
25	Ceremonial and Court Dress	1911	70p	£17.50
L25	Championship Golf Courses	1936	£1.20	£30.00
25	Characters from Dickens A Series (1-25)	1912	70p	£17.50
25	Characters from Dickens 2nd Series (26-50) ...	1912	70p	£17.50
50	Characters from Dickens (Re-issue)	1923	50p	£25.00
X10	Characters from Dickens	1914	£2.50	£25.00
L25	Characters from Fiction	1933	£1.00	£25.00
25	Characters from Thackeray	1913	50p	£12.50
50	Cities of the World	1900	£2.00	£100.00
L20	Clocks—Old & New	1928	£2.50	£50.00
25	Colonial & Indian Army Badges	1917	50p	£12.50
50	Coronation Series—Ceremonial Dress	1937	15p	£6.00
25	Counties and Their Industries (Numbered) ...	1914	40p	£10.00
25	Counties and Their Industries (Unnumbered) ...	1914	50p	£12.50
50	Countries Arms & Flags	1905	30p	£15.00
50	Country Seats and Arms (1-50)	1909	40p	£20.00
50	Country Seats and Arms 2nd Series (51-100) ...	1910	40p	£20.00
50	Country Seats and Arms 3rd Series (101-150) ...	1910	40p	£20.00
L25	Country Sports	1930	£1.00	£25.00
50	Cricketers 1930	1930	60p	£30.00
50	Cricketers 1934	1934	16p	£8.00
50	Cricketers 1938	1938	15p	£7.00
50	Cricketers, Caricatures by "RIP"	1926	60p	£30.00
25	Cries of London A Series	1913	60p	£15.00
X10	Cries of London A Series	1912	£2.50	£25.00
X10	Cries of London 2nd Series	1914	£2.00	£20.00
25	Cries of London 2nd Series	1916	30p	£7.50
50	Curious Beaks	1929	15p	£6.50
50	Cycling	1939	15p	£7.00
50	Cycling (Eire) (adhesive)	1939	60p	—
50	Cycling (Eire) (non-adhesive)	1939	60p	—
50	Dandies	1932	15p	£6.50
L25	Dandies	1932	60p	£15.00
50	Decorations & Medals	Unissued	£1.20	£60.00
50	Derby and Grand National Winners	1933	60p	£30.00
50	Derby and Grand National Winners (Transfers) ...	1933	15p	£7.50
50	Dogs (Scenic Background)	1925	35p	£17.50
X12	Dogs Scenic Background)	1924	£1.25	£15.00

JOHN PLAYER & SONS—cont.

Qty		Date	Odds	Sets
50	Dogs, by Wardle (Full Length)	1931	20p	£10.00
50	Dogs, by Wardle (Transfers)	1931	15p	£7.50
L25	Dogs, by Wardle (Full Length)	1933	£1.00	£25.00
50	Dogs, by Wardle (Heads)	1929	20p	£10.00
L20	Dogs, by Wardle A Series (Heads)	1926	£1.20	£24.00
L20	Dogs, by Wardle 2nd Series (Heads)	1928	£1.00	£20.00
25	Dogs, by Wardle (Eire) A Series (Heads) ...	1927	80p	£20.00
25	Dogs, by Wardle 2nd Series (Eire) (Heads) ...	1929	80p	£20.00
50	Dogs Heads by Biegel	Unissued	15p	£7.00
L25	Dogs (Heads)	Unissued	40p	£10.00
50	Dogs' Heads (Silver Background, Eire)	1940	£1.00	£50.00
50	Drum Banners & Cap Badges	1924	35p	£17.50
25	Egyptian Kings & Queens and Classical Deities ...	1912	60p	£15.00
X10	Egyptian Sketches	1915	£2.00	£20.00
25	England's Military Heroes (Narrow)	1898	£20.00	£500.00
25	England's Military Heroes (Wide)	1898	£30.00	—
25	England's Naval Heroes (Non-Descriptive Narrow)	1897	£16.00	£400.00
25	England's Naval Heroes (Non-Descriptive Wide)	1897	£25.00	—
25	England's Naval Heroes (Descriptive, Narrow) ...	1898	£16.00	£400.00
25	England's Naval Heroes (Descriptive, Wide) ...	1898	£25.00	—
25	Everyday Phrases by Tom Browne	1900	£10.00	£250.00
L25	Fables of Aesop	1927	£1.20	£30.00
20	Famous Authors & Poets (Narrow)	1900	£12.50	£250.00
20	Famous Authors & Poets (Wide)	1900	£20.00	£400.00
L25	Famous Beauties	1937	40p	£10.00
50	Famous Irish Bred Horses	1936	£1.00	£50.00
50	Famous Irish Greyhounds	1935	£1.50	—
X10	Famous Paintings	1913	£2.00	£20.00
50	Film Stars	1934	25p	£12.50
50	Film Stars Second Series	1934	16p	£8.00
50	Film Stars Second Series (Eire)	1934	60p	—
50	Film Stars Third Series	1938	15p	£6.00
L25	Film Stars	1934	£1.20	£30.00
L25	Film Stars (Eire)	1934	*£4.00*	—
50	Firefighting Appliances	1930	60p	£30.00
50	Fishes of the World	1903	£1.00	£50.00
50	Flags of the League of Nations	1928	15p	£6.00
50	Football Caricatures by "MAC"	1927	20p	£10.00
50	Footballers, Caricatures by "RIP"	1926	20p	£10.00
50	Footballers 1928	1928	20p	£10.00
25	Footballers 1928-9, 2nd Series	1929	20p	£5.00
50	Fresh-water Fishes (pink back)	1933	25p	£12.50
50	Fresh-water Fishes (white back)	1934	50p	£25.00
L25	Fresh-water Fishes	1935	£1.00p	£25.00
L25	Fresh-water Fishes (Eire, non-adhesive)	1935	£3.50	—
25	From Plantation to Smoker	1926	15p	£3.00
50	Gallery of Beauty Series	1896	£16.00	£800.00
50	Game Birds and Wild Fowl	1927	25p	£12.50
L25	Game Birds & Wild Fowl	1928	£1.60	£40.00
25	Gems of British Scenery	1917	30p	£7.50
50	Gilbert and Sullivan	1925	35p	£17.50
X25	Gilbert & Sullivan	1926	£1.50	£37.50
50	Gilbert and Sullivan 2nd Series	1927	25p	£12.50
L25	Gilbert & Sullivan 2nd Series	1928	£1.50	£37.50

U.K. Tobacco 1920s

Beauties. Hignett, BAT, Players, Wills

Scientific Inventions and Discoveries.
Hill

Ships of all Ages. Sarony

Curious Signs. Churchman

The Nose Game. Carreras

Regalia Series. Carreras

Around the World. Bucktrout

Dogs. Players, also ITC Canada, Wills

U.K. Tobacco 1930s

Interesting Customs of the Navy Army & Air Force. Lambert & Butler

Coronation. J. Wix

The Game of Poker. Copes

Miniature Playing Cards. Phillips

This Mechanized Age. Phillips

British Naval Craft. Players

Qty		Date	Odds	Sets
L25	Golf	1939	£1.00	£25.00
25	Hidden Beauties	1929	15p	£3.00
25	Highland Clans	1907	£1.20	£30.00
50	Hints on Association Football	1934	16p	£8.00
X10	Historic Ships	1910	£2.50	£25.00
50	History of Naval Dress	1930	25p	£12.50
L25	History of Naval Dress	1929	80p	£20.00
50	International Air Liners	1936	15p	£6.00
50	International Air Liners (Eire)	1936	40p	—
25	Irish Place Names A Series	1927	80p	£20.00
25	Irish Place Names 2nd Series	1929	80p	£20.00
M5	Jubilee Issue	1960	60p	£3.00
50	Kings & Queens of England	1935	30p	£15.00
L50	Kings & Queens of England	1935	80p	£40.00
50	Life on Board a Man Of War in 1805 and 1905	1905	£1.20	£60.00
25	Live Stock	1925	£1.60	£40.00
50	Military Head-dress	1931	40p	£20.00
50	Military Series	1900	£12.00	£600.00
50	Military Uniforms of the British Empire Overseas	1938	15p	£6.50
25	Miniatures	1923	20p	£5.00
50	Modern Naval Craft	1939	15p	£5.00
50	Modern Naval Craft (Eire)	1939	40p	—
50	Motor Cars A Series	1936	30p	£15.00
50	Motor Cars (Eire) A Series	1936	60p	£30.00
50	Motor Cars 2nd Series	1937	25p	£12.50
L20	Mount Everest	1925	£1.25	£25.00
25	Napoleon	1916	50p	£12.50
50	National Flags and Arms	1936	15p	£5.00
50	National Flags and Arms (Eire)	1936	40p	—
50	Natural History	1924	15p	£7.00
X12	Natural History	1924	60p	£7.50
X12	Natural History, 2nd Series	1924	60p	£7.50
50	Nature Series	1909	60p	£30.00
X10	Nature Series (Birds)	1908	£6.00	£60.00
X10	Nature Series (Mammals)	1913	£2.50	£25.00
50	Old England's Defenders	1898	£12.00	£600.00
L25	Old Hunting Prints	1938	70p	£17.50
L25	Old Naval Prints	1936	80p	£20.00
X25	Old Sporting Prints	1924	£1.20	£30.00
L25	Picturesque Bridges	1929	£1.00	£25.00
L25	Picturesque Cottages	1929	£1.00	£25.00
L25	Picturesque London	1931	£1.00	£25.00
25	Players Past & Present	1916	30p	£7.50
25	Polar Exploration A Series	1915	50p	£12.50
25	Polar Exploration, 2nd Series	1916	50p	£12.50
L25	Portals of the Past	1930	£1.00	£25.00
50	Poultry	1931	30p	£15.00
50	Poultry (Transfers)	1931	15p	£7.50
25	Products of the World	1908	24p	£6.00
50	Products of the World (Different)	1928	15p	£5.00
25	Racehorses	1926	£2.00	£50.00
40	Racing Caricatures	1925	30p	£12.00
L25	Racing Yachts	1938	80p	£20.00
50	R.A.F. Badges (No Motto)	1937	15p	£6.00

Qty		Date	Odds	Sets
50	R.A.F. Badges (With Motto)	1937	15p	£6.50
50	Regimental Colours & Cap Badges (Regulars) ...	1907	50p	£25.00
50	Regimental Colours & Cap Badges (Territorials, Blue Back)	1910	60p	£30.00
50	Regimental Colours & Cap Badges (Territorials, Brown Back)	1910	50p	£25.00
50	Regimental Standards and Cap Badges	1930	30p	£15.00
50	Regimental Uniforms (Blue)	1912	60p	£30.00
50	Regimental Uniforms (Brown)	1914	70p	£35.00
X10	Regimental Uniforms (Different)	1914	£4.00	£40.00
50	Regimental Uniforms 2nd Series (51-100) ...	1913	60p	£30.00
50	Riders of the World	1905	70p	£35.00
P30	Rulers & Views	1902	£50.00	—
50	Sea Fishes	1935	15p	£5.00
50	Sea Fishes (Eire)	1935	40p	—
50	Screen Celebrities (Eire)	1938	60p	—
25	Shakespearean Series	1917	30p	£7.50
L20	Ship-Models	1926	£1.50	£30.00
50	Shipping	Unissued	—	£40.00
25	Ships' Figure-heads	1912	50p	£12.50
L25	Ships' Figure-heads	1931	80p	£20.00
L8	Snap Cards	1930	£5.00	£40.00
50	Speedway Riders	1937	30p	£15.00
S150	Stereoscopic Series	1904	*£35.00*	—
50	Straight Line Caricatures	1926	25p	£12.50
25	Struggle for Existence	1923	15p	£3.50
50	Tennis	1936	15p	£7.50
116	The Corsair Game (Eire)	1965	50p	—
L25	The Nation's Shrines	1929	£1.00	£25.00
X1	The Royal Family	1937	—	£1.25
P6	The Royal Family	1901	£25.00	£150.00
25	Those Pearls of Heaven	1916	30p	£7.50
66	Transvaal Series	1902	£3.00	£200.00
L25	Treasures of Britain	1931	80p	£20.00
25	Treasures of Ireland	1930	80p	£20.00
L25	Types of Horses	1939	£1.00	£25.00
50	Uniforms of the Territorial Army	1939	15p	£6.50
50	Useful Plants & Fruits	1902	£1.00	£50.00
25	Victoria Cross	1914	60p	£15.00
90	War Decorations & Medals	1927	35p	£32.00
50	Wild Animals' Heads	1931	15p	£6.50
50	Wild Animals' Heads (Transfers)	1931	15p	£7.00
L25	Wild Animals (Heads) A Series	1927	£1.00	£25.00
L25	Wild Animals (Heads) 2nd Series ...	1932	£1.00	£25.00
45	Wild Animals of the World (Narrow) (no Ltd)	1901	£3.50	—
45	Wild Animals of the World (Narrow) (with Ltd)	1901	£3.50	—
50	Wild Animals of the World (Wide) (no Ltd)	1901	£1.60	£80.00
50	Wild Animals of the World (Wide) (with Ltd)	1901	£1.60	£80.00
50	Wild Birds	1932	15p	£5.00
50	Wild Birds (Transfers)	1932	15p	£7.00
L25	Wild Birds	1934	£1.00	£25.00
L25	Wildfowl	1937	80p	£20.00
50	Wonders of the Deep	1904	£1.00	£50.00
25	Wonders of the World (Blue Back)	1916	40p	£10.00
25	Wonders of the World (Grey Back, Eire)	1926	60p	£15.00

JOHN PLAYER & SONS—cont.

Qty		Date	Odds	Sets
X10	Wooden Walls	1908	£3.00	£30.00
25	Wrestling & Ju-Jitsu (Blue Back)	1913	40p	£10.00
25	Wrestling & Ju-Jitsu (Grey Back, Eire)	1925	60p	£15.00
26	Your Initials (Transfers)	1932	20p	£5.00
L25	Zoo Babies	1938	20p	£5.00
Overseas Issues				
50	Aeroplane Series	1926	£1.00	£50.00
50	Aircraft of the Royal Air Force	1938	35p	£17.50
50	Animals of the Countryside	1939	30p	£15.00
50	Arms & Armour (grey back)	1926	£1.60	£80.00
F50	Beauties	1925	80p	£40.00
BF50	Beauties (Coloured)	1925	£1.00	£50.00
F50	Beauties 2nd Series	1925	80p	£40.00
50	Birds & Their Young	1937	30p	£15.00
52	Birds of Brilliant Plumage	1927	£2.00	£100.00
25	"Bonzo" Dogs	1923	£1.60	£40.00
50	Boy Scouts	1924	£1.20	£60.00
L25	British Live Stock	1924	£3.50	£87.50
50	Butterflies (girls)	1928	£2.00	£100.00
50	Coronation Series Ceremonial Dress	1937	30p	£15.00
50	Cricketers 1938	1938	75p	£37.50
50	Cycling	1939	30p	£15.00
25	Dogs (Heads)	1927	40p	£10.00
32	Drum Horses	1911	£4.00	—
L25	Famous Beauties	1937	75p	—
50	Film Stars Third Series	1938	40p	—
25	Flag Girls of All Nations	1908	£4.00	—
L25	Golf	1939	£1.00	£25.00
50	Household Hints	1928	60p	£30.00
50	International Air Liners	1936	30p	£15.00
50	Lawn Tennis	1928	£1.20	£60.00
50	Leaders of Men	1925	80p	£40.00
50	Military Uniforms of the British Empire Overseas (adhesive)	1938	40p	£20.00
50	Military Uniforms of the British Empire Overseas (non-adhesive)	1938	50p	—
50	Modern Naval Craft	1939	30p	£15.00
50	Motor Cars A Series	1936	60p	£30.00
50	Motor Cars 2nd Series	1937	60p	£30.00
50	National Flags and Arms	1936	30p	£15.00
L25	Old Hunting Prints	1938	£1.00	£25.00
M22	Old Masters	1966	60p	—
L25	Old Naval Prints	1936	£1.20	£30.00
48	Pictures of the East	1931	£1.20	
25	Picturesque People of the Empire	1938	£1.20	£30.00
B53	Playing Cards	1929	75p	—
50	Pugilists in Action	1928	£1.00	£50.00
L25	Racing Yachts	1938	£1.50	—
50	R.A.F Badges	1937	30p	£15.00
50	Railway Working	1926	80p	£40.00
50	Sea Fishes	1935	30p	£15.00
50	Ships' Flags & Cap Badges	1930	80p	£40.00
50	Signalling Series	1926	80p	£40.00
F50	The Royal Family at Home & Abroad	1927	£1.00	—
L25	Types of Horses	1939	£1.50	—
25	Whaling	1930	80p	£20.00
L25	Zoo Babies	1937	75p	

JOHN PLAYER & SONS—cont.

Qty		Date	Odds	Sets
Modern Issues (Doncella)				
T32	Britain's Endangered Wildlife	1984	15p	£4.00
T30	Britain's Nocturnal Life	1987	—	—
T30	Britain's Wild Flowers	1986	15p	£4.50
T32	British Butterflies	1984	15p	£5.00
T30	British Mammals	1983	l5p	£3.50
T32	Country Houses and Castles	1981	15p	£3.50
T24	Golden Age of Flying	1977	15p	£3.50
T1	Golden Age of Flying Completion Ooffer ...	1978	—	40p
T24	Golden Age of Motoring	1975	15p	£3.50
T24	Golden Age of Motoring with Completion Offer	1976	£1.50	£36.00
T24	Golden Age of Sail	1978	15p	£3.50
T1	Golden Age of Sail Completion Offer	1979	—	40p
T24	Golden Age of Steam	1976	15p	£3.00
T1	Golden Age of Steam Completion Offer	1977	—	*£1.00*
T24	History of the V.C.	1980	25p	£6.00
T1	History of the V.C. Completion Offer	1980	—	£1.50
T24	Napoleonic Uniforms	1980	15p	£3.50
T1	Napoleonic Uniforms Completion Offer	1980	—	*£1.00*
T30	The Living Ocean	1985	15p	£4.50
Modern Issues (Grandee)				
T32	Britain's Endangered Wildlife	1984	15p	£5.00
T30	Britain's Wild Flowers	1986	20p	£6.00
T32	British Birds	1980	20p	£6.50
T32	British Butterflies	1983	15p	£5.00
T30	British Mammals (Imperial Tobacco Ltd) ...	1982	15p	£5.00
T30	British Mammals (Imperial Group PLC) ...	1983	15p	£5.00
T28	Famous M.G. Marques	1981	15p	£4.00
T30	The Living Ocean	1985	20p	£6.00
T25	Top Dogs	1979	40p	£10.00
T6	World of Gardening	1976	£3.50	£21.00
Modern Issues (Panama)				
T7	Limericks	1977	£3.50	—
T8	Panama Puzzles	1976	£3.50	—
T6	Play Ladbroke Spot Ball	1975	£3.50	—
T6	Play Panama Spot Six	1977	£3.50	—
Modern Issues (Tom Thumb)				
L32	Exploration of Space	1982	15p	£5.00
L30	History of Britain's Railways	1987	—	—
L30	History of Motor Racing	1986	20p	£6.50
L32	Myths & Legends	1981	50p	£16.00
L32	Wonders of the Ancient World	1984	20p	£6.50
L30	Wonders of the Modern World	1985	20p	£6.50

JAMES PLAYFAIR & CO.

25	How To Keep Fit	1912	£25.00	£625.00

PREMIER TOBACCO MFRS. LTD.

48	Eminent Stage & Screen Personalities	1936	80p	£40.00
K52	Miniature Playing Cards	1935	*£5.00*	—
100	Stage & Screen Personalities	1936	75p	£75.00

PRITCHARD & BURTON

51	Actors & Actresses "FROGA"	1899	£12.50	—
15	Beauties "PAC"	1899	£40.00	—
20	Boer War Cartoons	1900	£50.00	—
30	Flags & Flags with Soldiers (masts draped) ...	1902	£10.00	£300.00
15	Flags & Flags with Soldiers (masts undraped) ...	1902	£12.50	—
25	Holiday Resorts & Views	1902	£10.00	£250.00

PRITCHARD & BURTON—cont.

Qty		Date	Odds	Sets
40	Home & Colonial Regiments	1901	£35.00	—
25	Royalty Series	1902	£12.00	—
25	South African Series	1901	£10.00	£250.00
25	Star Girls	1900	£75.00	—

G. PRUDHOE

30	Army Pictures, Cartoons, etc.	1916	£50.00	—

JAS. QUINTON LTD

26	Actresses "FROGA"	1899	£100.00	—

Q.V. CIGARS

B?10	Barnum & Bailey's Circus Performers	1900	£100.00	—

RAY & CO. LTD.

K6	Flags of the Allies (shaped)	1916	£30.00	—
25	War Series (1-25)	1915	£8.00	—
75	War Series (26-100)	1915	£6.00	—
24	War Series (101-124)	1916	£15.00	—

RAYMOND REVIEWBAR

BF25	Striptease Artistes	1960	£6.00	

RECORD CIGARETTE CO.

X36	The Talkie Cigarette Card (Real Records)	1934	£20.00	—

REDFORD & CO.

20	Actresses "BLARM"	1900	£35.00	—
25	Armies of the World	1901	£35.00	—
25	Beauties "GRACC"	1899	£60.00	—
30	Colonial Troops	1902	£30.00	—
24	Nautical Expressions	1900	£50.00	—
40	Naval & Military Phrases	1904	£30.00	—
25	Picture Series	1906	£40.00	—
25	Sports & Pastimes	1906	£40.00	—
50	Stage Artistes of the Day	1908	£8.00	£400.00

RELIANCE TOBACCO MFG. CO.

24	British Birds	1934	£3.00	£72.00
35	Famous Stars	1934	£2.50	£87.50

A. S. RICHARDSON

B12	Manikin Cards	1915	£40.00	—

RICHMOND CAVENDISH CO. LTD.

26	Actresses "FROGA"	1900	£17.50	—
28	Actresses "PILPI I"	1902	£10.00	£280.00
F50	Actresses "PILPI II"	1903	£6.00	£300.00
?229	Actresses, Gravure	1904	£4.00	—
14	Beauties "AMBS"	1899	£30.00	—
52	Beauties P/C Inset	1897	£30.00	—
28	Chinese Actors & Actresses	1923	£2.50	£70.00
F50	Cinema Stars	1927	£1.25	—
40	Medals	1900	£8.00	£320.00
20	Music Hall Artistes	1901	£25.00	£500.00
12	Pretty Girl Series "RASH"	1899	£25.00	£300.00
20	Yachts (black back)	1900	£35.00	—
20	Yachts (white back)	1900	£35.00	—

ROBERTS & SONS

Qty		Date	Odds	Sets
26	Actresses "FROGA"	1899	£40.00	—
25	Armies of the World (plain back)	1900	£30.00	—
25	Armies of the World (printed back)	1900	£30.00	—
M50	Beautiful Women	1898	£125.00	—
50	Beauties "CHOAB"	1900	£50.00	—
50	Colonial Troops	1902	£25.00	—
B28	Dominoes	1905	£35.00	—
K52	Miniature Playing Cards	1905	£40.00	—
24	Nautical Expressions	1902	£40.00	—
70	Stories without Words	1904	£35.00	—
25	Types of British & Colonial Troops	1900	£30.00	—

ROBINSON & BARNSDALE LTD.

B25	Actresses, Colin Campbell	1898	£75.00	—
?14	Actresses, Cupola	1898	£80.00	—
1	Advertisement Card, Colin Campbell	1897	—	£75.00
?13	Beauties, Collotype	1895	£80.00	—
B?20	Beauties, Highest Honors	1895	£100.00	—

E. ROBINSON & SONS

10	Beauties	1897	£35.00	—
?50	Derbyshire and The Peak	1903	£65.00	—
25	Egyptian Studies	1914	£12.00	—
25	King Lud Problems	1934	£10.00	—
?10	Medals & Decorations	1902	£80.00	—
40	Nature Studies	1914	£12.00	—
25	Regimental Mascots	1916	£35.00	—
25	Wild Flowers	1915	£12.00	—

ROMAN STAR CIGARS

26	Actresses "FROGA"	1899	£80.00	—
24	Beauties "BOCCA"	1899	£75.00	—

ROTHMANS LTD.

40	Beauties of the Cinema	1939	50p	£20.00
L24	Beauties of the Cinema (Circular)	1939	£1.25	—
X25	Canterbury Bankstown District Rugby League Football Club (New Zealand)	1980	£2.50	—
24	Cinema Stars	1925	35p	£8.50
L25	Cinema Stars	1925	25p	£6.25
P30	Country Living Cards	1974	—	£6.50
L50	International Football Stars	1984	30p	—
36	Landmarks in Empire History	1936	50p	£18.00
?	Lucky Charms (metal)	1930	£2.00	—
50	Modern Inventions	1935	40p	£20.00
LF54	New Zealand	1933	40p	£20.00
24	Prominent Screen Favourites	1934	35p	£8.50
F50	Punch Jokes	1935	20p	£10.00
5	Rare and Historic Banknotes	1970	80p	£4.00

WM. RUDDELL LTD.

?	Couplet Cards	1924	£7.50	—
25	Grand Opera Series	1924	£3.50	£87.50
25	Rod & Gun	1924	£3.00	£75.00
50	Songs That Will Live For Ever	1924	£1.60	£80.00

I. RUTTER & CO.

Qty		Date	Odds	Sets
15	Actresses (printed back)	1900	£30.00	—
15	Actresses (rubber stamped back)	1900	£40.00	—
1	Advertisement Card	1899	—	£250.00
7	Boer War Celebrities	1901	£25.00	£175.00
54	Comic Phrases	1905	£10.00	£540.00
20	Cricketers Series	1902	£125.00	—
30	Flags & Flags with Soldiers	1901	£15.00	£450.00
24	Girls, Flags & Arms of Countries	1900	£25.00	£600.00
25	Proverbs	1904	£30.00	—
25	Shadowgraphs	1903	£20.00	—

S.D.V. TOBACCO CO. LTD.

Qty		Date	Odds	Sets
16	British Royal Family	1901	£100.00	—

SACCONE & SPEED

Qty		Date	Odds	Sets
F55	Beauties	1912	£4.00	—
F55	Beauties (red overprint)	1912	£3.00	—

ST. PETERSBURG CIGARETTE CO. LTD.

Qty		Date	Odds	Sets
?	Footballers	1904	£125.00	—

SALMON & GLUCKSTEIN LTD.

Qty		Date	Odds	Sets
X1	Advertisement Card (Snake Charmer)	1897	—	£300.00
15	Billiard Terms	1905	£35.00	—
12	British Queens	1902	£30.00	£360.00
X30	Castles, Abbeys & Houses (brown back) ...	1906	£12.00	£350.00
X30	Castles, Abbeys & Houses (red back)	1906	£15.00	—
32	Characters from Dickens	1903	£16.00	£500.00
25	Coronation Series	1911	£5.00	£125.00
L25	Famous Pictures (Brown)	1912	£6.00	£150.00
L25	Famous Pictures (Green, Different)	1912	£5.00	£125.00
6	Her Most Gracious Majesty Queen Victoria ...	1897	£30.00	£180.00
40	Heroes of the Transvaal War	1901	£7.00	£400.00
25	Magical Series	1923	£2.00	£50.00
30	Music Hall Celebrities	1902	£30.00	—
25	Occupations	1898	£200.00	—
20	Owners & Jockeys Series	1900	£30.00	—
L50	Pottery Types (Silk)	1916	£2.00	£100.00
6	Pretty Girl Series "RASH"	1900	£40.00	—
22	Shakespearian Series	1902	£15.00	£330.00
25	Star Girls	1899	£75.00	—
50	The Great White City	1908	£7.00	£350.00
48	The Post in Various Countries	1900	£17.50	£840.00
25	Traditions of the Army & Navy	1917	£6.00	£150.00
25	Wireless Explained	1923	£2.50	£62.50

W. SANDORIDES & CO. LTD.

Qty		Date	Odds	Sets
25	Aquarium Studies from the London Zoo	1925	£1.40	£35.00
L25	Aquarium Studies from the London Zoo	1925	£1.60	£40.00
25	Cinema Celebrities	1924	£1.50	£37.50
X25	Cinema Celebrities	1924	£2.00	—
25	Cinema Stars (As Above)	1924	£3.00	—

W. SANDORIDES & CO. LTD.—cont.

Qty		Date	Odds	Sets
X25	Cinema Stars (As Above)	1924	£1.00	£25.00
50	Famous Racecourses	1926	£1.20	£60.00
L50	Famous Racecourses	1926	£1.50	£75.00
50	Famous Racehorses	1923	80p	£40.00
25	Sports & Pastimes	1924	£7.50	—

SANSOM'S CIGAR STORES

?	London Views	1905	£100.00	—

NICHOLAS SARONY & CO.

25	A Day on the Airway	1928	40p	£10.00
L25	A Day on the Airway	1928	50p	£12.50
50	Around the Mediterranean	1926	40p	£20.00
L50	Around the Mediterranean	1926	60p	£30.00
?	Boer War Scenes	1901	£125.00	
100	Celebrities and Their Autographs	1923	30p	£30.00
L100	Celebrities and Their Autographs	1923	35p	£35.00
50	Cinema Stars	1933	40p	£20.00
P38	Cinema Stars	1930	£5.00	—
P42	Cinema Stars, 2nd Series	1930	£2.00	—
P50	Cinema Stars, 3rd Series	1930	£2.00	—
P42	Cinema Stars, 4th Series	1930	£2.00	—
P25	Cinema Stars, 5th Series	1930	£2.00	£50.00
25	Cinema Studies	1929	30p	£7.50
F54	Life at Whipsnade Zoo	1934	30p	£15.00
50	Links with the Past	1925	16p	£8.00
L50	Links with the Past	1925	16p	£8.00
25	Links with the Past (Australia)	1926	30p	—
L25	Links with the Past (Australia)	1926	35p	—
25	Links with the Past (New Zealand)	1926	30p	£7.50
L25	Links with the Past (New Zealand)	1926	24p	£6.00
L25	Links with the Past (Presentation Issue)	1926	£1.00	—
25	Museum Series	1927	16p	£4.00
L25	Museum Series	1927	16p	£4.00
L25	Museum Series (Australia)	1927	30p	—
25	Museum Series (New Zealand)	1927	24p	£6.00
L25	Museum Series (New Zealand)	1927	30p	—
L25	Museum Series (Presentation Issue)	1927	30p	£7.50
F36	National Types of Beauty	1928	16p	£6.00
MF36	National Types of Beauty	1928	20p	£7.50
15	Origin of Games	1923	£1.50	£22.50
L15	Origin of Games	1923	£1.60	£24.00
50	Saronicks	1929	15p	£6.00
M50	Saronicks	1929	15p	£6.00
50	Ships of All Ages	1929	15p	£7.00
M50	Ships of All Ages	1929	15p	£7.00
25	Tennis Strokes	1923	£1.20	£30.00

T. S. SAUNT

30	Army Pictures, Cartoons, etc.	1916	£50.00	—

SCOTTISH C.W.S.

Qty		Date	Odds	Sets
25	Burns	1924	40p	£10.00
20	Dogs	1925	£5.00	—
25	Dwellings of All Nations	1924	£1.00	£25.00
L25	Famous Pictures	1924	£4.00	—
L25	Famous Pictures—Glasgow Galleries (Adhesive)	1927	70p	£17.50
L25	Famous Pictures—Glasgow Galleries (Non-Adhesive) ...	1927	£1.20	£30.00
L25	Famous Pictures—London Galleries (Adhesive)	1927	70p	£17.50
L25	Famous Pictures—London Galleries (Non-Adhesive)	1927	£1.20	£30.00
50	Feathered Favourites (Adhesive)	1926	70p	£35.00
50	Feathered Favourites (Non-Adhesive)	1926	80p	£40.00
25	Racial Types	1925	£4.00	£100.00
50	Triumphs of Engineering	1926	£1.20	£60.00
50	Wireless	1924	£1.60	£80.00

SELBY

B12	Manikin Cards	1915	£50.00	—

SHARPE & SNOWDEN

?	Views of England	1905	£80.00	—
?	Views of London	1905	£80.00	—

W. J. SHEPHERD

25	Beauties "FECKSA"	1901	£60.00	—

SHORTS

L?20	House Views	1924	£20.00	—

SIMONETS LTD. (Channel Isles)

MF36	Beautiful Women	1928	£2.50	£90.00
F24	Cinema Scenes Series	1926	£2.50	—
F27	Famous Actors & Actresses	1929	£1.75	£47.50
50	Local Footballers	1925	£1.75	£87.50
25	Picture Series	1925	£2.00	—
F27	Sporting Celebrities	1929	£3.00	—
LF50	Views of Jersey (Plain Back)	1926	£1.20	—

JOHN SINCLAIR LTD.

B?65	Actresses	1902	£35.00	—
F48	Birds (numbered)	1924	£1.20	—
F48	Birds ("specimen cigarette card")	1924	£3.50	—
LF50	Birds	1924	£2.50	—
50	British Sea Dogs	1928	£1.75	£87.50
F54	Champion Dogs	1938	16p	£8.50
LF52	Champion Dogs	1938	20p	£10.00
F54	Champion Dogs, 2nd Series	1939	£1.25	—
LF52	Champion Dogs, 2nd Series	1939	£1.50	—
F50	English & Scottish Football Stars	1935	30p	£15.00
F54	Film Stars (Series of 54 Real Photos) ...	1934	60p	£30.00
F54	Film Stars (Series of Real Photos)	1937	50p	£27.50
F54	Film Stars (55-108)	1937	30p	£16.00

JOHN SINCLAIR LTD.—cont.

Qty		Date	Odds	Sets
M12	Flags (Numbered, Silk) (25-36)	1914	£10.00	—
M24	Flags (Unnumbered Silk, blue captions)	1914	£6.00	—
M24	Flags (Unnumbered, Silk, myrtle green captions)	1914	£5.00	—
M24	Flags (Unnumbered, Silk, olive green captions)	1914	£5.00	—
M24	Flags (Unnumbered, Silk, grey captions)	1914	£7.50	—
M24	Flags (Unnumbered, Silk, red captions)	1914	£6.00	—
M50	Flags, 4th Series (Silk)	1914	£4.00	—
M50	Flags, 5th Series (Silk)	1914	£4.00	—
D50	Flags, 6th Series (Silk)	1914	£5.00	—
G10	Flags, 7th Series (Silk)	1914	£25.00	—
F96	Flowers & Plants (numbered)	1924	£1.20	£120.00
F96	Flowers & Plants ("specimen cigarette card") ...	1924	£3.50	—
F50	Football Favourites	1906	£30.00	—
4	North Country Celebrities	1904	£30.00	—
F?81	Northern Gems	1902	£30.00	—
50	Picture Puzzles & Riddles Series	1916	£12.50	—
F54	Radio Favourites	1935	75p	£40.00
L50	Regimental Badges (Silk)	1915	£3.50	—
D24	Regimental Colours (Silk) (38-61)	1914	£10.00	—
K53	Rubicon Cards (Miniature P/C)	1934	£4.00	—
G1	The Allies Flags (No. 37, Silk)	1915	£25.00	—
50	Trick Series	1916	£12.50	—
50	Well Known Footballers—N.E. Counties	1938	20p	£10.00
50	Well Known Footballers—Scottish	1938	15p	£7.00
50	World's Coinage	1914	£8.00	—

ROBERT SINCLAIR TOBACCO CO. LTD.

Qty		Date	Odds	Sets
X4	Battleships & Crests (Silk)	1915	£30.00	—
10	Billiards, 1st Set	1928	£3.00	£30.00
15	Billiards, 2nd Set	1928	£3.00	£45.00
3	Billiards, 3rd Set	1928	£5.00	—
28	Dominoes	1902	£35.00	—
M9	Flags (Silk)	1915	£17.50	—
?	Footballers	1900	£150.00	—
P6	Great War Area (Silk)	1915	£25.00	—
M10	Great War Heroes (Silk)	1915	£20.00	—
12	Policemen of the World	1899	£75.00	—
X1	Red Cross Nurse (Silk)	1915	£30.00	—
M5	Regimental Badges (Silk)	1915	£17.50	—
12	The Smiler Series	1924	£2.50	—
L12	The Smiler Series	1924	£5.00	£60.00

J. SINFIELD

Qty		Date	Odds	Sets
24	Beauties "HUMPS"	1899	£150.00	—

SINGLETON & COLE LTD.

Qty		Date	Odds	Sets
50	Atlantic Liners	1910	£12.00	£600.00
25	Bonzo Series	1928	£3.00	£75.00
50	Celebrities—Boer War Period	1901	£12.00	—
110	Crests & Badges of the British Army (Silk)	1915	£3.00	—
35	Famous Boxers	1930	£4.00	—
25	Famous Film Stars	1930	£4.00	—
35	Famous Officers	1915	£10.00	£500.00

SINGLETON & COLE LTD.—cont.

Qty		Date	Odds	Sets
50	Footballers	1905	£30.00	—
40	Kings & Queens	1902	£10.00	£400.00
B12	Manikin Cards	1915	*£50.00*	–
25	Maxims of Success	1906	£15.00	—
8	Orient Royal Mail Line	1904	£30.00	£240.00
25	The Wallace-Jones Keep Fit System	1910	£12.00	—

F. & J. SMITH
36 Page Reference Book – £2.25

Qty		Date	Odds	Sets
24	Advertisement Cards	1897	£125.00	£3000.00
50	A Tour Round the World (Postcard Backs) ...	1901	£30.00	—
50	A Tour Round the World (Script Backs)	1901	£16.00	£800.00
50	A Tour Round the World (Descriptive) ...	1906	£5.00	£250.00
50	Battlefields of Great Britain	1913	£7.00	£350.00
25	Boer War Series (Black & White)	1901	£40.00	—
50	Boer War Series (Coloured)	1901	£16.00	£800.00
50	Champions of Sport (Blue Back)	1902	£35.00	—
50	Champions of Sport (Red Back)	1902	£30.00	—
25	Cinema Stars	1920	£3.00	£75.00
50	Cricketers (1-50)	1912	£7.50	£375.00
20	Cricketers, 2nd Series (51-70)	1912	£16.00	£320.00
50	Derby Winners	1913	£6.00	£300.00
50	Famous Explorers	1911	£5.00	£250.00
50	Football Club Records	1917	£5.00	£250.00
50	Football Club Records (Different)	1922	£5.00	£250.00
120	Footballers (Brown Back)	1906	£12.50	—
100	Footballers (Blue Back, No Series Title) ...	1908	£4.00	£400.00
150	Footballers (Titled)	1912	£4.00	£600.00
50	Fowls, Pigeons & Dogs	1908	£4.00	£200.00
25	Holiday Resorts	1925	£4.00	£100.00
50	Medals (Numbered Smith back)	1902	£5.00	£250.00
50	Medals (Numbered, Imperial Tobacco Co. back)	1903	£25.00	—
50	Medals (Numbered, Imperial Tobacco Company)	1906	£5.00	£250.00
20	Medals (Unnumbered)	1905	£7.50	£150.00
50	Nations of the World	1923	£2.50	£125.00
50	Naval Dress & Badges (descriptive back) ...	1911	£5.00	—
50	Naval Dress & Badges (non-descriptive) ...	1914	£5.00	—
50	Phil May Sketches (Brown Back)	1924	£2.50	£125.00
50	Phil May Sketches (Grey Back)	1908	£4.00	£200.00
25	Prominent Rugby Players	1924	£4.00	£100.00
40	Races of Mankind (no series title)	1900	£40.00	—
40	Races of Mankind (with series title)	1900	£30.00	—
25	Shadowgraphs	1915	£3.00	£75.00
25	War Incidents	1914	£3.50	£87.50
25	War Incidents 2nd Series	1915	£3.50	£87.50

SNELL & CO.

Qty		Date	Odds	Sets
25	Boer War Celebrities "STEW"	1901	*£80.00*	—

SOROKO

Qty		Date	Odds	Sets
6	Jubilee Series	1935	*£12.50*	—
L6	Jubilee Series	1935	*£12.50*	—

S. E. SOUTHGATE & SON

Qty		Date	Odds	Sets
25	Types of British & Colonial Troops	1900	£100.00	—

SOUTH WALES TOB. MFG. CO. LTD.

30	Army Pictures, Cartoons, etc.	1915	£50.00	—
?91	Game of Numbers	1912	£40.00	—
25	Views of London	1912	£12.00	—

T. SPALTON

30	Army Pictures, Cartoons, etc.	1916	£50.00	

SPIRO VALLERI & CO.

?15	Noted Footballers	1905	£150.00	—

G. STANDLEY

B12	Manikin Cards	1915	£45.00	

STAPLETON

B12	Manikin Cards	1915	£45.00	—

STAR OF THE WORLD

20	Boer War Cartoons	1901	£60.00	—
?50	Boer War Celebrities "JASAS"	1901	£75.00	—
30	Colonial Troops	1901	£40.00	—

H. STEVENS & CO.

20	Dogs	1923	£3.50	—
25	Zoo Series	1926	£2.50	—

A. STEVENSON

50	War Portraits	1916	£40.00	—

ALBERT STOCKWELL

30	Army Pictures, Cartoons, etc.	1916	£50.00	—

STRATHMORE TOBACCO CO.

M25	British Aircraft	1938	50p	£12.50

SWEET ALVA CIGARETTES

?50	Boer War Celebrities "JASAS"	1901	£50.00	—

T.S.S.

24	Nautical Expressions	1900	£50.00	—

TADDY & CO.

72	Actresses, Collotype	1897	£60.00	—
25	Actresses with Flowers	1899	£50.00	£1500.00
37	Admirals & Generals—The War	1914	£8.00	£500.00
25	Admirals & Generals—The War (South Africa)	1914	£30.00	£750.00

TADDY & CO.—cont.

Qty		Date	Odds	Sets
25	Autographs	1912	£8.00	£200.00
20	Boer Leaders	1901	£10.00	£200.00
50	British Medals & Decorations, Series 2	1912	£6.00	£300.00
50	British Medals & Ribbons	1912	£6.00	£300.00
20	Clowns & Circus Artistes	—	£400.00	—
30	Coronation Series	1902	£12.50	£375.00
238	County Cricketers	1907	£20.00	
50	Dogs	1900	£12.50	£625.00
5	English Royalty	1897	*£300.00*	—
25	Famous Actors/Famous Actresses	1903	£8.00	£200.00
50	Famous Horses and Cattle	1908	£50.00	—
25	Famous Jockeys (No Frame)	1910	£16.00	£400.00
25	Famous Jockeys (With Frame)	1910	£12.00	£300.00
50	Footballers (New Zealand)	1900	£45.00	
25	Heraldry Series	1911	£10.00	£250.00
25	Honours & Ribbons	1906	£12.00	£300.00
10	Klondyke Series	1900	£40.00	£400.00
60	Leading M.L.A.'s (South Africa)	1900	*£350.00*	—
25	Natives of the World	1899	£30.00	£750.00
25	Orders of Chivalry	1911	£12.00	£300.00
25	Orders of Chivalry 2nd Series	1912	£16.00	£400.00
595	Prominent Footballers (No Footnote)	1907	£5.00	—
400	Prominent Footballers (With Footnote)	1908	£5.00	—
?350	Prominent Footballers (London Mixture)	1913	£17.50	—
20	Royalty, Actresses & Soldiers	1898	£125.00	—
25	Royalty Series	1903	£10.00	£250.00
25	Russo Japanese War (1-25)	1904	£8.00	£200.00
25	Russo Japanese War (26-50)	1904	£12.00	£300.00
16	South African Cricket Team, 1907	1907	£35.00	—
26	South African Football Team, 1906-7	1906	£16.00	£400.00
25	Sports & Pastimes	1912	£10.00	£250.00
25	Territorial Regiments	1908	£12.00	£300.00
25	Thames Series	1903	£25.00	£625.00
20	Victoria Cross Heroes (1-20)	1901	£30.00	£600.00
20	Victoria Cross Heroes (21-40)	1901	£30.00	£600.00
20	VC Heroes—Boer War (41-60)	1902	£8.00	£160.00
20	VC Heroes—Boer War (61-80)	1902	£10.00	£200.00
20	VC Heroes—Boer War (81-100)	1902	£12.00	£240.00
25	Victoria Cross Heroes (101-125)	1904	£35.00	—
2	Wrestlers	1908	£150.00	£300.00

TADDY (re-registered, no connection with earlier Co.)

8	Advertisement Cards	1980	25p	£2.00
26	Motor Cars (Clown Cigarettes)	1980	—	£1.50
26	Motor Cars (Myrtle Grove Cigarettes)	1980	—	£1.50
26	Railway Locomotives (Clown Cigarettes)	1980	—	£1.50
26	Railway Locomotives (Myrtle Grove Cigs.)	1980	—	£1.50

W. & M. TAYLOR

8	The European War Series	1915	£30.00	—
25	War Series	1915	£8.00	£200.00

TAYLOR WOOD

Qty		Date	Odds	Sets
18	Motor Cycle Series	1914	£50.00	—

TEOFANI & CO. LTD.

Qty		Date	Odds	Sets
25	Aquarium Studies from the London Zoo	1925	£7.50	—
50	Cinema Celebrities	1926	£2.00	—
25	Cinema Stars	1924	£2.50	—
X25	Cinema Stars	1924	£3.00	—
25	Famous Boxers	1925	£3.50	—
F32	Famous British Ships & Officers	1934	£1.25	£40.00
12	Film Actors & Actresses (Plain Back)	1936	16p	£2.00
20	Great Inventors	1924	£3.00	£60.00
20	Head-dress of all Nations (Plain back)	1926	£7.00	£140.00
LF50	Icelandic Employees	1926	£3.50	—
12	London Views (Plain Back)	1936	15p	£2.00
48	Modern Movie Stars & Cinema Celebrities ...	1934	20p	£10.00
50	Natives in Costume (Plain back)	1926	£8.00	—
24	Past & Present "A"—The Army	1938	40p	£10.00
24	Past & Present "B"—Weapons of War	1938	20p	£5.00
4	Past & Present "C"—Transport	1939	£2.00	£8.00
50	Public Schools & Colleges	1923	£2.50	£125.00
50	Ships and Their Flags	1925	£1.20	£60.00
25	Sports & Pastimes (Plain Back)	1924	£2.00	£50.00
25	Sports & Pastimes (Printed Back)	1924	£7.50	—
22	Teofani Gems	1925	£1.50	—
28	Teofani Gems	1925	50p	—
36	Teofani Gems	1925	£1.50	—
48	Transport Then & Now	1939	15p	£7.00
50	Views of London	1925	£1.50	—
F36	Views of the British Empire	1927	50p	£18.00
24	Well Known Racehorses	1923	£3.00	—
50	Worlds Smokers (Plain back)	1926	£8.00	—
50	Zoological Studies	1924	£2.50	—
L50	Zoological Studies	1924	£5.00	—

TETLEY & SONS

Qty		Date	Odds	Sets
1	The Allies	1915	£125.00	—
50	War Portraits	1916	£40.00	—
25	World's Coinage	1914	£35.00	—

THEMANS & CO.

Qty		Date	Odds	Sets
?10	Anecdotes & Riddles	1913	£125.00	—
55	Dominoes	1913	£50.00	—
18	Motor Cycle Series	1914	£40.00	—
50	War Portraits	1915	£25.00	—
14	War Posters	1916	£75.00	—

THOMSON & PORTEOUS

Qty		Date	Odds	Sets
50	Arms of British Towns	1905	£7.50	£375.00
25	Boer War Celebrities "STEW"	1901	£35.00	—
25	Shadowgraphs	1902	£20.00	—
20	The European War Series	1915	£6.50	£130.00
41	V.C. Heroes	1916	£6.00	£250.00

TOPSY CIGARETTES

Qty		Date	Odds	Sets
F?10	Actresses	1896	*£100.00*	—

TURKISH MONOPOLY CIGARETTE CO. LTD.

X?12	Boer War Scenes	1901	*£75.00*	—

UNITED KINGDOM TOBACCO CO. LTD.

50	Aircraft	1933	50p	£25.00
P48	Beautiful Britain	1929	75p	£36.00
P48	Beautiful Britain 2nd Series	1929	75p	£36.00
25	British Orders of Chivalry & Valour	1936	40p	£10.00
24	Chinese Scenes	1933	15p	£3.50
32	Cinema Stars	1933	50p	£16.00
50	Cinema Stars	1934	50p	£25.00
36	Officers Full Dress	1936	60p	£21.50
?50	Soldiers (Metal)	1935	£7.50	—
36	Soldiers of the King	1937	50p	£18.00

UNITED SERVICES MFG. CO. LTD.

50	Ancient Warriors	1938	50p	£25.00
25	Ancient Warriors	1957	£2.00	—
50	Bathing Belles	1939	16p	£8.00
100	Interesting Personalities	1935	£1.25	£125.00
50	Popular Footballers	1936	£1.60	£80.00
50	Popular Screen Stars	1937	£1.60	£80.00

UNITED TOBACCONISTS ASSOCIATION LTD.

10	Actresses "MUTA"	1901	*£100.00*	—
12	Pretty Girl Series "RASH"	1900	*£100.00*	—

WALKERS TOBACCO CO. LTD. (W.T.C.)

60	British Beauty Spots	1924	*£10.00*	—
28	Dominoes (Old Monk)	1908	*£35.00*	—
28	Dominoes (W.T.C.)	1924	*£2.00*	—
F31/32	Film Stars (Tatleys)	1936	50p	£16.00
F48	Film Stars (Walkers)	1935	*£2.00*	—

WALTERS TOBACCO CO. LTD.

L6	Angling Information	1939	50p	£3.00

E. T. WATERMAN

30	Army Pictures, Cartoons, etc.	1916	*£50.00*	—

WEBB & RASSELL

50	War Portraits	1916	*£40.00*	—

HENRY WELFARE & CO.

?25	Prominent Politicians	1912	*£40.00*	—

WESTMINSTER TOBACCO CO. LTD.

Qty		Date	Odds	Sets
F36	Australia, 1st Series	1932	15p	£4.50
F36	Australia, 2nd Series (Plain Back)	1933	15p	£3.00
F48	British Royal and Ancient Buildings			
	(Unnumbered)	1925	50p	£25.00
F48	British Royal and Ancient Buildings			
	(Numbered)	1925	35p	£17.50
F48	British Royal and Ancient Buildings 2nd Series ...	1926	16p	£8.00
F36	Canada 1st Series	1926	30p	£11.00
F36	Canada 2nd Series	1928	30p	£11.00
F48	Indian Empire 1st Series	1925	16p	£8.00
F48	Indian Empire 2nd Series	1926	16p	£8.00
F36	New Zealand 1st Series	1928	20p	£7.50
F36	New Zealand 2nd Series	1929	15p	£4.00
F36	South Africa 1st Series	1928	25p	£9.00
F36	South Africa 2nd Series	1928	25p	£9.00

Overseas Issues

Qty		Date	Odds	Sets
L?200	Adamson's Oplevelser	1926	*£12.50*	—
MF50	Beauties	1924	£1.50	—
MF100	Beautiful Women	1915	£1.25	—
M50	Birds, Beasts & Fishes	1923	£1.40	£70.00
B100	British Beauties (Hand coloured)	1915	£1.75	—
B102	British Beauties (Uncoloured)	1915	£1.50	—
F48	British Royal and Ancient Buildings ...	1925	60p	£30.00
B50	Butterflies & Moths	1920	£1.50	—
F36	Canada 1st Series	1926	60p	—
F36	Canada 2nd Series	1928	60p	—
30	Celebrated Actresses	1921	£3.00	£90.00
100	Cinema Artistes (Green Back)	1928	£1.25	—
50	Cinema Artistes (Grey Back)	1931	£1.25	—
48	Cinema Celebrities (C)	1935	£1.50	—
F50	Cinema Stars	1927	£1.25	—
MF50	Cinema Stars (Coloured)	1926	£1.50	—
MF50	Cinema Stars (Uncoloured)	1930	£1.50	—
B27	Dancing Girls	1917	£2.50	£65.00
50	Do You Know?	1922	£1.00	—
24	Fairy Tales (Booklets)	1926	£2.50	—
M100	Famous Beauties (Blue Caption)	1916	£1.25	—
M100	Famous Beauties (Brown Caption)	1916	£1.25	—
MF52	Film Favourites (Coloured)	1927	£1.50	—
MF52	Film Favourites (Uncoloured)	1927	£1.50	—
M50	Film Personalities	1931	£1.50	—
M50	Garden Flowers of the World	1917	£1.25	£62.50
M50	Garden Flowers of the World (Silk)	1913	£2.50	£125.00
F48	Indian Empire, 1st Series	1925	60p	—
F48	Indian Empire 2nd Series	1926	60p	—
MF50	Islenzkar Eimskipamyndir	1931	£1.50	£75.00
MF50	Islenzkar Landslagsmyndir	1928	£1.25	£62.50
MF50	Islenzkar Landslagsmyndir Nr2	1929	£1.25	£62.50
40	Merrie England Studies	1914	£3.50	—
X24	Miniature Rugs	1924	£8.00	—
36	Modern Beauties	1938	*£1.50*	—
MF52	Movie Stars	1925	£1.50	—
F36	New Zealand 1st Series	1928	60p	—

U.K. Tobacco 1930s

CHINESE

Ancient Warriors. United Services

THE CHAIR THAT GREW

Believe it or Not. Carreras

THE ROYAL WARWICKSHIRE REGIMENT

Soldiers of the King. United Kingdom
Tobacco, Phillips

Treasure Trove. Churchman

Romance of the Royal Mail. Woods

Stars of Stage & Screen. Gallaher

Bathing Belles. Murray. United
Services

Garden Flowers. Wills

Post War U.K. Issues – Tobacco

Famous Footballers. Carreras Turf

Advert Card. Taddy

Western Stars. C.W.S.

Vintage Cars. Carreras Black Cat

Coins of the World.
Amalgamated also Amaran Tea, Cede

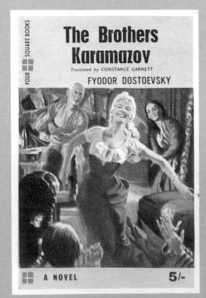

Four Square Books. Dobie

Punchlines. Wills Embassy

Qty		Date	Odds	Sets
F36	New Zealand 2nd Series	1929	60p	—
55	Playing Cards	1934	£1.00	—
M55	Playing Cards (blue back)	1934	75p	—
M55	Playing Cards (red back)	1934	75p	—
F50	Popular Film Stars	1926	£1.50	—
L?200	Skjeggen's Oplevelser	1926	£12.50	—
F36	South Africa, 1st Series	1928	60p	—
F36	South Africa, 2nd Series	1928	60p	—
M49	South African Succulents	1937	15p	£6.00
M100	Stage & Cinema Stars (Black Caption)	1921	£1.50	—
M100	Stage & Cinema Stars (Grey Caption)	1921	75p	£75.00
MF50	Stars of Filmland	1927	£1.50	£75.00
50	Steamships of the World	1920	£4.00	—
40	The Great War Celebrities	1914	£4.00	—
50	The World of Tomorrow	1938	35p	f17.50
M50	Uniforms of All Ages	1917	£6.00	—
F50	Views of Malaya	1930	£3.00	£150.00
25	Wireless	1923	£2.00	£50.00
M50	Women of Nations	1922	£2.50	£125.00

WHALE & COMPANY

?12	Conundrums	1900	£85.00	—

M. WHITE & CO.

20	Actresses "BLARM"	1900	£75.00	—

WHITFIELD'S

30	Army Pictures, Cartoons etc.	1916	£50.00	—

WHITFORD & SONS

20	Inventors	1924	£25.00	—

WHOLESALE TOBACCO CO.

25	Armies of the World	1903	£40.00	—
40	Army Pictures	1902	£50.00	—

P. WHYTE

30	Army Pictures, Cartoons, etc.	1916	£50.00	—

W. WILLIAMS & CO.

30	Aristocrats of the Turf A Series	1924	£3.50	—
36	Aristocrats of the Turf 2nd Series	1924	£10.00	—
25	Boer War Celebrities "STEW"	1901	£35.00	—
25	Boxing	1923	£3.00	—
50	Interesting Buildings	1912	£8.00	—
12	Views of Chester	1912	£15.00	£180.00
12	Views of Chester, 2nd Series (As it Was)	1913	£16.00	£190.00

W. D. & H. O. WILLS LTD.

?	Actresses (typeset back)	1895	£300.00	—
52	Actresses (Brown Back, P/C Inset)	1898	£10.00	£520.00
52	Actresses (Grey Back, P/C Inset)	1897	£10.00	£520.00
52	Actresses (Grey Back, No Inset)	1897	£12.50	—
25	Actresses, Collotype (Wills')	1894	£50.00	—
50	Actresses & Celebrities, Collotype (Wills's)	1894	£65.00	—

W. D. & H. O. WILLS LTD.—cont.

Qty		Date	Odds	Sets
1	Advertisement Card (Serving Maid)	1890	—	£400.00
4	Advertisement Cards (Cigarette Packets)	1891	£400.00	—
11	Advertisement Cards (Tobacco Packings)	1891	£300.00	—
3	Advertisement Cards (Showcards)	1893	£200.00	—
6	Advertisement Cards (Showcards)	1893	£175.00	—
1	Advertisement Card—Three Castles	1965	—	50p
L1	Advertisement Card—Wants List	1935	—	25p
50	Air Raid Precautions	1938	15p	£6.50
40	Air Raid Precautions (Eire)	1938	40p	£16.00
50	Allied Army Leaders	1917	65p	£32.50
50	Alpine Flowers	1913	30p	£15.00
49	And When Did You Last See Your Father? (Sect.)	1932	50p	£25.00
50	Animals & Birds (Descriptive)	1900	£10.00	£500.00
50	Animals & Birds in Fancy Costume	1896	£35.00	—
48	Animalloys (Sect.)	1929	15p	£5.00
L25	Animals and Their Furs	1929	£1.00	£25.00
50	Arms of Companies	1913	30p	£15.00
50	Arms of Foreign Cities	1912	30p	£15.00
L42	Arms of Oxford & Cambridge Colleges	1922	80p	£33.00
L25	Arms of Public Schools 1st Series	1933	70p	£17.50
L25	Arms of Public Schools 2nd Series	1934	70p	£17.50
50	Arms of the Bishopric	1907	50p	£25.00
50	Arms of the British Empire	1910	35p	£17.50
L25	Arms of the British Empire 1st Series	1933	70p	£17.50
L25	Arms of the British Empire 2nd Series	1933	70p	£17.50
L25	Arms of Universities	1923	70p	£17.50
50	Association Footballers (Frame on back)	1935	20p	£10.00
50	Association Footballers (No Frame on back) ...	1939	20p	£10.00
50	Association Footballers (Eire)	1939	40p	—
L25	Auction Bridge	1926	80p	£20.00
50	Aviation	1910	75p	£37.50
?100	Beauties, Collotype	1894	£65.00	—
K52	Beauties, Playing Card Inset	1896	£16.00	—
52	Beauties, Playing Card Insets	1897	£10.00	£520.00
?	Beauties (No inset, scroll back)	1897	£75.00	—
?	Beauties (No inset, type set back)	1897	£100.00	—
?	Beauties, Girl Studies	1895	£300.00	—
L25	Beautiful Homes	1930	80p	£20.00
48	Between Two Fires (Sect.)	1930	15p	£6.50
50	Billiards	1909	60p	£30.00
K9	Boer War Medallions	1900	£40.00	—
50	Borough Arms (Scroll Back, Numbered)	1903	£6.00	£300.00
50	Borough Arms (Scroll Back, Unnumbered) ...	1903	50p	£25.00
50	Borough Arms (1-50 descriptive)	1904	50p	£25.00
50	Borough Arms Second Edition (1-50)	1906	30p	£15.00
50	Borough Arms 2nd Series (51-100)	1904	30p	£15.00
50	Borough Arms Second Edition (51-100) ...	1906	30p	£15.00
50	Borough Arms 3rd Series (101-150 Red Print)	1905	30p	£15.00
50	Borough Arms 3rd Series (101-150 Grey Print)	1905	35p	£17.50
50	Borough Arms Second Edition (101-150) ...	1906	30p	£15.00
50	Borough Arms 4th Series (151-200)	1905	30p	£15.00
24	Britain's Part in the War	1917	50p	£12.00
50	British Birds	1915	50p	£25.00

W. D. & H. O. WILLS LTD.—cont.

Qty		Date	Odds	Sets
50	British Butterflies	1927	25p	£12.50
L25	British Castles	1925	80p	£20.00
L25	British School of Painting	1927	70p	£17.50
M48	British Sporting Personalities	1937	25p	£12.00
50	Builders of the Empire	1898	£3.50	£175.00
L40	Butterflies & Moths	1938	20p	£8.00
1	Calendar for 1911	1910	—	£7.50
1	Calendar 1912	1911	—	£4.00
L25	Cathedrals	1933	£1.00	£25.00
L25	Celebrated Pictures A Series	1916	£1.00	£25.00
L25	Celebrated Pictures 2nd Series	1916	£1.20	£30.00
50	Celebrated Ships	1911	50p	£25.00
25	Cinema Stars 1st Series	1928	40p	£10.00
25	Cinema Stars 2nd Series	1928	30p	£7.50
50	Cinema Stars 3rd Series	1931	40p	£20.00
P12	Cities of Britain	1929	£4.00	£48.00
25	Conundrums (no album clause)	1898	£3.00	£75.00
25	Conundrums (with album clause)	1898	£3.00	£75.00
60	Coronation Ser. (narrow arrows)	1902	£3.00	£180.00
60	Coronation Ser. (wide arrows)	1902	£2.50	£150.00
50	Cricketers	1896	£40.00	£2000.00
50	Cricketer Series 1901	1901	£12.00	£600.00
25	Cricketers (WILLS'S)	1908	£3.00	£75.00
50	Cricketers (WILLS's)	1908	£2.50	£125.00
50	Cricketers, 1928	1928	50p	£25.00
50	Cricketers 2nd Series	1929	50p	£25.00
50	Dogs	1937	16p	£8.00
50	Dogs (Eire)	1937	50p	£25.00
L25	Dogs A Series	1914	£1.60	£40.00
L25	Dogs 2nd Series	1915	£1.60	£40.00
50	Double Meaning	1898	£5.00	£250.00
52	Double Meaning (P/C Inset)	1898	£6.00	£300.00
50	Do You Know A Series	1922	15p	£6.50
50	Do You Know 2nd Series	1924	15p	£5.00
50	Do You Know 3rd Series	1926	15p	£6.00
50	Do You Know 4th Series	1933	20p	£10.00
50	Engineering Wonders	1927	16p	£8.00
50	English Period Costumes	1929	30p	£15.00
L25	English Period Costumes	1927	80p	£20.00
L40	Famous British Authors	1937	30p	£12.00
L30	Famous British Liners A Series	1934	£1.50	£45.00
L30	Famous British Liners 2nd Series	1935	£1.00	£30.00
L25	Famous Golfers	1930	£1.60	£40.00
50	Famous Inventions	1915	40p	£20.00
50	First Aid (No Album Clause)	1913	30p	£15.00
50	First Aid (With Album Clause)	1913	30p	£15.00
50	Fish & Bait	1910	35p	£17.50
25	Flags of the Empire A Series	1926	30p	£7.50
25	Flags of the Empire 2nd Series	1929	30p	£7.50
50	Flower Culture in Pots	1925	15p	£5.00
L30	Flowering Shrubs	1934	50p	£15.00
50	Flowering Trees & Shrubs	1924	16p	£8.00
66	Football Series	1902	£3.00	£200.00
50	Garden Flowers	1933	15p	£6.50

Qty		Date	Odds	Sets
50	Garden Flowers by Sudell	1939	15p	£4.00
50	Garden Flowers by Sudell (Eire)	1939	15p	£7.50
L40	Garden Flowers—New Varieties A Series ...	1938	15p	£6.00
L40	Garden Flowers—New Varieties 2nd Series ...	1939	15p	£4.00
50	Garden Hints	1938	15p	£4.00
50	Garden Hints (Eire)	1938	15p	£7.50
50	Gardening Hints	1923	15p	£5.00
50	Garden Life	1914	30p	£15.00
50	Gems of Belgian Architecture	1915	30p	£15.00
50	Gems of French Architecture	1916	60p	£30.00
F50	Gems of Italian Architecture (Reproduction) ...	—	—	£6.50
50	Gems of Russian Architecture	1917	30p	£15.00
L25	Golfing	1924	£1.60	£40.00
X32	Happy Families	1939	—	£95.00
L25	Heraldic Signs & Their Origin	1925	80p	£20.00
50	Historic Events	1912	50p	£25.00
F54	Homeland Events	1932	15p	£5.00
50	Household Hints	1927	15p	£6.00
50	Household Hints 2nd Series	1930	16p	£8.00
50	Household Hints (Different)	1936	15p	£4.00
50	Household Hints (Eire)	1936	15p	£7.50
50	Hurlers (Eire)	1927	50p	£25.00
2	Indian Series	1900	£150.00	—
P12	Industries of Britain	1930	£4.00	£48.00
25	Irish Beauty-Spots	1924	£2.00	£50.00
25	Irish Holiday Resorts	1924	£2.00	£50.00
50	Irish Industries	1937	40p	£20.00
25	Irish Rugby Internationals	1926	£3.00	£75.00
50	Irish Sportsmen	1936	£1.50	£75.00
50	Japanese Series	1900	£25.00	£1250.00
50	Kings & Queens (Short Card, Brown Back) ...	1898	£6.00	£300.00
50	Kings & Queens (Short Card, Grey Back) ...	1898	£2.50	£125.00
50/51	Kings & Queens (Long Card, "Wills" at Base) ...	1902	£2.50	£125.00
50	Kings & Queens (Long Card, "Wills" at Top) ...	1902	£6.00	—
L25	Lawn Tennis, 1931	1931	£1.20	£30.00
50	Life in the Hedgerow	Unissued	—	£7.50
50	Life in the Royal Navy	1939	15p	£5.00
50	Life in the Treetops	1925	15p	£6.00
50	Locomotives & Rolling Stock (No Clause) ...	1901	£3.00	£150.00
50	Locomotives & Rolling Stock (With ITC Clause)	1902	£3.50	£175.00
50	Lucky Charms	1923	15p	£6.00
100	Maori Series	1900	£50.00	—
50	Medals	1906	£1.40	£70.00
50	Merchant Ships of the World	1924	30p	£15.00
50	Military Motors (Not Passed by Censor) ...	1916	50p	£25.00
50	Military Motors (Passed by Censor)	1916	50p	£25.00
52	Miniature Playing Cards (Blue Back, Numbered)	1931	25p	£12.50
52	Miniature Playing Cards (Blue Back, Unnumbered)	1931	25p	£12.50
52	Miniature Playing Cards (Blue Back, Red Overprints)	1931	25p	£12.50
52	Miniature Playing Cards (Pink Back)	1931	40p	£20.00

W. D. & H. O. WILLS LTD.—cont.

Qty		Date	Odds	Sets
52	Miniature Playing Cards (Eire)	1931	75p	—
50	Mining	1916	35p	£17.50
L25	Modern Architecture	1931	80p	£20.00
L30	Modern British Sculpture	1928	75p	£22.50
48	Mother & Son (Sect.)	1931	15p	£6.00
50	Musical Celebrities	1912	80p	£40.00
50	Musical Celebrities 2nd Series	1914	£1.40	£70.00
25	National Costumes	1895	£120.00	—
?	National Types	1893	*£250.00*	—
50	Naval Dress & Badges	1909	£1.20	£60.00
50	Nelson Series	1905	£1.30	£65.00
50	Old English Garden Flowers	1910	30p	£15.00
50	Old English Garden Flowers Second Series ...	1913	30p	£15.00
L25	Old Furniture 1st Series	1923	£1.20	£30.00
L25	Old Furniture 2nd Series	1924	£1.20	£30.00
L40	Old Inns A Series	1936	£1.00	£40.00
L40	Old Inns Second Series	1939	45p	£18.00
L25	Old London	1929	£1.40	£35.00
L30	Old Pottery & Porcelain	1934	60p	£18.00
L25	Old Silver	1924	£1.00	£25.00
L25	Old Sundials	1928	80p	£18.00
20	Our Gallant Grenadiers	1902	£20.00	£400.00
50	Our King & Queen	1937	15p	£5.00
50	Overseas Dominions (Australia)	1915	30p	£15.00
50	Overseas Dominions (Canada)	1914	30p	£15.00
50	Physical Culture	1914	35p	£17.50
25	Pond & Aquarium 1st Series	Unissued	—	£4.00
25	Pond & Aquarium 2nd Series	Unissued	—	£5.00
50	Portraits of European Royalty (1-50) ...	1908	50p	£25.00
50	Portraits of European Royalty (51-100) ...	1908	70p	£35.00
L25	Public Schools	1927	80p	£20.00
L25	Punch Cartoons 1st Series	1916	£2.00	£50.00
L25	Punch Cartoons 2nd Series	1917	£10.00	£250.00
L40	Racehorses & Jockeys 1938	1939	40p	£16.00
50	Radio Celebrities A Series	1934	25p	£12.50
50	Radio Celebrities A Series (Eire)	1934	60p	—
50	Radio Celebrities 2nd Series	1934	25p	£12.50
50	Radio Celebrities 2nd Series (Eire)	1934	60p	—
50	Railway Engines	1924	40p	£20.00
50	Railway Engines (adhesive)	1936	30p	£15.00
50	Railway Engines (Eire)	1936	60p	—
50	Railway Equipment	1938	15p	£5.00
50	Railway Locomotives	1930	60p	£30.00
12	Recruiting Posters	1915	£3.00	£36.00
L25	Rigs of Ships	1929	£1.40	£35.00
50	Romance of the Heavens	1928	20p	£10.00
50	Roses A Series (1-50)	1912	30p	£15.00
50	Roses Second Series (51-100)	1913	30p	£15.00
50	Roses (Different)	1926	15p	£6.50
L40	Roses (Different)	1936	30p	£12.00
M48	Round Europe	1936	15p	£6.50
50	Rugby Internationals	1929	50p	£25.00
50	Safety First	1934	16p	£8.00
50	Safety First (Eire)	1934	60p	—

W. D. & H. O. WILLS LTD.—cont.

Qty		Date	Odds	Sets
50	School Arms	1906	35p	£17.50
50	Seaside Resorts	1899	£5.00	£250.00
40	Shannon Electric Power Scheme (Eire)	1931	70p	£28.00
25	Ships (Three Castles Back)	1895	£18.00	£450.00
25	Ships (No "Wills" on Front)	1895	£18.00	£450.00
50	Ships (With "Wills" on Front)	1896	£12.00	£600.00
100	Ships (Brownish Card)	1897	£12.50	—
50	Ships' Badges	1925	15p	£6.00
50	Signalling Series	1911	35p	£17.50
50	Soldiers & Sailors (Blue Back)	1894	£30.00	£1500.00
50	Soldiers & Sailors (Grey back)	1894	£30.00	£1500.00
100	Soldiers of the World (Ltd. back)	1895	£4.00	£400.00
100/101	Soldiers of the World (no Ltd. on back)	1895	£4.00	£400.00
52	Soldiers of the World (P/C Inset)	1896	£15.00	£780.00
100	South African Personalities (Collotype)	1901	£60.00	—
50	Speed	1930	60p	£30.00
50	Speed (Different)	1938	15p	£5.00
50	Speed (Eire)	1938	30p	£15.00
50	Sports of All Nations	1901	£5.00	£250.00
50	Strange Craft	1931	30p	£15.00
48	The Boyhood of Raleigh (Sect.)	1931	15p	£7.50
P12	The British Empire	1929	£4.00	£48.00
50	The Coronation Series	1911	50p	£25.00
L40	The King's Art Treasures	1938	15p	£5.00
48	The Laughing Cavalier (Sect.)	1931	15p	£7.50
48	The Laughing Cavalier (Sect. Eire)	1931	75p	—
50	The Life of H.M. King Edward VIII	Unissued	£10.00	
50	The Reign of King George V	1935	16p	£8.00
50	The Sea Shore	1938	15p	£5.00
50	The Sea Shore (Eire)	1938	30p	£15.00
48	The Toast (Sect.)	1931	15p	£6.00
48	The Toast (Sect., Eire)	1931	75p	—
25	The World's Dreadnoughts	1910	70p	£17.50
50	Time & Money in different Countries	1908	80p	£40.00
50	Transvaal Series (Black Border)	1901	£5.00	
66	Transvaal Series (White Border)	1901	£1.00	£66.00
66	Transvaal Series (Non Descriptive Back)	1902	£2.50	£165.00
L40	Trees	1937	35p	£14.00
L25	University Hoods & Gowns	1926	£1.40	£35.00
50	Vanity Fair Series (Unnumbered)	1902	£2.50	£125.00
50	Vanity Fair 1st Series	1902	£2.50	£125.00
50	Vanity Fair 2nd Series	1902	£2.50	£125.00
50	Waterloo	Unissued	£50.00	—
50	Wild Animals of the World (Green Scroll Back)	1900	£3.00	£150.00
15	Wild Animals of the World (Grey Descriptive Back)	1902	£20.00	£300.00
52	Wild Animals of the World (P/C Inset)	1900	£7.50	£400.00
50	Wild Flowers	1923	15p	£5.00
50	Wild Flowers A Series (adhesive)	1936	15p	£5.00
50	Wild Flowers (Eire)	1936	25p	£12.50
50	Wild Flowers 2nd Series	1937	15p	£4.00
50	Wild Flowers 2nd Series (Eire)	1937	25p	£12.50
50	Wonders of the Past	1926	25p	£12.50
50	Wonders of the Sea	1928	25p	£12.50

W. D. & H. O. WILLS LTD.—cont.

Qty		Date	Odds	Sets
MODERN ISSUES (EMBASSY)				
T48	Familiar Phrases	1986	30p	—
L30	History of Britain's Railways	1987	40p	—
L30	History of Motor Racing	1987	40p	—
T5	Pica Punchline	1984	40p	£2.00
L144	Punch Lines	1983	25p	—
T288	Punch Lines	1983	25p	—
T48	Ring the Changes	1985	30p	£15.00
56	Wonders of the World	1986	30p	—
M56	Wonders of the World	1986	30p	—
T56	Wonders of the World	1986	30p	—
M36	World of Firearms	1982	15p	£2.00
M36	World of Speed	1981	15p	£2.00
AUSTRALIAN ISSUES				
100	Actresses	1903	£1.75	—
1	Advertisement Card (Capstan)	1902	—	£125.00
60	Animals (cut-outs)	1916	50p	£30.00
60	Animals (cut-outs Havelock)	1916	£1.00	—
50	Arms & Armour	1910	80p	£40.00
50	Arms & Armour (Havelock)	1910	£1.50	—
50	Arms of the British Empire	1910	40p	£20.00
50	Arms of the British Empire (Havelock)	1910	£1.00	—
M50	Arms of the British Empire (Silk)	1910	£1.60	£80.00
50	A Tour Round the World	1907	£1.60	£80.00
25	Australian & English Cricketers (Numbered)	1903	£8.00	£200.00
25	Australian & English Cricketers (Blue/Red Frame)	1909	£8.00	£200.00
59	Australian & English Cricketers (Titled)	1911	£8.00	£475.00
50	Australian & English Cricketers (Havelock)	1911	£25.00	—
24	Australian & South African Cricketers (dark background—SA only)	1910	£10.00	£240.00
60	Australian & South African Cricketers (light background)	1910	£8.00	£480.00
60	Australian & South African Cricketers (Havelock)	1910	£25.00	—
M50	Australian Butterflies (Silk)	1914	£1.60	£80.00
40/46	Australian Club Cricketers	1905	£10.00	—
MF100	Australian Scenic Series	1925	35p	£35.00
50	Australian Wild Flowers	1913	35p	£17.50
50	Australian Wild Flowers (Havelock)	1913	£1.00	—
75	Aviation (Black Back)	1910	70p	£52.50
75	Aviation (Black Back, Havelock)	1910	£1.50	—
75	Aviation (Green Back)	1910	80p	—
75	Aviation (Green Back, Havelock)	1910	£1.75	—
85	Aviation	1910	£1.00	£85.00
50	Best Dogs of their Breed	1914	£2.00	—
50	Best Dogs of Their Breed (Havelock)	1914	£3.50	—
M50	Birds and Animals of Australia (Silk)	1915	£1.60	£80.00
100	Birds of Australasia (Green Back)	1912	50p	£50.00
100	Birds of Australasia (Green Back, Havelock)	1912	£1.00	—
100	Birds of Australasia (Yellow Back)	1912	40p	£40.00
100	Birds of Australasia (Yellow Back, Havelock)	1912	£1.00	—
50	Britain's Defenders (1-50)	1914	60p	£30.00
50	Britain's Defenders (Havelock)	1914	£1.50	£75.00
8	Britain's Defenders (51-8)	1914	£5.00	—
50	British Empire Series	1912	35p	£17.50
50	British Empire Series (Havelock)	1912	80p	£40.00

Qty		Date	Odds	Sets
M68	Crests and Colours of Australian Universities Colleges and Schools	1929	30p	£20.00
M50	Crests and Colours of Australian Universities Colleges and Schools (Silk)	1929	£1.75	£87.50
M1	Crests and Colours of Australian Schools (Silk, Unnumbered)	1929	—	£10.00
50	Cricketer Series (Grey Scroll Back, No Frame) ...	1901	£50.00	—
25	Cricketer Series (Grey Scroll Back, Fancy Frame) ...	1902	£50.00	—
F63	Cricketers (Plain Back)	1926	£4.00	£250.00
F40/48	Cricket Season, 1928-29	1929	£1.00	£40.00
L20	Dogs A Series	1927	£1.00	£25.00
L20	Dogs 2nd Series	1928	£1.00	£25.00
L25	English Period Costumes	1929	60p	£15.00
100	Famous Film Stars	1930	30p	£30.00
M100	Famous Film Stars	1933	50p	—
MF100	Famous Film Stars	1933	£1.25	—
B20	Fiestas (Cartons)	1968	40p	—
50	Fish of Australasia	1912	35p	£17.50
50	Fish of Australasia (Havelock)	1912	80p	—
50	Flag Girls of All Nations	1908	£1.20	£60.00
8	Flags (Shaped, Metal)	1915	£4.00	—
M13	Flags (Lace)	1916	£3.00	£40.00
28	Flags of the Allies (Silk)	1915	£1.00	£28.00
25	Flags of the Empire	1926	£4.00	—
28	Football Club Colours & Flags	1913	£1.75	—
28	Football Club Colours & Flags (Havelock)	1913	£3.00	—
200	Footballers 1933	1933	25p	£50.00
M200	Footballers 1933	1933	40p	—
?6	Footballers (Shaped)	1910	£40.00	—
?	Football Pennants (Shaped)	1905	£25.00	—
?	Football Pennants (Shaped Havelock)	1905	£25.00	—
50	Girls of All Nations	1908	£1.20	£60.00
X?	Havelock Comics	1904	£50.00	—
50	Historic Events	1913	50p	£25.00
50	Historic Events (Havelock)	1913	80p	£40.00
L25	History of Naval Dress	1929	£12.50	—
50	Horses of Today	1906	£1.00	£50.00
50	Horses of Today (Havelock)	1906	£2.00	—
50	Interesting Buildings	1905	80p	£40.00
5	Islands of the Pacific	1917	£60.00	—
38	Kings & Queens of England (Silk)	1910	£2.50	£95.00
45	Melbourne Cup Winners	1906	£2.50	—
40	Merrie England Studies	1916	£2.50	£100.00
50	Modern War Weapons	1915	60p	£30.00
50	Modern War Weapons (Havelock)	1915	£1.25	—
50	Past & Present Champions	1908	£2.50	£125.00
M50	Popular Flowers (Silk)	1913	£2.00	£100.00
L70	Practical Wireless	1923	£1.25	—
50	Prominent Australian & English Cricketers (1-50)	1907	£7.00	£450.00
23	Prominent Australian & English Cricketers (51-73)	1907	£8.00	£175.00
10	Recruiting Posters (Anon back)	1915	£3.00	£30.00
50	Riders of the World	1913	60p	£30.00
50	Riders of the World (Havelock)	1913	£1.25	—
50	Royal Mail	1913	£1.40	£70.00

W. D. &. H. O. WILLS LTD.—cont.

Qty		Date	Odds	Sets
50	Royal Mail (Havelock)	1913	£2.50	—
50	Signalling Series	1912	40p	£20.00
50	Signalling Series (Havelock)	1912	80p	£40.00
40	Sketches in Black & White	1905	£1.25	—
50	Soldiers of the World	1902	£3.50	£175.00
25	Sporting Terms	1905	£4.00	—
50	Sports of the World	1917	£1.75	—
50	Stage & Music Hall Celebrities (Oval Frame)	1904	£1.20	£60.00
50	Stage & Music Hall Celebrities (Havelock)	1904	£2.50	—
50	Stage & Music Hall Celebrities (Square Frame)	1904	£1.20	£60.00
L25	The Nation's Shrines	1928	70p	£17.50
25	The World's Dreadnoughts	1910	70p	£17.50
50	Time & Money in Different Countries ... .:. ...	1908	60p	£30.00
50	Time & Money in Different Countries (Havelock)	1908	£1.25	£62.50
50	Types of the British Army	1912	£1.20	£60.00
50	Types of the Commonwealth Forces	1910	£1.50	£75.00
50	Types of the Commonwealth Forces (Havelock)	1910	£3.00	—
P1	Union Jack (Silk)	1915	—	£8.00
25	United States Warships	1911	£1.40	£35.00
25	United States Warships (Havelock)	1911	£2.50	—
25	Victoria Cross Heroes	1915	£1.20	£30.00
25	Victoria Cross Heroes (Havelock)	1915	£2.50	£62.50
29	Victorian Football Pennants	1910	£1.75	—
29	Victorian Football Pennants (Havelock)	1910	£3.00	—
FS165	Views of the World	1908	50p	—
50	War Incidents A Series	1915	60p	£30.00
50	War Incidents A Series (Havelock)	1915	£1.25	—
50	War Incidents, 2nd Series	1915	60p	£30.00
50	War Incidents 2nd Series (Havelock)	1915	£1.50	—
L67	War Medals (Silk)	1916	£1.75	£120.00
50	War Pictures	1915	60p	£30.00
50	War Pictures (Havelock)	1915	£1.25	£62.50
50	Wild Animals (Heads)	1934	20p	£10.00
M25	Wild Animals (as above)	1934	50p	£12.50
50	Wild Animals of the World	1906	£2.00	£100.00
LF50	Zoological Series	1922	£1.00	£50.00

BRAND ISSUES

(A) Autocar Cigarettes

40	Chinese Trades	1905	£3.00	—

(B) Flag Cigarettes

67	International Footballers, Season 1909-1910 ...	1910	£4.00	—
50	Jiu Jitsu	1911	£2.50	—
50	Types of the British Army	1912	£3.00	—

(C) Four Aces Cigarettes

52	Birds of Brilliant Plumage (P/C Inset)	1924	£1.50	£80.00
75	Film Favourites	1928	80p	£60.00
25	Modes of Conveyance	1928	80p	£20.00
50	Stage & Film Stars (numbered)	1926	80p	£40.00
50	Stage & Film Stars (unnumbered)	1926	£1.00	£50.00
F52	Stars of the Cinema	1926	£1.75	—

W. D. & H. O. WILLS LTD.—cont.

Qty		Date	Odds	Sets
(D)	**Pirate Cigarettes**			
G?	Advertisement Cards	1910	£35.00	—
?100	Baseball Series	1912	*£15.00*	—
52	Birds of Brilliant Plumage (P/C Inset frame line)	1914	£2.50	—
52	Birds of Brilliant Plumage (P/C Inset no frame) ...	1914	£2.00	£100.00
100	China's Ancient Warriors	1911	65p	£65.00
28	Chinese Actors & Actresses	1907	£1.25	£35.00
50	Chinese Beauties	1907	70p	£35.00
50	Chinese Costumes	1928	£1.75	—
P25	Chinese Pagodas	1911	*£12.50*	—
50	Chinese Proverbs (Brown)	1928	80p	£40.00
50	Chinese Proverbs (Coloured)	1914	80p	£40.00
33	Houses of Parliament	1914	60p	£20.00
50	Products of the World	1913	80p	£40.00
(E)	**Purple Mountain Cigarettes**			
20	Flowers (Numbered)	1914	*£7.50*	—
100	Flowers (Unnumbered)	1915	*£6.00*	—
25	Roses	1912	£3.00	£75.00
(F)	**Ruby Queen Cigarettes**			
30	Birds & Animals	1911	£1.50	£45.00
50	Birds of the East	1912	80p	£40.00
30	Chinese Children's Games	1911	£1.00	—
50	Chinese Proverbs	1927	£1.00	—
50	Chinese Transport	1914	£1.50	—
(G)	**Scissors Cigarettes**			
50	Actresses (Black & White)	1904	*£5.00*	—
50	Actresses (Four Colour Surround)	1904	£3.50	—
30	Actresses (Green Surround)	1905	£2.00	—
30	Actresses (Mauve Surround)	1916	80p	£24.00
30	Actresses (Orange Surround)	1916	£1.25	£37.50
30	Actresses (Purple Brown, Brown Back)	1908	£1.25	£37.50
30	Actresses (Purple Brown, Red Back)	1908	80p	£24.00
30	Actresses (Purple Brown, Long Card)	1909	80p	£24.00
25	Army Life	1914	£1.00	£25.00
30	Beauties (Green Surround)	1921	£3.00	—
52	Beauties (P/C Inset) (lattice background) ...	1911	£1.75	£90.00
52	Beauties (P/C Inset, no lattice on back) ...	1911	£3.00	—
32	Beauties (Picture Hat)	1914	£1.50	£48.00
40	Beauties (Brown Tint)	1913	80p	£32.00
30	Beauties & Children	1910	£1.25	£45.00
36	Boxers	1911	£3.50	£125.00
50	Britain's Defenders (Green Back)	1914	80p	£40.00
50	Britain's Defenders (Red Back & Front) ...	1914	70p	£35.00
50	Britain's Defenders (Red Back, Blue Front) ...	1914	70p	£35.00
43	British Army Boxers Series	1913	£2.50	£100.00
25	Cinema Stars	1916	£1.20	£30.00
F50	Cinema Stars	1926	*£2.50*	—
27	Dancing Girls (Series of 27)	1915	£1.50	£40.00
27/28	Dancing Girls (Series of 28)	1915	£1.50	£40.00
25	Derby Day Series	1914	£2.00	£50.00
25	Derby Day Series A (no series title)	1914	£3.50	—

Qty		Date	Odds	Sets
32	Drum Horses (Horizontal back)	1909	£3.50	£105.00
32	Drum Horses (Vertical back)	1909	£5.00	—
50	Famous Footballers	1914	£2.50	£125.00
25	Flag Girls of All Nations	1908	£5.00	—
50	Football Club Colours	1907	£2.50	£125.00
25	Governors-General of India	1912	£3.50	£87.50
30	Heroic Deeds	1913	£1.25	£37.50
50	Indian Regiments Series	1912	£3.50	£175.00
67	International Footballers, Season 1909-1910 ...	1910	£3.50	£235.00
50	Jiu Jitsu	1910	£3.00	£150.00
53	Jockeys & Owners Colours (P/C Inset)	1914	£3.00	—
25	Military Portraits	1917	£2.50	£62.50
50	Music Hall Celebrities	1911	£3.50	—
K52	Playing Cards	1906	£7.50	—
25	Puzzle Series (United Service Backs)	1910	£3.00	—
50	Regimental Colours & Cap Badges	1907	80p	£40.00
33	Regimental Pets	1911	£3.50	£115.00
30	Sporting Girls	1913	£3.50	—
50	Types of the British Army	1908	£3.00	£150.00
25	Victoria Cross Heroes	1915	£1.40	£35.00
50	War Incidents	1915	80p	£40.00
30	What It Means	1916	65p	£20.00
F50	"Zoo"	1927	£2.50	—

(H) United Service Cigarettes

Qty		Date	Odds	Sets
50	Arms & Armour	1910	£1.50	£75.00
32	Drum Horses	1909	£3.50	£105.00
25	Flag Girls of All Nations	1908	£1.40	£35.00
67	International Footballers, Season 1909-1910 ...	1910	£3.50	—
	Puzzle Series—See Scissors Cigarettes			
50	Regimental Colours & Cap Badges			
	(Blue Back)	1907	60p	£30.00
50	Regimental Colours & Cap Badges			
	(Red Back)	1907	70p	£35.00

(I) Wild Woodbine Cigarettes

Qty		Date	Odds	Sets
50	British Army Uniforms	1909	£3.00	£150.00

CHANNEL ISLANDS ISSUES (Similar to British Sets)

Qty		Date	Odds	Sets
50	Air Raid Precautions	1938	25p	£12.50
50	Association Footballers	1935	35p	£17.50
50	Dogs	1937	35p	£17.50
50	Garden Flowers by Sudell	1939	16p	£8.00
50	Garden Hints	1938	16p	£8.00
50	Household Hints	1936	16p	£8.00
50	Life in the Royal Navy	1939	20p	£10.00
50	Our King & Queen	1937	20p	£10.00
50	Railway Equipment	1938	20p	£10.00
50	Speed	1938	16p	£8.00
50	The Sea Shore	1938	16p	£8.00
50	Wild Flowers A Series	1936	25p	£12.50
50	Wild Flowers 2nd Series	1937	16p	£8.00

NEW ZEALAND ISSUES

Qty		Date	Odds	Sets
F50	A Sporting Holiday in New Zealand	1928	25p	£12.50
LF50	A Sporting Holiday in New Zealand (Different) ...	1928	40p	£20.00

Qty		Date	Odds	Sets
F50	Beautiful New Zealand	1928	15p	£6.00
50	Birds, Beasts and Fishes	1924	25p	£12.50
F48	British Royal and Ancient Buildings	1925	16p	£8.00
45	British Rugby Players	1930	70p	£31.50
50	Children of All Nations	1925	20p	£10.00
50	Coaches and Coaching Days	1925	50p	£25.00
50	Dogs	1926	30p	£15.00
F25	English Cricketers	1926	80p	£20.00
26	Etchings (Dogs)	1925	35p	£10.00
L26	Etchings (Dogs)	1925	80p	£20.00
50	Famous Inventions	1926	30p	£15.00
L25	Heraldic Signs & Their Origin	1925	60p	£15.00
F50	Homeland Events	1927	15p	£6.00
50	Household Hints	1927	15p	£6.00
50	Lighthouses	1926	25p	£12.50
50	Merchant Ships of the World	1925	30p	£15.00
48	Motor Cars	1923	75p	£36.00
F50	Motor Cars	1926	50p	£25.00
50	Motor Cycles	1926	£1.00	£50.00
50	New Zealand Birds	1925	30p	£15.00
F50	New Zealand—Early Scenes & Maori Life	1926	15p	£7.50
F50	New Zealand Footballers	1927	15p	£6.50
50	New Zealand Racehorses	1928	35p	£17.50
50	N.Z. Butterflies, Moths & Beetles	1925	30p	£15.00
25	Past & Present	1929	50p	£12.50
25	Picturesque People of the Empire	1928	30p	£7.50
25	Pirates & Highwaymen	1925	25p	£6.25
50	Products of the World	1929	15p	£7.50
50	Railway Engines	1925	35p	£17.50
50	Railway Working	1927	£1.00	£50.00
50	Regimental Standards and Cap Badges	1928	20p	£10.00
50	Riders of the World	1931	35p	£17.50
50	Romance of the Heavens	1928	£1.00	—
50	Safety First	1935	30p	£15.00
F50	Ships and Shipping	1928	15p	£7.00
50	Ships' Badges	1925	40p	£20.00
F50	The Royal Family at Home and Abroad	1927	30p	£15.00
F50	The Royal Navy	1929	80p	£40.00
F50	Units of the British Army and R.A.F.	1928	15p	£6.50
50	U.S.S. Co's. Steamers	1930	£1.25	—
50	V.C's.	1926	60p	£30.00
25	Village Models Series	1925	50p	£12.50
L25	Village Models Series	1925	£3.00	—
50	Warships	1926	60p	£30.00
25	Wonders of the World	1926	25p	£6.25
F50	"Zoo"	1926	15p	£6.00

OTHER OVERSEAS ISSUES

Qty		Date	Odds	Sets
50	Actors & Actresses "WALP"	1905	£1.40	£70.00
250	Actresses "ALWICS"	1905	80p	£200.00
25	Actresses, Tabs Type (101-125)	1902	£7.00	£175.00
50	Actresses, Four Colour Surround	1904	£1.40	£70.00
50	Aeroplanes	1926	£1.25	—
50	Animals & Birds (With Series Title)	1912	£2.00	£100.00

W. D. & H. O. WILLS LTD.—cont.

Qty		Date	Odds	Sets
50	Animals & Birds (No Series Title)	1909	£2.00	£100.00
50	Arms of the British Empire	1911	50p	£25.00
50	Art Photogravures—Set 1	1912	30p	£15.00
B50	Art Photogravures—Set 1	1912	40p	£20.00
50	Art Photogravures—Set 2	1913	30p	£15.00
50	Aviation Series	1911	£1.20	£60.00
50	Beauties "LAWHA" (Red Tinted)	1905	80p	£40.00
40	Beauties (Brown Tinted)	1913	£1.50	—
52	Beauties (P/C Inset)	1911	£3.00	—
32	Beauties—Picture Hats	1914	£3.00	£100.00
M72	Beauties	1923	£7.50	—
BF50	Beauties (Hand Coloured)	1925	£1.50	—
F25	Beauties	1925	£1.75	—
F50	Beauties, 2nd Series	1925	£1.75	—
52	Birds of Brilliant Plumage (P/C Inset)	1914	£3.00	£150.00
36	Boxers	1911	£3.50	£125.00
50	Britain's Defenders	1914	£1.00	£50.00
101	British Beauties	1915	£1.00	£100.00
50	British Costumes from 100 BC to 1904	1905	£40.00	—
50	Chateaux	1925	£2.00	£100.00
50	Conundrums	1903	£5.00	£250.00
25	Derby Day Series	1914	£4.00	—
32	Drum Horses	1909	£3.50	£110.00
26	Etchings (Gold Flake Cigs)	1925	£3.50	—
26	Etchings (Dutch Text)	1925	£3.50	—
50	Famous Footballers	1914	£3.00	—
25	Flag Girls of All Nations	1908	£1.20	£30.00
126	Flags & Ensigns	1904	60p	£75.00
6	Flags of the Allies (Shaped)	1915	£7.50	£45.00
50	Girls of All Nations	1908	£1.50	—
32	Houses of Parliament	1912	80p	£25.00
50	Indian Regiments Series	1912	£4.00	—
24	Merveilles Du Monde	1927	£3.00	—
M25	Miniatures (Metal)	1914	£30.00	£750.00
F48	Movie Stars	1927	£2.00	—
50	National Flags and Arms	1936	80p	
FS50	Nature Studies	1928	£1.00	—
25	Police of the World	1910	£4.00	£100.00
25	Products of the World	1913	£1.00	£25.00
50	Races of Mankind	1911	£7.50	£375.00
100	Royalty, Notabilities & Events, 1900-2	1902	£1.00	£100.00
27	Rulers of the World	1911	£3.50	—
100	Russo Japanese Series (black front)	1905	80p	£80.00
50	Russo Japanese Series (red front)	1905	£5.00	—
LF48	Scenes from the Empire	1939	£1.00	—
30	Semaphore Signalling	1910	£1.25	£37.50
36	Ships & Their Pennants	1913	£2.00	—
75	Soldiers of the World	1903	£5.00	—
F52	Stars of the Cinema	1926	£2.50	—
25	The Evolution of the British Navy	1915	£1.40	£35.00
25	The World's Dreadnoughts	1910	£1.00	£25.00
50	Wild Animals of the World (Star, Circle & Leaves)	1906	£5.00	—

WILSON & CO.

Qty		Date	Odds	Sets
50	War Portraits	1916	£40.00	—

W. WILSON

30	Army Pictures, Cartoons, etc.	1916	£45.00	—

A. & M. WIX

D250	Cinema Cavalcade	1940	24p	£60.00
D250	Cinema Cavalcade, Volume 2	1940	24p	£60.00
100	Film Favourites	1930	£1.25	—
100	Film Favourites, 2nd Series	1931	£1.25	—
100	Film Favourites, 3rd Series	1932	50p	£50.00
L?23	Maxims of Max (Package Issue)	1952	£4.00	—
X100	Men of Destiny	1934	£1.50	£150.00
D250	Speed—Through the Ages	1938	20p	£50.00
D250	This Age of Power & Wonder	1935	16p	£40.00

J. WIX & SONS LTD.

F?	Animals	1928	£25.00	—
P80	Bridge Favours & Place Cards	1937	£7.50	—
P50	Bridge Hands	1937	£7.50	—
L48	British Empire Flags (Silk)	1934	35p	£16.50
L48	British Empire Flags (Silk, Printed in U.S.A.)	1934	30p	£15.00
50	Builders of Empire	1937	15p	£6.00
42	Card Tricks	1938	£2.00	—
M42	Card Tricks	1938	£2.00	—
50	Coronation (Kensitas)	1937	15p	£5.00
50	Coronation (Wix)	1937	15p	£5.00
L50	Henry	1935	20p	£10.00
P25	Henry	1935	£1.40	£35.00
L50	Henry, 2nd Series	1936	40p	£20.00
P25	Henry, 2nd Series	1936	£1.40	£35.00
L50	Henry, 3rd Series	1936	16p	£8.00
L50	Henry, 4th Series	1936	15p	£7.50
L50	Henry, 5th Series	1937	15p	£7.50
L182	Jenkynisms (Yellow)	1932	50p	—
?150	Jenkynisms (Red Borders)	1931	£2.00	—
L?150	Jenkynisms (Red Borders)	1931	£2.00	—
P96	Ken-Cards	1969	20p	£20.00
60	Kensitas Flowers (Silk, plain back)	1933	£1.00	£60.00
60	Kensitas Flowers (Silk, printed back)	1933	£1.00	£60.00
L60	Kensitas Flowers (Silk, plain back)	1933	£1.50	£90.00
L60	Kensitas Flowers (Silk, printed back)	1933	£1.50	£90.00
P30	Kensitas Flowers (Silk)	1933	£12.50	£375.00
40	Kensitas Flowers 2nd Series (Silk)	1934	£2.00	£100.00
L40	Kensitas Flowers 2nd Series (Silk)	1934	£3.00	£150.00
25	Love Scenes from Famous Films, 1st Series ...	1932	£1.40	£35.00
L25	Love Scenes from Famous Films, 1st Series ...	1932	£1.40	£35.00
P25	Love Scenes from Famous Films, 1st Series ...	1932	£2.00	—
19/25	Love Scenes from Famous Films, 2nd Series ...	1932	£1.40	£35.00
L19/25	Love Scenes from Famous Films, 2nd Series ...	1932	£2.00	—
P19/25	Love Scenes from Famous Films, 2nd Series ...	1932	£5.00	—
K53	Miniature Playing Cards (Blue Scroll)	1938	15p	£5.00
K53	Miniature Playing Cards (Red Scroll)	1938	15p	£5.00
K53	Miniature Playing Cards (Revenge)	1938	15p	£6.50

J. WIX & SONS LTD.—cont.

Qty		Date	Odds	Sets
K53	Miniature Playing Cards (Victory)	1938	15p	£6.50
L60	National Flags (Silk)	1934	35p	£25.00
F24	Royal Tour in New Zealand	1928	£6.00	—
25	Scenes from Famous Films, 3rd Series	1932	£1.50	£37.50
P25	Scenes from Famous Films, 3rd Series	1932	£3.00	—

T. WOOD & SONS

30	Army Pictures, Cartoons, etc.	1916	*£45.00*	—

WOOD BROS.

28	Dominoes	1910	*£35.00*	—

JOHN J. WOODS

?	Views of London	1905	*£85.00*	—

W. H. & J. WOODS LTD.

25	Aesop's Fables	1932	70p	£17.50
F50	Modern Motor Cars	1936	£1.75	£87.50
25	Romance of the Royal Mail	1931	50p	£12.50
25	Types of Volunteer & Yeomanry	1902	£16.00	£400.00

J. & E. WOOLF

50	Beauties "KEWA"	1898	*£125.00*	—

M. H. WOOLLER

24	Beauties "BOCCA"	1899	*£150.00*	—

T. E. YEOMANS & SONS LTD.

M72	Beauties	1900	*£100.00*	—
50	War Portraits	1916	*£40.00*	—

JOHN YOUNG & SONS LTD.

12	Naval Skits	1904	£100.00	—
12	Russo Japanese Series	1904	£40.00	—

A. ZICALIOTTI

1	Milly-Totty Advertisement Card	1900	*£250.00*	—

THE "NOSTALGIA" ALBUM

We believe our album to be the finest on the market – yet this year it is even better. Our pages are now being made from a material which contains no potentially harmful plasticiser and has a crystal-clear appearance. Only available from Murray Cards (International) Ltd. and approved stockists. Note also the following features:–

★★ Album leaves are made from clear plastic, enabling the entire card to be examined easily without handling!

★★ Cards easily removed and inserted!

★★ Wide margin enables pages to be turned in album without removing retention clip!

★★ A planned range of page formats allows most cards to be housed in one cover. Ten different pages now available!

★★ Handsome loose leaf PVC binders for easy removal and insertion of pages. Matching slip cases. Four different colours available.

★★ Black or coloured interleaving to enhance the appearance of your cards.

★★ Album with 40 pages only £8.00 ★★

Extra pages	13p each	Matching slip case	£2.00 each
Pastel interleaving	50p per 8	Cover only	£2.80 each
Black interleaving	£1.20 per 40	Tweezers	£1.00 each

Slip cases only supplied with covers. All prices post paid.

Page sizes available:–

- K. holds 15 cards smaller than standard. Size up to 51 x 41 mm.
- A. holds 10 standard size cards. Size up to 80 x 41 mm.
- B. holds 8 cards larger than standard. Size up to 80 x 46 mm.
- M. holds 8 medium size cards. Size up to 80 x 52 mm.
- L. holds 6 large size cards. Size up to 80 x 71 mm.
- T. holds 6 Doncella/Typhoo cards. Size up to 110 x 54 mm.
- X. holds 4 extra large size cards. Size up to 80 x 110 mm.
- C. holds 4 long cards. Size up to 165 x 50 mm.
- P. holds 2 post card size cards. Size up to 165 x 105 mm.
- G. holds 1 card cabinet size. Size up to 223 x 165 mm.

Covers, size 303 x 182 x 60 mm., are available in blue, gold, green or red.

Nostalgia – Collect with Confidence!

Overseas Issues of U.K. Manufacturers

Whos Who in Sport. Lambert & Butler,
BAT, Machado

Personality Football Series. Carreras

Riders of the World. Ogdens, Players,
Wills, UTC

War Incidents. Wills Scissors, BAT

Arms & Armour. Players, Hignett,
Wills

Flag Girls. Wills, BAT, Players,
Lambert & Butler

Actresses Alwics. Wills, BAT,
Lambert & Butler, Calcutta

Birds of Brilliant Plumage. Ogdens,
BAT, Players, Wills

Pre War Trade Issues

Transport. Cadbury

Makes of Motor Cars & Index Marks.
Amalgamated

In Victoria's Days.
English & Scottish CWS

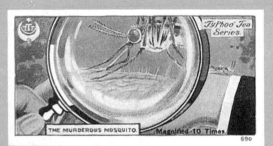

Common Objects Highly Magnified.
Typhoo

Birds & Poultry. Frys

Animals. Hustler. African Tobacco.
Dunns

Speed. Thomson

Part 2

OVERSEAS TOBACCO
MANUFACTURERS

AFRICAN TOBACCO MANUFACTURERS (S. Africa)

Qty		Date	Odds	Sets
L18	All Blacks South African Tour, 1928	1928	£6.00	—
60	Animals	1922	£2.00	—
MF48	British Aircraft	1926	£2.00	—
50	Chinese Transport	1923	£2.00	—
MF48	Cinema Artistes	1926	£1.75	—
50	Cinema Stars "OMBI", 1st Series	1923	75p	—
50	Cinema Stars "OMBI", 2nd Series	1923	75p	—
B50	Famous & Beautiful Women	1938	£1.00	—
L50	Famous & Beautiful Women	1938	75p	—
33	Houses of Parliament	1923	£4.00	—
?60	Miniatures	1924	£4.00	—
MF48	National Costumes	1926	£2.00	—
53	Playing Cards (MP)	1929	75p	—
53	Playing Cards (OK)	1929	75p	—
53	Playing Cards (Scots)	1929	75p	—
MF48	Popular Dogs	1926	£2.00	—
B100	Postage Stamps—Rarest Varieties	1930	75p	£75.00
B80	Prominent N.Z. & Australian Rugby Players and Springbok 1937 Touring Team	1937	75p	—
L80	Prominent N.Z. & Australian Rugby Players and Springbok 1937 Touring Team	1937	75p	—
29	S.A. Rugby Football Team, 1912-13	1912	*£10.00*	—
L30	Some Beautiful Roses (Silk)	1928	£4.00	£120.00
?115	S. African Members of the Legislative Assembly	1919	*£15.00*	—
25	The Arcadia Fair	1923	£4.00	—
25	The Racecourse	1923	£4.00	—
B100	The World of Sport	1939	80p	—
L100	The World of Sport	1939	80p	—
L25	Types of British Birds (Silk)	1928	£5.00	£125.00
L20	Types of British Butterflies (Silk)	1928	£5.00	—
L25	Types of Railway Engines (Silk)	1928	£12.50	—
L25	Types of Sea Shells (Silk)	1928	£6.50	—

ALLEN & GINTER (U.S.A.)

50	American Editors	1887	£12.00	£600.00
X50	American Editors	1887	£16.00	—
50	Arms of All Nations	1887	£10.00	£500.00
50	Birds of America	1890	£6.00	£300.00
X50	Birds of America	1890	£13.00	£650.00
50	Birds of the Tropics	1889	£6.00	£300.00
X50	Birds of the Tropics	1889	£13.00	—
50	Celebrated American Indian Chiefs	1888	£8.00	£400.00
50	City Flags	1888	£6.00	£300.00
50	Fans of the Period	1886	£12.00	£600.00
50	Fish from American Waters	1889	£6.00	£300.00
X50	Fish from American Waters	1889	£13.00	—
48	Flags of All Nations, 1st Series	1887	£4.00	£200.00
50	Flags of All Nations, 2nd Series	1890	£5.00	£250.00
47	Flags of The States & Territories	1890	£5.00	£235.00
50	Fruits	1891	£10.00	£500.00
50	Game Birds	1889	£6.00	£300.00
X50	Game Birds	1889	£13.00	—
50	General Government & State Capitol Buildings	1889	£6.00	£300.00
50	Great Generals	1886	£15.00	—

ALLEN & GINTER (U.S.A.)—cont.

Qty		Date	Odds	Sets
50	Natives in Costume	1886	£15.00	—
50	Naval Flags	1887	£6.00	£300.00
50	Parasol Drill	1888	£12.00	£600.00
F?	Photographic Cards (Many Types)	1885	From £1.00	
50	Pirates of the Spanish Main	1888	£12.00	£600.00
50	Prize & Game Chickens	1892	£7.00	£350.00
50	Quadrupeds	1889	£6.00	£300.00
X50	Quadrupeds	1889	£13.00	—
50	Racing Colours of the World (no border) ...	1888	£10.00	—
50	Racing Colours of the World (white border) ...	1888	£8.00	£400.00
50	Song Birds of the World	1890	£6.00	£300.00
X50	Song Birds of the World	1890	£13.00	—
X50	The American Indian	1888	£14.00	£700.00
50	The World's Beauties, 1st Series	1888	£8.00	
50	The World's Beauties, 2nd Series	1888	£8.00	—
50	The World's Champions, 1st Series	1888	£7.00	—
50	The World's Champions, 2nd Series	1889	£8.00	—
X50	The World's Champions, 2nd Series	1889	£16.00	—
50	The World's Decorations	1890	£6.00	£300.00
X50	The World's Decorations	1890	£13.00	£650.00
50	The World's Racers	1888	£8.00	
50	Types of All Nations	1887	£10.00	£500.00
50	Wild Animals of the World	1888	£7.00	£350.00
50	World's Dudes	1888	£10.00	£500.00
50	World's Smokers	1888	£8.00	£400.00
50	World's Sovereigns	1887	£14.00	£700.00

Printed Albums (exchanged for coupons)

		Date	Odds	Sets
	American Editors	1887	—	£60.00
	Birds of America	1890	—	£40.00
	Birds of the Tropics	1889	—	£40.00
	Celebrated American Indian Chiefs	1888	—	£60.00
	City Flags	1888	—	£50.00
	Decorations of Principal Orders	1890	—	£45.00
	Fish from American Waters	1889	—	£40.00
	Flags of All Nations	1890	—	£45.00
	Game Birds	1889	—	£40.00
	General Government & State Capitol Buildings of the United States	1889	—	£40.00
	George Washington	1889	—	£50.00
	Napoleon	1889	—	£50.00
	Our Navy	1889	—	£50.00
	Paris Exhibition 1889	1889	—	£40.00
	Quadrupeds	1889	—	£60.00
	Racing Colours of the World	1888	—	£60.00
	Song Birds of the World	1890	—	£40.00
	With the Poets in Smokeland	1890	—	£40.00
	World's Beauties, 1st Series	1888	—	£50.00
	World's Beauties, 2nd Series	1888	—	£50.00
	World's Champions, 1st Series	1888	—	£150.00
	World's Champions, 2nd Series	1889	—	£150.00
	World's Inventors	1888	—	£50.00
	World's Racers	1888	—	£50.00

ALLEN TOBACCO CO. (U.S.A.)

Qty		Date	Odds	Sets
X?300	Views & Art Studies	1912	£2.50	—

AMERICAN CIGARETTE CO. (China)

Qty		Date	Odds	Sets
10	Admirals & Generals	1900	£35.00	—
25	Beauties (Black Back)	1902	£10.00	—
?25	Beauties (Green Back)	1901	£12.00	—
52	Beauties, Playing Card Inset	1901	£25.00	—
?	Chinese Girls	1900	*£40.00*	—
50	Flowers	1902	£8.00	£400.00

AMERICAN EAGLE TOBACCO CO. (U.S.A.)

36	Flags of All Nations	1890	£17.50	—
36	Flags of States	1890	£17.50	—
50	Occupations for Women	1892	£25.00	—
F?	Photographic Cards	1886	£3.00	—
LF?	Photographic Cards	1886	£6.00	—
23	Presidents of U.S.	1890	£25.00	—

AMERICAN TOBACCO CO. (U.S.A.)

Early Issues

F100	Actresses (Black Back)	1901	£1.00	—
F300	Actresses (Blue Back)	1901	£1.00	—
44	Australian Parliament	1901	£1.75	£75.00
25	Battle Scenes	1901	£4.00	£100.00
177	Beauties (Typeset Back)	1901	75p	—
350	Beauties (Old Gold Back)	1901	75p	—
101	Beauties (Label Back)	1901	£1.00	—
?500	Beauties (Green Net Back)	1901	75p	—
?75	Beauties (Blue Net Back)	1901	£3.50	—
24	Beauties (Plain Back, Carton)	1901	£1.50	£36.00
25	Beauties, Black Background	1900	£4.00	£100.00
25	Beauties, Blue Frame Line	1900	£10.00	—
25	Beauties, Curtain Background	1900	£3.50	£87.50
28	Beauties, Domino Girls	1900	£10.00	£280.00
25	Beauties, Flower Girls	1900	£3.50	£87.50
25	Beauties, Flowers Inset	1900	£3.00	£75.00
25	Beauties, International Code of Signals, 1st	1900	£3.00	£75.00
25	Beauties, International Code of Signals, 2nd	1900	£3.00	£75.00
50	Beauties, Marine & Universe Girls	1900	*£10.00*	—
25	Beauties, Numbered	1900	£8.00	—
25	Beauties, Orange Framelines	1900	£12.50	—
25	Beauties, Palette Girls	1900	£4.00	£100.00
F?	Beauties, Photographic	1894	*£7.50*	—
52	Beauties, Playing Card Inset, Set 1	1900	£4.00	£200.00
52	Beauties, Playing Card Inset, Set 2	1900	£5.00	—
53	Beauties, Playing Card Superimposed, Set 3	1900	£4.00	£200.00
25	Beauties, Star Girls	1900	£7.50	—
25	Beauties, Star Series	1900	£7.50	—
25	Beauties, Stippled Background	1900	£3.50	£87.50
100	Beauties, Thick Borders	1895	*£10.00*	—
25	Boer War, Series A	1901	£2.00	£50.00
22	Boer War, Series B	1901	£3.00	£65.00
50	Butterflies	1895	£10.00	—
32	Celebrities	1900	£2.50	£80.00
25	Chinese Girls	1900	£5.00	—
1	Columbian & Other Postage Stamps	1895	—	£4.00
25	Comic Scenes	1900	£4.00	£100.00

Qty		Date	Odds	Sets
50	Congress of Beauty, World's Fair	1893	£10.00	—
25	Dancers	1895	£5.00	—
50	Dancing Women	1895	£7.50	—
50	Fancy Bathers	1895	£7.50	—
25	Fish From American Waters (Green Net)	1900	£3.50	£87.50
50	Fish From American Waters (List Back)	1895	£5.00	—
28	Flags, Dominoes Superimposed (Carton)	1900	£2.00	£56.00
50	Flags of All Nations	1895	£5.00	—
50	Heroes of The Spanish American War (Carton)	1900	£2.00	£100.00
?36	Japanese Girls	1900	£20.00	—
25	Military Uniforms, A	1894	£8.00	—
25	Military Uniforms, B	1896	£6.00	£150.00
27	Military Uniforms, C (Green Net)	1900	£3.00	£80.00
27	Military Uniforms, C (Typeset)	1900	£3.50	£95.00
25	Military Uniforms, D	1900	£6.00	—
50	Musical Instruments	1895	£8.00	—
50	National Flags & Arms	1895	£4.00	—
25	National Flags & Flower-Girls	1900	£8.00	—
25	Old Ships, 1st Series	1900	£2.00	£50.00
25	Old Ships, 2nd Series	1900	£3.50	£87.50
50	Savage & Semi Barbarous Chiefs & Rulers	1895	£10.00	—
25	Songs A	1900	£5.00	—
25	Songs B	1900	£6.00	—
25	Songs C, 1st Group	1900	£3.00	£75.00
25	Songs C, 2nd Group	1900	£5.00	—
25	Songs D	1900	£3.00	£75.00
27	Songs E	1900	£4.00	—
25	Songs F	1900	£4.00	—
25	Songs G	1900	£3.00	£75.00
25	Songs H	1900	£7.50	—
25	Songs I	1900	£10.00	—
F150	Views	1901	£1.25	—

Later Issues

Qty		Date	Odds	Sets
L50	Actors	1907	£1.75	—
L50	Actresses "Between The Acts"	1902	£3.50	—
G25	Actresses "Turkish Trophies" (Premiums)	1902	£7.00	—
B85	Actress Series	1904	£3.00	—
L80	Animals	1912	75p	£60.00
L25	Arctic Scenes	1916	£1.20	£30.00
M15	Art Gallery Pictures	1904	£2.50	—
M50	Art Reproductions	1904	£3.00	—
21	Art Series (Grand Duke)	1902	£7.50	—
P10	Artistic Pictures	1910	£6.00	—
18	Ask Dad	1905	£7.50	—
L50	Assorted Standard Bearers of Different Countries	1910	£3.00	—
B25	Auto-Drivers	1908	£4.00	£100.00
M50	Automobile Series	1908	£4.00	£200.00
L50	Baseball Folders	1907	£4.00	—
M121	Baseball Series (T204)	1907	£5.00	—
208	Baseball Series (T205, Gold Borders)	1907	£4.00	—
522	Baseball Series (T206, White Borders)	1907	£3.00	—
200	Baseball Series (T207, Brown Background)	1907	£5.00	—
?578	Baseball Series (T210, Red Borders)	1907	£6.00	—
75	Baseball Series (T211, Southern Association)	1907	£7.50	—

Qty		Date	Odds	Sets
376	Baseball Series (T212, "Obak")	1907	£4.00	—
180	Baseball Series (T213, "Coupon")	1907	£6.00	—
?90	Baseball Series (T214, Victory Tobacco)	1907	£6.00	—
159	Baseball Series (T215, Red Cross)	1907	£6.00	—
L76	Baseball Triple Folders	1907	£7.50	—
50	Bird Series (Gold Borders)	1912	75p	£37.50
50	Bird Series (White Border)	1912	75p	£37.50
30	Bird Series (Fancy Gold Frame)	1911	£1.00	£30.00
M361	Birthday Horoscopes	1910	£1.00	—
P80	Bridge Favors & Place Cards	1938	£2.00	—
P100	Bridge Game Hands	1938	£2.50	—
M24	British Buildings	1937	£1.25	£30.00
M42	British Sovereigns	1939	£1.00	£42.00
M50	Butterfly Series	1908	£1.50	—
L153	Champion Athlete & Prizefighter Series	1910	80p	£120.00
X50	Champion Athlete & Prizefighter Series			
	(Prizefighters Only)	1910	£1.75	—
L50	Champion Pugilists	1908	£3.00	—
X100	Champion Women Swimmers	1906	£3.50	—
M150	College Series	1914	60p	£90.00
G25	College Series (Premiums)	1904	£5.00	£125.00
M50	Costumes and Scenery for All Countries of			
	The World	1912	£1.75	£87.50
X49	Cowboy Series	1914	£2.00	—
M?38	Cross Stitch	1906	£5.00	—
L?17	Embarrassing/Emotional Moments	1906	£10.00	—
M50	Emblem Series	1908	£1.00	£50.00
L100	Fable Series	1913	75p	£75.00
PF?53	Famous Baseball Players, American Athletic			
	Champions & Photoplay Stars	1910	£7.50	—
100	Fish Series	1909	75p	£75.00
200	Flags of All Nations Series	1909	75p	£150.00
L100	Flags of All Nations Series (Red Cross)	1904	£4.00	—
50	Foreign Stamp Series	1906	£2.50	—
L505	Fortune Series	1907	75p	—
G12	Hamilton King Girls (1-12 Sketches)	1902	£7.50	—
G12	Hamilton King Girls (13-24 Girls)	1902	£6.00	—
G12	Hamilton King Girls (25-36 Bathing Girls) ...	1902	£6.00	—
G25	Hamilton King Girls (37-61 Period Gowns) ...	1902	£6.00	—
G25	Hamilton King Girls (62-86 Flag Girls)	1902	£6.00	—
G25	Hamilton King Girls (1-25)	1913	£6.00	—
L?3	Helmar Girls	1902	£20.00	—
M79	Henry	1937	75p	—
X50	Heroes of History	1912	£1.50	£75.00
M50	Historic Homes	1913	£1.00	£50.00
X25	Historical Events Series	1911	£1.75	—
M25	Hudson-Fulton Series	1908	£2.50	—
45	Imitation Cigar Bands	1909	75p	—
L50	Indian Life in The 60's	1914	£1.75	—
L221	Jig Saw Puzzle Pictures	1910	£2.50	—
L50	Lighthouse Series	1912	£1.25	£62.50
X50	Men of History	1912	£1.50	£75.00
B100	Military Series (White Borders)	1908	£2.00	—
50	Military Series (Gold Borders)	1908	£2.50	—

AMERICAN TOBACCO CO. (U.S.A.)—cont.

Qty		Date	Odds	Sets
50	Military Series (Recruit)	1908	£2.00	—
50	Movie Stars	1915	£1.00	—
L100	Movie Stars	1915	£1.25	—
B15	Moving Picture Stars Series	1915	*£12.50*	—
X50	Murad Post Card Series	1905	£3.00	—
100	Mutt & Jeff Series (Black & White)	1908	£2.00	—
100	Mutt & Jeff Series (Coloured)	1908	£2.50	—
F16	National League & American League Teams	1910	*£15.00*	—
G126	Prominent Base Ball Players & Athletes (Premium)	1911	*£12.50*	—
50	Pugilistic Subjects	1908	*£5.00*	—
X18	Puzzle Picture Series	1904	*£7.50*	—
L200	Riddle Series	1907	£1.00	—
X?60	Royal Bengal Souvenir Cards	1906	£3.00	—
M150	Seals of The United States & Coats of Arms ...	1912	70p	£105.00
L25	Series of Champions	1906	*£4.00*	—
X50	Sights & Scenes of The World	1912	£1.50	£75.00
X50	Silhouettes	1908	£2.50	—
L25	Song Bird Series	1905	*£3.00*	—
32	Sports Champions	1908	*£4.00*	—
45	Stage Stars (Transfers)	1910	*£3.50*	—
B25	State Girl Series	1910	£2.50	—
L50	Theatres Old & New Series	1912	£1.50	£75.00
L25	The World's Greatest Explorers	1914	£1.20	£30.00
L50	Toast Series (Sultan)	1910	*£2.50*	—
M550	Toast Series (Mogul)	1910	60p	—
M25	Toasts	1910	*£5.00*	—
50	Types of Nations	1912	£1.00	£50.00
M25	Up To Date Baseball Comics	1908	£5.00	—
L26	Up To Date Comics	1908	£3.00	—
F?500	World Scenes & Portraits	1910	£1.25	—
250	World War I Scenes	1916	80p	—
X50	World's Champion Athletes	1909	£2.50	—

Silk Issues

Qty		Date	Odds	Sets
M111	Actresses	1910	£2.00	—
X2	Actresses ... ... ,,, ...	1910	*£30.00*	—
L15	Animals	1910	£3.00	—
P250	Athlete and College Seal	1910	£2.00	—
G250	Athlete and College Seal	1910	£2.50	—
B?6	Automobile Pennants	1910	*£35.00*	—
M?100	Baseball—Actress Series	1910	£3.00	—
M?100	Baseball Players	1910	*£6.00*	—
G25	Baseball Players	1910	*£12.50*	—
M25	Bathing Beach Girls	1910	£5.00	—
G6	Bathing Girls	1910	£7.50	—
X50	Birds, Set 1	1910	£2.50	—
B26	Birds, Set 2	1910	£2.50	—
B30	Birds, Set 3	1910	£2.50	—
L20	Birds in Flight	1910	£2.50	—
L25	Breeds of Dogs	1910	£4.00	—
L10	Breeds of Fowls	1910	£3.50	—
P6	Butterflies	1910	£7.50	—
L50	Butterflies & Moths, Set 1	1910	£2.00	—
L50	Butterflies & Moths, Set 2	1910	£2.00	—

Qty		Date	Odds	Sets
L25	Butterflies & Moths, Set 3	1910	£2.00	—
B77	City Seals	1910	£1.50	—
G50	College Flag, Seal, Song, Yell	1910	£3.50	—
X24	College Pennants	1910	*£3.50*	—
B145	College Seals	1910	£1.25	—
G?7	College Yells	1910	*£10.00*	—
L10	Comics	1910	£4.00	—
M25	Domestic Animals' Heads	1910	£3.00	—
G6	Domestic Animals' Heads	1910	£7.50	—
M50	Emblem Series	1910	£2.50	—
L15	Famous Queens	1910	£4.00	—
L11	Feminine Types	1910	£4.00	—
D322	Flags & Arms (Woven)	1910	£1.25	—
P24	Flag Girls of Nations	1910	£3.00	—
G24	Flag Girls of Nations	1910	£4.00	—
X50	Flowers, Set 1	1910	£3.00	—
M25	Flowers, Set 2	1910	£2.50	—
L50	Flowers, Set 2	1910	£3.00	—
L52	Flowers, Set 3	1910	£3.00	—
L10	Fruits	1910	£3.50	—
G5	Generals	1910	*£40.00*	—
M10	Girls (Portrait in Circle)	1910	*£15.00*	—
L10	Girls (Portrait in Circle)	1910	*£25.00*	—
G10	Girls (Portrait in Circle)	1910	*£35.00*	—
G?50	Hatbands	1910	£7.50	—
M50	Indian Portraits	1910	£3.00	—
G6	Indian Portraits	1910	£7.50	—
L25	Indian Portraits & Scenes	1910	£4.00	—
P10	Indian Portraits & Scenes	1910	£6.00	—
G12	King Girls	1910	*£6.00*	—
G20	Kink Series	1910	*£30.00*	—
B51	Military & Lodge Medals	1910	£2.00	—
L?5	Miniature National Flags	1910	*£15.00*	—
L10	Mottoes & Quotations	1910	£3.50	—
L25	National Arms (Silko)	1910	£2.00	—
B42	National Arms (Woven)	1910	£1.50	—
L154	National Flags	1910	£1.00	—
G?150	National Flags (Many Styles)	1910	£2.00	—
L25	National Flags & Arms	1910	£1.50	—
X40	National Flags & Arms	1910	£1.50	—
P53	National Flags & Arms (Many Styles)	1910	£2.00	—
X27	National Flags, Song & Flower	1910	£2.50	—
P20	National Flags, Song & Flower	1910	£2.50	—
G17	National Flags, Song & Flower	1910	£4.00	—
M?37	Orders & Military Medals	1910	*£4.00*	—
B24	Presidents of U.S.	1910	£3.00	—
P27	Ruler With Flags	1910	£5.00	—
P24	Ruler With National Arms	1910	£6.00	—
P10	Rulers of The Balkans & Italy	1910	£6.00	—
L120	Silk National Flags	1910	£1.00	—
M36	State Flags	1910	£2.50	—
B?11	State Flowers	1910	*£5.00*	—
M25	State Flowers	1910	£4.00	—
L25	State Girl & Flower	1910	£4.00	—

Qty		Date	Odds	Sets
M50	State Maps & Maps of Territories	1910	£3.50	—
M48	State Seals	1910	£1.50	—
X?75	Twelfth Night Miscellany	1910	£5.00	—
M25	Women of Ancient Egypt	1910	£5.00	—
L10	Zira Girls	1910	£5.00	—

Blanket Issues

Qty		Date	Odds	Sets
P?	Animal Pelts	1908	£3.00	—
G90	Baseball Players	1908	£6.00	—
P?	Butterflies	1908	£1.25	—
G?	Butterflies	1908	£1.50	—
P135	College Athlete, Pennant, Seals	1908	£1.25	—
G10	College Pennants	1908	£3.00	—
G53	College Seals	1908	£1.25	—
X?	Conventional Rug Designs	1908	60p	—
P?	Conventional Rug Designs	1908	75p	—
G?	Conventional Rug Designs	1908	£1.00	—
X5	Domestic Pets	1908	£3.50	—
P?	Miniature Indian Blankets	1908	75p	—
G?	Miniature Indian Blankets	1908	£1.00	—
E6	National Arms	1908	£2.00	—
P45	National Flags	1908	60p	—
G71	National Flags	1908	75p	—
E31	National Flags	1908	£1.25	—
G?	National Flags and Arms	1908	£1.50	—
X9	Nursery Rhymes	1908	£4.00	—
X13	Soldiers	1908	£6.00	—

Leather Issues

Qty		Date	Odds	Sets
B15	Breeds of Dogs	1908	£3.50	—
X97	College Building, Shield, Etc.	1908	£2.00	—
P19	College Buildings	1908	£2.00	—
M14	College Fraternity Seals	1908	£3.50	—
M159	College Pennants	1908	60p	—
M112	College Pennants (Shaped)	1908	80p	—
X23	College Pennant, Yell, Emblem	1908	£2.50	—
M144	College Seals	1908	60p	—
M122	College Seals (Shaped)	1908	80p	—
M29	College Seals (Card Suit Shaped)	1908	£1.50	—
M19	Comic Designs	1908	£1.50	—
B23	Flowers	1908	£2.00	—
B9	Girls	1908	£2.50	—
M26	Girls (Alphabet Background)	1908	£3.50	—
M94	Mottoes & Quotations	1908	£1.50	—
M5	Movie Film Personalities	1908	£5.00	—
M21	National Flags	1908	£2.50	—
M45	Nursery Rhymes Illustrated	1908	£2.50	—
M56	State Seals	1908	60p	—
M18	State Seals (Pennant Shaped)	1908	75p	—

Celluloid Buttons & Pins

Qty		Date	Odds	Sets
K245	Actresses	1901	£1.50	—
K152	Baseball Players	1901	£6.00	—
K8	Boer War Leaders	1901	£30.00	—
K362	Comic Pictures	1901	£1.50	—
K425	Comic Sayings	1901	£1.50	—

AMERICAN TOBACCO CO. (U.S.A.)—cont.

Qty		Date	Odds	Sets
K14	Cricketers	1901	£50.00	—
K125	Flags	1901	£1.25	—
K48	Girls' Heads	1901	*£4.00*	—
K25	Jockeys	1901	*£5.00*	—
K48	State Arms	1901	£1.50	—
K187	Yellow Kid Designs	1901	*£4.00*	—

AMERICAN TOBACCO CO. OF NEW SOUTH WALES (Australia)

Qty		Date	Odds	Sets
25	Beauties, Group 1	1902	£4.00	£100.00
25	Beauties, Group 2	1902	£5.00	£125.00

AMERICAN TOBACCO COMPANY OF VICTORIA LTD. (Australia)

Qty		Date	Odds	Sets
100?	Beauties	1902	£5.00	—

ATLAM CIGARETTE FACTORY (Malta)

Qty		Date	Odds	Sets
150	Beauties	1924	*£2.00*	—
B65	Beauties	1924	£1.25	—
B519	Celebrities	1924	75p	—
L50	Views of Malta	1924	*£2.00*	—
B128	Views of The World	1924	*£2.00*	—

BANNER TOBACCO CO. (U.S.A.)

Qty		Date	Odds	Sets
X25	Beauties	1890	£12.50	—

AUG. BECK & CO. (U.S.A.)

Qty		Date	Odds	Sets
24	Actors & Actresses	1885	*£35.00*	—
?	Beauties—Burdick 488	1888	£30.00	—
25	National Dances	1889	*£35.00*	—
F?	Photographic Cards	1886	£3.00	—
?	Picture Cards	1888	£25.00	—
24	Presidents of U.S.A.	1890	*£30.00*	—
?	State Seals	1887	*£30.00*	—

DE BEER & CO. (Australia)

Qty		Date	Odds	Sets
20	Admirals & Warships of U.S.A	1908	£25.00	—

BOOKER TOBACCO CO. (U.S.A.)

Qty		Date	Odds	Sets
35	Indian Series	1906	£20.00	—
?20	U.S. Battleships	1906	£15.00	—

BRITISH AMERICAN TOBACCO CO. LTD. (B.A.T.)

(1)   SERIES WITH FIRM'S NAME

Qty		Date	Odds	Sets
48	A Famous Picture Series, The Toast (Sect.)	1931	*£1.50*	—
BF50	Beauties	1925	75p	—
BF40	Beauties	1925	75p	—
25	Beauties, Art Series	1903	£5.00	—
25	Beauties, Black Background	1903	£5.00	—
25	Beauties, Blossom Girls	1903	£20.00	—
25	Beauties, Flower Girls	1903	£4.00	£100.00
25	Beauties, Fruit Girls	1903	£6.00	£150.00
25	Beauties, Girls in Costumes	1903	£5.00	£125.00
20	Beauties, Group 1	1903	£5.00	£100.00
25	Beauties, Lantern Girls	1903	£4.00	£100.00
50	Beauties, Marine & Universe Girls	1903	£4.00	£200.00

BRITISH AMERICAN TOBACCO CO. LTD. (B.A.T.)—cont.

Qty		Date	Odds	Sets
25	Beauties, Numbered	1903	£10.00	—
25	Beauties, Palette Girls	1903	£5.00	£125.00
25	Beauties, Palette Girls (Red Border)	1903	£7.50	—
53	Beauties, Playing Cards	1903	£4.00	—
24	Beauties, Smoke Girls	1903	£8.00	£200.00
25	Beauties, Star Girls	1903	£7.50	—
25	Beauties, Stippled Background	1903	£4.00	£100.00
25	Beauties, Water Girls	1903	£4.00	£100.00
M50	Birds, Beasts & Fishes	1934	75p	—
50	Buildings	1905	£4.00	—
25	Chinese Girls "A"	1904	£4.00	—
25	Chinese Girls "B"	1904	£4.00	—
25	Chinese Girls "C"	1904	£4.00	—
25	Chinese Girls "D"	1904	£3.50	—
25	Chinese Girls "E"	1904	£3.50	—
25	Chinese Girls "F1"	1904	£3.50	—
25	Chinese Girls "F2"	1904	£3.50	—
50	Chinese Girls "F3"	1904	£3.50	—
40	Chinese Trades	1904	£3.50	£140.00
50	Danish Athletes	1906	£5.00	—
28	Dominoes	1908	£3.00	—
48	Fairy Tales	1928	*£2.00*	—
25	New York Views	1908	£5.00	—
53	Playing Cards	1908	£5.00	—
M50	Wild Animals	1930	75p	—

(2) SERIES WITH BRAND NAMES

(A) Albert Cigarettes (Belgium Etc.)

Qty		Date	Odds	Sets
L50	Aeroplanes (Civils)	1935	*£3.00*	—
50	Artistes De Cinema (1-50)	1932	*£1.00*	—
50	Artistes De Cinema (51-100)	1933	75p	—
50	Artistes De Cinema (101-150)	1934	*£1.00*	—
M48	Beauties	1928	*£1.00*	—
M75	Belles Vues De Belgique	1926	*£1.25*	—
M50	Birds, Beasts & Fishes	1934	*£1.00*	—
M50	Butterflies (Girls)	1926	*£2.00*	—
M50	Cinema Stars, Set 1 (Brown)	1927	*£1.00*	—
M100	Cinema Stars, Set 2	1928	£1.00	—
M208	Cinema Stars, Set 3 (Unnumbered)	1928	*£1.00*	—
M100	Circus Scenes	1930	*£1.25*	—
M100	Famous Beauties	1916	*£2.00*	—
M100	La Faune Congolaise	1934	75p	—
M50	L'Afrique Equatoriale De L'est A L'ouest	1932	*£1.50*	—
M50	Les Grande Paquebots Du Monde	1924	*£2.50*	—
M50	Merveilles du Monde	1927	*£2.50*	—
M50	Women of Nations	1922	*£2.00*	—

(B) Atlas Cigarettes (China)

Qty		Date	Odds	Sets
50	Buildings	1907	*£2.50*	—
25	Chinese Beauties	1912	£1.00	£25.00
50	Chinese Trades, Set 4	1908	£1.00	—
85	Chinese Trades, Set 6	1912	*£1.00*	—

(C) Battle Ax Cigarettes

Qty		Date	Odds	Sets
M100	Famous Beauties	1916	£2.00	—
M50	Women of Nations	1922	£2.50	—

123

BRITISH AMERICAN TOBACCO CO. LTD. (B.A.T.)—cont.

Qty		Date	Odds	Sets
(D)	**Copain Cigarettes (Belgium)**			
52	Birds of Brilliant Plumage (P/C Inset)	1927	£3.00	—
(E)	**Domino Cigarettes (Mauritius)**			
25	Animaux et Reptiles	1961	—	£1.25
25	Coursaires et Boucaniers	1961	—	£1.00
25	Figures Historiques, 1st Series	1961	—	£1.50
25	Figures Historiques, 2nd Series	1961	—	£4.00
25	Fleures De Culture	1961	—	£1.00
25	Les Oiseaux et L'art Japonais	1961	—	£7.50
25	Les Produits Du Monde	1961	—	£1.00
50	Voitures Antiques	1961	—	£25.00
(F)	**Eagle Bird Cigarettes (China & Siam)**			
50	Animal & Birds	1909	£1.20	£60.00
50	Aviation Series	1912	£1.25	—
25	Birds of the East	1912	80p	—
25	China's Famous Warriors	1911	80p	—
25	Chinese Beauties, 1st Series	1908	£2.00	—
25	Chinese Beauties, 2nd Series	1909	£1.00	—
50	Chinese Trades	1908	75p	—
25	Cock Fighting	1911	£1.60	£40.00
60	Flags & Pennons	1926	60p	£36.00
50	Romance of the Heavens	1929	£1.00	£50.00
50	Siamese Alphabet	1922	60p	£30.00
50	Siamese Dreams & Their Meaning	1923	60p	£30.00
50	Siamese Horoscopes	1916	50p	£25.00
50	Siamese Play—Inao	1916	70p	—
50	Siamese Play—Khun Chang Khun Phaen 1st ...	1917	50p	£25.00
50	Siamese Play—Khun Chang Khun Phaen 2nd ...	1917	50p	£25.00
36	Siamese Play—Phra Aphai, 1st	1918	40p	£15.00
36	Siamese Play—Phra Aphai, 2nd	1919	40p	£15.00
150	Siamese Play—Ramakien I	1913	50p	£75.00
50	Siamese Play—Ramakien II	1914	50p	£25.00
50	Siamese Uniforms	1915	£1.00	£50.00
50	Views of Bangkok	1928	60p	£30.00
50	Views of Siam	1928	50p	£25.00
30	War Weapons	1914	80p	£24.00
(G)	**Gold Dollar Cigarettes (Germany)**			
M270	Auf Deutscher Scholle	1934	60p	—
M270	Der Weltkrieg	1933	60p	—
M270	Deutsche Kolonien	1931	60p	—
M270	Die Deutsche Wehrmacht	1935	60p	—
?50	Do You Know?	1928	£3.00	—
B100	Filmbilder	1935	60p	£60.00
B100	Im Prarie Und Urwald	1930	60p	£60.00
100	Wild-West	1932	60p	£60.00
(H)	**Kong Beng Cigarettes (China)**			
50	Animals	1912	£3.00	—
(I)	**Mascot Cigarettes (Germany)**			
100	Cinema Stars	1931	£1.50	—
M208	Cinema Stars	1924	£1.50	—
(J)	**Motor Cigarettes (Denmark)**			
50	Aviation Series	1911	£5.00	—

Qty		Date	Odds	Sets
50	Butterflies & Moths	1911	£3.00	—
50	Flag Girls of All Nations	1908	£5.00	—
50	Girls of All Nations	1908	£5.00	—
(K)	**Pedro Cigarettes (India)**			
50	Actors & Actresses	1906	£2.00	—
37	Nautch Girls (Red Border)	1907	£1.00	—
40	Nautch Girls (Coloured)	1907	£1.25	—
52	Nautch Girls (P/C) Inset)	1907	£1.50	—
(L)	**Pinhead Cigarettes (China)**			
50	Chinese Modern Beauties	1912	75p	£37.50
33	Chinese Heroes, Set 1	1912	75p	—
50	Chinese Heroes, Set 2	1913	75p	—
50	Chinese Trades, Set III	1908	70p	£35.00
50	Chinese Trades, Set IV	1909	70p	£35.00
50	Chinese Trades, Set V	1910	70p	£35.00
50	Types of the British Army	1909	£1.50	—
(M)	**Railway Cigarettes (India)**			
37	Nautch Girls Series	1907	£1.00	£35.00
(N)	**Shantung Cigarettes (China)**			
50	Chinese Curios	1928	£3.50	—
(O)	**Sunflower Cigarettes (China)**			
50	Chinese Trades	1906	£3.50	—
(P)	**Teal Cigarettes (Siam)**			
30	Chinese Beauties	1917	£2.00	—
50	Cinema Stars	1930	80p	£40.00
30	Fish Series	1916	£1.00	£30.00
50	War Incidents	1916	£1.00	£50.00
(Q)	**Tiger Cigarettes (India)**			
52	Nautch Girl Series (P/C Inset)	1911	£1.00	—
(3)	**SERIES WITH PRINTED BACK, NO MAKER'S NAME OR BRAND**			
	(See also Imperial Tobacco Co. (Canada & India), United Tobacco Co.)			
250	Actresses "ALWICS" (Design Back)	1906	£1.00	—
50	Aeroplanes (Gilt Border)	1926	80p	£40.00
50	Aeroplanes of Today	1936	30p	£15.00
25	Angling	1930	£1.00	£25.00
L25	Arabic Proverbs (Silk)	1913	£7.50	—
50	Arms & Armour	1910	£2.00	—
L50	Arms of the British Empire (Silk)	1911	£1.60	£80.00
25	Army Life	1908	£3.00	—
50	Art Photogravures	1912	60p	—
1	Australia Day	1915	—	£4.00
L50	Australian Wild Flowers (Silk)	1913	£1.60	£80.00
75	Aviation	1910	£1.50	—
50	Aviation Series	1911	£1.20	£60.00
50	Beauties, Red Tinted (Design Back)	1906	£1.00	—
52	Beauties, Tobacco Leaf Back (P/C Inset)	1908	£1.20	£60.00
52	Beauties, Tobacco Leaf Back (No Inset)	1908	£2.50	—
F50	Beauties, Set 1	1925	50p	—
BF50	Beauties, Set 1 (Hand Coloured)	1925	60p	—
F50	Beauties, 2nd Series	1926	40p	£20.00
F50	Beauties, 3rd Series	1926	35p	£17.50

BRITISH AMERICAN TOBACCO CO. LTD. (B.A.T.)—cont.

Qty		Date	Odds	Sets
F50	Beauties of Great Britain	1930	25p	£12.50
F50	Beautiful England	1928	20p	£10.00
50	Best Dogs of their Breed	1916	£1.40	£70.00
L50	Best Dogs of their Breed (Silk)	1913	£2.50	£125.00
50	Billiards	1929	80p	£40.00
50	Birds Beasts & Fishes	1937	16p	£8.00
M50	Birds Beasts & Fishes	1937	60p	—
24	Birds of England	1924	£1.25	£30.00
50	Boy Scouts	1930	80p	£40.00
50	Britain's Defenders (Blue Front)	1914	60p	—
50	Britain's Defenders (Mauve Front)	1914	50p	£25.00
50	British Butterflies	1930	40p	£20.00
50	British Empire Series	1913	£1.25	—
25	British Trees & Their Uses	1930	80p	£20.00
50	British Warships and Admirals	1915	£1.50	£75.00
50	Butterflies & Moths	1911	75p	—
50	Butterflies (Girls)	1928	£1.20	£60.00
M50	Butterflies (Girls)	1928	£2.00	£100.00
M50	Celebrities of Film and Stage	1930	75p	—
LF48	Channel Islands, Past & Present	1939	15p	£6.00
38/40	Characters from the Works of Charles Dickens ...	1919	25p	£10.00
50	Cinema Artistes (Black & White 1-50)	1928	50p	—
50	Cinema Artistes (Black & White 101-150) ...	1930	50p	—
60	Cinema Artistes, Set 1 (Brown)	1929	50p	—
50	Cinema Artistes, Set 2 (Brown)	1931	50p	—
M48	Cinema Artistes, Set 3	1932	75p	—
48	Cinema Celebrities (C)	1935	30p	£15.00
L48	Cinema Celebrities (C)	1935	40p	£20.00
L56	Cinema Celebrities (D)	1937	£1.00	—
50	Cinema Favourites	1929	£1.50	—
50	Cinema Stars, Set 2 (1-50)	1928	35p	—
50	Cinema Stars, Set 3 (51-100)	1930	35p	—
50	Cinema Stars, Set 4 (101-150)	1932	35p	—
100	Cinema Stars (Coloured)	1931	£1.00	—
F50	Cinema Stars, Set 1	1924	60p	—
F50	Cinema Stars, Set 2	1924	40p	£20.00
F50	Cinema Stars, Set 3	1925	60p	—
MF52	Cinema Stars, Set 4	1925	75p	—
MF52	Cinema Stars, Set 5	1926	75p	—
MF52	Cinema Stars, Set 6	1927	£1.00	—
LF48	Cinema Stars, Set 7	1927	£1.25	—
F50	Cinema Stars, Set 8	1928	60p	—
F50	Cinema Stars, Set 9 (51-100)	1929	60p	—
F50	Cinema Stars, Set 10 (101-150)	1930	60p	—
F50	Cinema Stars, Set 11	1931	50p	—
110	Crests & Badges of the British Army (Silk)	1915	£1.50	—
M108	Crests & Badges of the British Army (Silk) ...	1915	£1.25	—
M50	Crests & Colours of Australian Universities, Colleges & Schools (Silk)	1916	£1.40	—
25	Derby Day Series	1914	£4.00	—
50	Do You Know?	1923	20p	£10.00
50	Do You Know? 2nd Series	1931	16p	£8.00
25	Dracones Posthistorici	1938	£3.00	—
25	Dutch Footballers	1913	£3.50	—

Qty		Date	Odds	Sets
25	Dutch Scenes	1928	£1.20	£30.00
50	Engineering Wonders	1930	25p	£12.50
40	English Costumes of Ten Centuries	1919	80p	£32.00
F25	English Cricketers	1926	£1.00	£25.00
26	Etchings (of Dogs)	1926	50p	£13.00
F50	Famous Bridges	1935	35p	£17.50
50	Famous Footballers, Set 1	1923	80p	£40.00
50	Famous Footballers, Set 2	1924	80p	£40.00
50	Famous Footballers, Set 3	1925	80p	£40.00
25	Famous Racehorses	1926	80p	£20.00
25	Famous Railway Trains	1929	£1.00	£25.00
50	Favourite Flowers	1923	35p	£17.50
50	Film and Stage Favourites	1926	50p	£25.00
75	Film Favourites	1928	50p	£37.50
50	Flags of the Empire	1928	40p	£20.00
50	Foreign Birds	1930	25p	£12.50
50	Game Birds & Wild Fowl	1929	60p	£30.00
LF45	Grace & Beauty (1-45)	1938	15p	£7.00
LF45	Grace & Beauty (46-90)	1939	15p	£6.00
LF48	Guernsey, Alderney & Sark, 1st Series	1937	15p	£7.00
LF48	Guernsey, Alderney & Sark, 2nd Series	1938	15p	£6.00
L80	Guernsey Footballers, Priaulx League	1938	15p	£12.00
F52	Here There & Everywhere	1929	15p	£7.50
25	Hints & Tips for Motorists	1929	£1.00	—
F50	Homeland Events	1928	35p	—
50	Horses of Today	1906	£3.00	—
32	Houses of Parliament (Red Back)	1912	£1.00	£32.00
32	Houses of Parliament (Brown, Back with Verse)	1912	£5.00	—
50	Indian Chiefs	1930	£1.75	£87.50
50	Indian Regiments Series	1912	£4.00	—
50	International Air Liners	1937	30p	£15.00
25	Java Scenes	1929	£4.00	—
LF48	Jersey Then & Now, 1st Series	1935	25p	£12.50
LF48	Jersey Then & Now, 2nd Series	1937	15p	£6.00
50	Jiu Jitsu	1911	£1.50	—
50	Keep Fit	1939	25p	£12.50
M?48	La Belgique Monumentale et Pittoresque	1926	£2.00	—
50	Leaders of Men	1929	£1.50	—
50	Life in the Treetops	1931	25p	£12.50
50	Lighthouses	1926	40p	£20.00
40	London Ceremonials	1929	75p	—
F50	London Zoo	1927	40p	—
50	Lucky Charms	1930	£1.00	—
25	Marvels of the Universe Series	1925	£1.40	£35.00
45	Melbourne Cup Winners	1906	£3.00	—
50	Merchant Ships of the World	1925	£2.00	—
25	Merchant Ships of the World	1925	£2.00	—
25	Military Portraits	1917	£1.00	£25.00
LF36	Modern Beauties	1939	16p	£6.00
XF36	Modern Beauties	1936	40p	£15.00
36	Modern Beauties 1st Series	1938	15p	£5.00
MF54	Modern Beauties 1st Series	1937	25p	£13.50
36	Modern Beauties 2nd Series	1938	15p	£4.00
MF54	Modern Beauties 2nd Series	1938	25p	£13.50

Qty		Date	Odds	Sets
XF36	Modern Beauties 2nd Series	1936	30p	£10.00
MF36	Modern Beauties 3rd Series	1938	25p	£9.00
XF36	Modern Beauties 3rd Series	1936	15p	£5.00
MF36	Modern Beauties 4th Series	1939	25p	£9.00
XF36	Modern Beauties 4th Series	1937	15p	£4.50
XF36	Modern Beauties 5th Series	1938	15p	£4.50
XF36	Modern Beauties 6th Series	1938	15p	£4.50
XF36	Modern Beauties 7th Series	1938	15p	£4.50
LF36	Modern Beauties 8th Series	1939	15p	£4.50
LF36	Modern Beauties 9th Series	1939	15p	£4.50
50	Modern Warfare	1936	30p	£15.00
25	Modes of Conveyance	1928	80p	£20.00
48	Motor Cars (Coloured)	1926	£1.50	—
36	Motor Cars (Brown)	1929	£1.50	—
50	Motor Cycles	1927	£1.40	£70.00
F50	Native Life in Many Lands	1932	30p	£15.00
F50	Natural & Man Made Wonders of the World ...	1937	25p	£12.50
F50	Nature Studies	1928	30p	£15.00
50	Naval Portraits	1917	£1.00	£50.00
25	Notabilities	1917	£1.00	£25.00
25	Past & Present	1929	80p	£20.00
FS48	Pictures of the East	1930	25p	£12.50
M48	Picturesque China	1925	60p	£30.00
B53	Playing Cards	1940	15p	£4.00
36	Popular Stage, Cinema & Society Celebrities ...	1928	£1.50	—
25	Prehistoric Animals	1931	80p	£20.00
50	Prominent Australian & English Cricketers ...	1911	£20.00	—
25	Puzzle Series	1916	£2.50	—
50	Railway Working	1927	80p	£40.00
33	Regimental Pets	1911	£3.00	£100.00
50	Regimental Uniforms	1936	75p	£37.50
50	Romance of the Heavens	1929	30p	£15.00
FS50	Round the World in Pictures	1931	40p	—
50	Royal Mail	1912	£2.00	—
27	Rulers of the World	1911	£3.50	—
40	Safety First	1931	30p	£12.00
25	Ships' Flags & Cap Badges, 1st Series	1930	60p	£15.00
25	Ships' Flags & Cap Badges, 2nd Series	1930	60p	£15.00
F50	Ships & Shipping	1928	35p	£17.50
50	Signalling Series	1913	£1.25	—
100	Soldiers of the World (Tobacco Leaf Back) ...	1902	£6.00	—
50	Speed	1938	30p	£15.00
25	Sports & Games in Many Lands	1930	80p	—
50	Stage & Film Stars	1926	75p	—
M50	Stars of Filmland	1927	75p	—
F50	The Royal Navy	1930	£1.25	—
F50	The World of Sport	1927	60p	£30.00
100	Transfers, Set 1	1930	£1.25	—
100	Transfers, Set 2	1930	£1.25	—
32	Transport of the World	1911	*£5.00*	—
20	Types of North American Indians	1931	£2.50	—
F50	Types of the World	1936	40p	£20.00
F52	Ur Ollum Attum	1930	£1.50	—
FS270	Views of the World	1908	*£2.00*	—

German Tobacco Issues

Cartoons. Aviatik

Castles. Borg

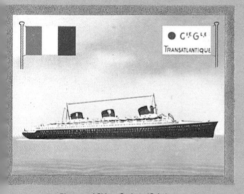

Pictures of Ships. Garbaty (Saba)

The World War. Bergmann

People of the World. Eckstein Halpaus

German Peasant Costumes. Zuban

Old Army Uniforms. Waldorf Astoria

Early American Cards

Coins of All Nations. Duke

Birds of America.
Allen & Ginter

Fishers & Fish. Duke

Perilous Occupations. Duke

Postage Stamps. Duke

National Dances. Kinney

Novelties. Kinney

Fancy Bathers. Kimball & ATC

BRITISH AMERICAN TOBACCO CO. LTD. (B.A.T.)—cont.

Qty		Date	Odds	Sets
25	Warriors of All Nations (Gold Panel)	1937	60p	£15.00
50	War Incidents (Blue Black)	1915	60p	£30.00
50	War Incidents (Brown Back)	1916	60p	£30.00
50	Warships	1926	£1.00	—
25	Whaling	1930	80p	£20.00
F50	Who's Who in Sport	1927	60p	£30.00
50	Wild Animals of the World (Tobacco Leaf back)	1903	£4.00	—
25	Wireless	1923	£1.20	£30.00
50	Wonders of the Past	1930	40p	£20.00
50	Wonders of the Sea	1929	40p	£20.00
25	Wonders of the World	1928	40p	£10.00
40	World Famous Cinema Artistes	1933	40p	£16.00
L40	World Famous Cinema Artistes	1933	50p	£20.00
50	World's Products	1929	30p	£15.00
F50	Zoo	1935	40p	—
50	Zoological Studies	1928	30p	£15.00

(4) SERIES WITH PLAIN BACKS

Qty		Date	Odds	Sets
50	Actors & Actresses "WALP"	1906	£1.00	£50.00
50	Actresses "ALWICS"	1907	£1.00	—
50	Actresses, Four Colours Surround	1905	£1.00	£50.00
30	Actresses, Unicoloured (Light Brown)	1910	35p	£10.00
30	Actresses, Unicoloured (Purple Brown)	1910	40p	£12.00
50	Animals & Birds	1912	£1.00	£50.00
60	Animals—Cut-Outs	1912	75p	—
50	Art Photogravures	1912	75p	—
50	Aviation Series	1911	£1.50	—
40	Beauties (Brown Tinted)	1913	£1.25	—
50	Beauties, Coloured Backgrounds	1911	£1.25	£62.50
50	Beauties, "LAWHA"	1906	£1.25	—
32	Beauties, Picture Hats I	1914	80p	£25.00
45	Beauties, Picture Hats II	1914	80p	£36.00
30	Beauties & Children	1912	£2.50	—
52	Birds of Brilliant Plumage (P/C Inset)	1914	£1.40	£72.50
25	Bonzo Series	1923	£1.50	£37.50
30	Boys Scouts Signalling	1922	£1.50	£45.00
50	Butterflies & Moths	1910	80p	—
50	Cinema Artistes	1930	50p	—
50	Cinema Stars (1-50)	1927	50p	—
50	Cinema Stars (51-100)	1928	50p	—
50	Cinema Stars (101-150)	1930	50p	—
100	Cinema Stars (201-300)	1932	40p	—
50	Cinema Stars "BAMT"	1928	50p	£25.00
50	Cinema Stars, "FLAG"	1929	50p	—
27	Dancing Girls	1913	60p	£16.00
32	Drum Horses	1910	£2.00	£65.00
50	English Period Costumes	1929	40p	£20.00
50	Flag Girls of All Nations	1911	80p	£40.00
165	Flags, Pennons & Signals	1907	30p	—
20	Flowers	1915	35p	£7.00
50	Girls of All Nations	1908	£1.00	£50.00
30	Heroic Deeds	1913	65p	£20.00
25	Hindoo Gods	1909	£4.00	—
32	Houses of Parliament	1914	£2.00	—
25	Indian Mogul Paintings	1909	£5.00	—

BRITISH AMERICAN TOBACCO CO. LTD. (B.A.T.)—cont.

Qty		Date	Odds	Sets
53	Jockeys & Owners Colours (P/C Inset)	1914	£1.20	£62.50
K36	Modern Beauties, 1st Series	1938	£1.25	—
36	Modern Beauties, 2nd Series	1939	£1.00	—
F48	Movie Stars	1928	60p	—
F50	New Zealand, Early Scenes & Maori Life	1929	75p	—
50	Poultry & Pigeons	1926	£1.25	—
25	Products of the World	1914	50p	—
50	Royal Mail	1912	£2.50	—
36	Ships & Their Pennants	1913	75p	£27.00
75	Soldiers of the World	1904	£3.50	—
30	Sporting Girls	1913	£1.20	—
50	Sports of the World (Brown)	1917	£1.50	—
50	Sports of the World (Coloured)	1917	80p	—
B50	Stars of Filmland	1927	75p	—
32	Transport of the World	1917	35p	£11.50
50	Types of the British Army (Numbered)	1908	£1.00	—
50	Types of the British Army (Unnumbered)	1908	£1.00	—
F50	Types of the World	1936	£1.25	—
F50	Units of the British Army & R.A.F.	1930	£1.00	—
FS50	Views of the World	1908	75p	—
50	War Leaders and Scenes	1916	£3.00	—
M50	Women of Nations (Flag Girls)	1922	£1.50	—

BRITISH-AUSTRALIAN TOBACCO CO. (Australia)

?100	Flags of All Nations	1910	£4.00	—

BRITISH CIGARETTE CO. (China)

25	Actresses and Beauties (FECKSA)	1900	£40.00	—
25	South African War Scenes	1900	£12.00	£300.00

BRITISH NEW GUINEA DEVELOPMENT CO.

50	Papuan Series 1	1910	£25.00	—

BRITISH LEAF TOBACCO CO. (India)

?20	Cinema Stars	1930	£5.00	—

BROWN & WILLIAMSON TOBACCO CORP. (U.S.A.)

B50	Modern American Warplanes Series A	1940	60p	£30.00
B50	Modern American Warplanes Series B	1941	75p	£37.50
B50	Modern American Warplanes Series C	1942	75p	£37.50
50	Movie Stars	1940	£2.00	—

D. BUCHNER & CO. (U.S.A.)

B45	Actors	1888	£12.50	—
X?100	Actresses	1888	£15.00	—
X?60	American Scenes with Policeman	1888	£25.00	—
B120	Baseball Players	1888	£40.00	—
X?10	Butterflies & Bugs	1888	£35.00	—
P200	Defenders & Offenders	1888	£20.00	—
B31	Jockeys	1888	£15.00	—
X52	Morning Glory Maidens	1888	£25.00	—
X31	Morning Glory Maidens & American Flowers ...	1888	£35.00	—
X25	Musical Instruments	1888	£30.00	—
X25	New York City Scenes	1888	£25.00	—

D. BUCHNER & CO. (U.S.A.)—cont.

Qty		Date	Odds	Sets
B101	Police Inspectors	1888	£12.50	—
X100	Police Inspectors & Captains	1888	£12.50	—
X12	Presidential Puzzle Cards	1888	*£35.00*	—
X25	Yacht Club Colours	1888	£30.00	—

CALCUTTA CIGARETTE CO. (India)

25	Actresses (Blue Front)	1906	£12.50	—
25	Actresses (Brown Front)	1906	£15.00	—

A. G. CAMERON & SIZER (U.S.A.)

24	Occupations for Women	1890	£25.00	—
F?	Photographic Cards	1890	£2.00	—
25	The New Discovery	1890	£15.00	£375.00

V. CAMILLERI (Malta)

BF104	Popes of Rome	1922	70p	£70.00

CAMLER TOBACCO COY. (Malta)

F250	Footballers	1926	£1.75	—
B96	Maltese Families' Coats of Arms	1925	50p	£48.00

CASTELANO BROS. (India)

52	Beauties, Playing Card Inset	1899	£15.00	—

C. COLOMBOS (Malta)

MF?200	Actresses	1902	£1.25	—
BF?25	Actresses	1902	*£7.50*	—
50	Actresses (Coloured)	1900	£5.00	—
BF?25	Celebrities	1900	£7.50	—
F136	Dante's Divine Comedy	1914	£1.00	£135.00
MF72	Famous Oil Paintings, Serie A	1910	50p	£36.00
MF108	Famous Oil Paintings, Serie B	1911	50p	£50.00
MF240	Famous Oil Paintings, Serie C	1912	50p	£120.00
MF100	Famous Oil Paintings, Serie D	1913	50p	£50.00
XF100	Famous Oil Paintings	1911	£3.50	—
BF100	Life of Napoleon Bonaparte	1914	£1.00	£100.00
BF70	Life of Nelson	1914	£1.00	£70.00
BF70	Life of Wellington	1914	£1.00	£70.00
MF100	National Types and Costumes	1908	£1.20	£120.00
F?25	Opera Singers	1899	*£15.00*	—
120	Paintings and Statues	1913	40p	£50.00
B112	Royalty and Celebrities	1908	£1.50	£165.00

COLONIAL TOBACCOS (PTY.) LTD. (South Africa)

X150	World's Fairy Tales	1930	£2.00	—

D. CONDACHI & SON (Malta)

?10	Beauties	1910	£10.00	—

CONSOLIDATED CIGARETTE CO. (U.S.A.)

25	Ladies of the White House	1893	£16.00	—
B14	Ladies of the White House	1898	£20.00	£280.00
B25	Turn Cards	1894	£30.00	—
M25	Turn Cards	1894	*£30.00*	—

A. G. COUSIS & CO. (Malta)

Qty		Date	Odds	Sets
254	Actors & Actresses	1924	30p	—
KF100	Actors & Actresses (Hand Coloured)	1906	60p	—
F100	Actors & Actresses (Hand Coloured)	1906	75p	—
KF100	Actresses Serie I	1907	60p	—
KF80	Actresses Serie II	1907	60p	—
F1900	Actresses Serie I to Serie XIX	1907	75p	—
KF?2000	Actresses (Unnumbered)	1905	30p	—
F?1300	Actresses (Unnumbered)	1905	35p	—
MF?150	Actresses (White Border)	1902	£4.00	—
KF100	Actresses, Partners & National Costumes (Cousis')	1906	75p	—
KF200	Actresses, Partners & National Costumes (Cousis's)	1906	75p	—
F100	Actresses, Partners & National Costumes	1906	75p	—
50	Beauties, Couples & Children (Red Back) ...	1923	£1.00	—
MF50	Beauties, Couples & Children, Collection No. 1 ...	1908	£1.25	—
MF50	Beauties, Couples & Children, Collection No. 2 ...	1908	£1.25	—
MF50	Beauties, Couples & Children, Collection No. 3 ...	1908	£1.25	—
F402	Celebrities (Numbered)	1906	40p	—
KF?2156	Celebrities (Unnumbered)	1905	30p	—
F?2156	Celebrities (Unnumbered)	1905	30p	—
XF?30	Celebrities & Warships (White Border)	1902	£4.00	—
MF72	Grand Masters of the Order of St. John	1909	75p	—
F100	National Costumes	1908	75p	—
MF100	Paris Exhibition, 1900	1900	£10.00	—
MF102	Paris Series	1902	£10.00	—
MF182	Popes of Rome (To A.D. 1241)	1904	50p	£90.00
MF81	Popes of Rome (Dubec, After A.D. 1241)	1904	£1.00	—
F100	Statues & Monuments (Numbered)	1905	75p	—
F100	Statues & Monuments (Unnumbered)	1905	75p	—
KF127	Views of Malta	1903	60p	—
F?100	Views of Malta (Numbered)	1903	40p	—
BF?127	Views of Malta (Numbered)	1903	40p	—
BF?65	Views of Malta (Unnumbered)	1903	40p	—
F?30	Views of the Mediterranean	1903	£2.00	—
BF?100	Views of the Mediterranean	1903	£2.00	—
F?555	Views of the World	1903	40p	—
BF?555	Views of the World	1903	40p	—
F99	Warships (White Border)	1910	£1.00	—
KF850	Warships	1904	40p	—
BF850	Warships	1904	60p	—
BF?75	Warships & Liners (Dubec)	1904	£1.50	—
BF?25	Warships & Liners (Excelsior)	1904	£1.50	—
MF?50	Warships & Liners (Superior)	1904	£2.00	—

CROWN TOBACCO CO. (India)

X24	Actresses	1900	£30.00	—
96	National Types, Costumes & Flags	1900	£15.00	—
B96	National Types, Costumes & Flags	1900	£25.00	—
?	Photo Series	1900	£30.00	—

CHARLES C. DAVIS (U.S.A.)

?15	Actresses	1890	£30.00	

DIAMOND INDIAN CIGARETTES

?25	Beauties	1924	£7.00	—

DIXSON (Australia)

Qty		Date	Odds	Sets
50	Australian M.P.s & Celebrities	1900	£6.00	—

DOMINION TOBACCO CO. (Canada)

100	Photos (Actresses)	1905	£15.00	—
50	The Smokers of the World	1904	£25.00	—

DOMINION TOBACCO CO. LTD (New Zealand)

50	Coaches & Coaching Days	1927	80p	£40.00
50	People & Places Famous in New Zealand History	1933	£1.00	£50.00
50	Products of the World	1929	50p	£25.00
50	USS Co's Steamers	1928	£1.00	—

DRUMMOND TOBACCO CO. (U.S.A.)

?20	Actresses	1895	*£40.00*	—
?50	Bathing Girls	1895	*£40.00*	—
50	Beauties "CHOAB"	1897	*£60.00*	—
X?25	Girls	1896	£35.00	—

DUDGEON & ARNELL (Australia)

B16	1934 Australian Test Team	1934	£3.00	£48.00
B55	Famous Ships	1933	£1.50	—

W. DUKE & SONS LTD. (U.S.A.)

50	Actors & Actresses, Series 1	1889	£7.00	£350.00
B50	Actors & Actresses, Series 1	1889	*£25.00*	—
50	Actors & Actresses, Series 2	1889	£7.00	£350.00
B50	Actors & Actresses, Series 2	1889	*£25.00*	—
X30	Actors & Actresses (As Above)	1889	£14.00	—
X25	Albums of American Stars	1886	£20.00	—
X25	Battle Scenes	1887	£12.00	—
X25	Beauties, Black Border	1886	£12.00	£300.00
X25	Beauties, Folders	1886	£25.00	—
X25	Bicycle & Trick Riders	1891	£14.00	—
X25	Breeds of Horses	1892	£12.00	£300.00
X25	Bridges	1888	£12.00	£300.00
X25	Burlesque Scenes	1887	£12.50	—
50	Coins of All Nations	1889	£7.00	£350.00
X25	Comic Characters	1887	£12.00	£300.00
X25	Cowboy Scenes	1888	£16.00	—
X50	Fairest Flowers of the World	1887	£12.00	—
F45	Famous Ships	1884	*£5.00*	—
50	Fancy Dress Ball Costumes	1887	£7.00	£350.00
B50	Fancy Dress Ball Costumes	1887	*£25.00*	—
X50	Fancy Dress Ball Costumes	1887	£12.00	—
50	Fishers & Fish	1888	£7.00	£350.00
X25	Fishers & Fish	1888	£12.50	—
X25	Flags & Costumes	1892	£15.00	£375.00
50	Floral Beauties & Language of Flowers ...	1893	£7.00	£350.00
X25	French Novelties	1892	£12.00	—
X25	Gems of Beauty	1884	£12.00	—
50	Great Americans	1888	£8.00	£400.00
X16	Great Americans	1888	£14.00	—
25	Gymnastic Exercises	1887	£12.00	£300.00
X25	Habitations of Man	1890	£10.00	£250.00

W. DUKE & SONS LTD. (U.S.A.)—cont.

Qty		Date	Odds	Sets
X50	Histories of Generals	1888	£12.00	—
50	Histories of Generals (Booklets)	1888	£8.00	£400.00
50	Histories of Poor Boys & Other Famous People	1888	£10.00	£500.00
50	Holidays	1890	£7.00	£350.00
X25	Illustrated Songs	1893	£12.50	—
X25	Industries of States	1889	£15.00	—
50	Jokes	1890	£8.00	—
X25	Jokes	1890	£12.00	—
X25	Lighthouses (Die Cut)	1890	£12.00	£300.00
X25	Miniature Novelties	1891	£12.00	£300.00
50	Musical Instruments	1888	£10.00	£500.00
X25	Musical Instruments of the World	1888	£12.50	—
36	Ocean & River Steamers	1887	£10.00	—
F?	Photographic Cards	1885	50p	—
MF?	Photographic Cards	1885	£1.00	—
XF?	Photographic Cards	1885	75p	—
53	Playing Cards	1887	£6.00	£300.00
50	Popular Songs & Dancers	1894	£10.00	—
50	Postage Stamp Cards	1888	£8.00	£400.00
X25	Presidential Possibilities	1888	£12.00	£300.00
X15	Puzzles	1887	£16.00	—
50	Rulers, Flags & Arms (Folders)	1889	£7.00	£350.00
X50	Rulers, Flags & Arms	1889	£10.00	—
50	Scenes of Perilous Occupations	1888	£10.00	—
X25	Sea Captains	1887	£16.00	£400.00
50	Shadows	1890	£7.00	£350.00
X25	Snapshots from "Puck"	1889	£12.00	£300.00
X25	Stars of the Stage, 1st Series	1891	£12.00	£300.00
X25	Stars of the Stage, 2nd Series	1891	£12.00	£300.00
X25	Stars of the Stage, 3rd Series	1892	£12.00	£300.00
X25	Stars of the Stage, 4th Series (Die Cut)	1893	£12.00	£300.00
48	State Governors, Arms & Maps (Folders)	1889	£7.00	£350.00
X48	State Governors, Arms & Maps	1889	£10.00	—
X25	Talk of the Diamond	1893	£16.00	—
50	The Terrors of America & Their Doings	1890	£7.50	£375.00
M50	The Terrors of America & Their Doings	1890	*£25.00*	—
X50	The Terrors of America & Their Doings	1890	£12.50	—
50	Tinted Photos	1887	£10.00	—
X25	Transparencies	1888	£30.00	—
X24	Tricks with Cards	1887	£15.00	£360.00
X25	Types of Vessels (Die Cut)	1889	£12.00	£300.00
50	Vehicles of the World	1888	£10.00	—
X50	Yacht Club Colors of the World	1890	£12.50	—
50	Yacht Colors of the World	1890	£7.00	£350.00
B50	Yacht Colors of the World	1890	*£25.00*	—

Printed Albums (exchanged for coupons)

		Date	Odds	Sets
	Costumes of All Nations (3 Sets)	1890	—	£50.00
	Governors, Coats of Arms, etc.	1889	—	£35.00
	Postage Stamp Album	1888	—	£50.00
	Shadows	1890	—	£40.00
	Sporting Girls	1888	—	*£100.00*
	The Heroes of the Civil War	1889	—	*£75.00*
	The Rulers, Flags, Coats of Arms	1889	—	£40.00
	The Terrors of America	1890	—	£45.00
	Yacht Colors of the World (3 Sets)	1890	—	£50.00

DUNGEY, RALPH & CO. (Australia)

Qty		Date	Odds	Sets
50	Australian Footballers	1906	*£15.00*	—
?55	Australian Racehorses	1906	£15.00	—

EGYPTIAN CIGARETTE COY. (Malta)

F120	Actresses	1906	£2.50	—
LF?150	Actresses	1906	*£12.50*	—
264	Decorations & Medals	1908	£4.00	—
F100	Maltese Band Players	1910	£7.50	—

EGYPTIAN CIGARETTES MFG. CO. (China)

?50	Actresses	1900	£20.00	—
25	Armies of the World	1900	£30.00	—
?	Beauties	1900	*£40.00*	—
30	Beauties "Nymphs"	1900	£30.00	—
?30	Chinese & South African Series	1900	*£30.00*	—
25	National Flags & Flowers—Girls	1900	£35.00	—
30	Old Masters	1900	£20.00	—
?55	Russo–Japanese War Series	1903	*£30.00*	—
25	Types of British & Colonial Troops	1900	£30.00	—
25	Warships	1900	£20.00	—

H. ELLIS & CO. (U.S.A.)

25	Breeds of Dogs	1890	£20.00	£500.00
25	Costumes of Women	1890	£40.00	—
25	Generals of the Late Civil War	1890	£35.00	—
F?	Photographic Cards	1887	£3.00	—

D. FANCIULLI & CO. (Malta)

50	Il Paradiso Perduta	1906	£3.00	—

JOHN FINZER & BROS. (U.S.A.)

X10	Inventors & Inventions	1891	£17.50	£175.00

G. W. GAIL & AX (U.S.A.)

X25	Battle Scenes	1891	£12.50	—
X25	Bicycle & Trick Riders	1891	£20.00	—
X25	French Novelties	1891	£15.00	—
X25	Industries of States	1891	£15.00	—
X25	Lighthouses (Die Cut)	1891	£15.00	—
X25	Novelties (Die Cut)	1890	£20.00	—
XF?	Photographic Cards	1885	£1.50	—
X25	Stars of the Stage	1891	£15.00	—

GENERAL CIGAR CO. LTD. (Canada)

X36	Northern Birds	1977	50p	£18.00

GOODWIN & CO. (U.S.A.)

50	Champions	1888	£12.00	—
50	Dogs of the World	1890	£10.00	£500.00
50	Flowers	1890	£8.00	—
50	Games & Sports Series	1889	£10.00	£500.00
50	Holidays	1889	*£12.50*	—
50	Occupations for Women	1887	£35.00	—
F?	Photographic Cards	1886	£1.00	—
50	Vehicles of the World	1888	*£15.00*	—

GOODWIN & CO. (U.S.A.)—cont.

Qty		Date	Odds	Sets
Printed Albums (exchanged for coupons)				
	Champions	1888	—	£125.00
	Floral Album	1890	—	£60.00
	Games & Sports	1889	—	£75.00

L. O. GROTHE LTD. (Canada)

52	Bridge Hands	1927	£2.50	—

THOS. W. HALL (U.S.A.)

B155	Actors & Actresses (Dull Background)	1881	£4.00	—
B142	Actors & Actresses (Black Background)	1882	£5.00	—
B?200	Actors & Actresses (Fancy Corners)	1884	£10.00	—
B?150	Actors & Actresses (Sun's Rays)	1890	£7.50	—
B?50	Actresses (Tiled Wall)	1888	£12.50	—
B?50	Actresses (No Borders)	1892	£15.00	—
T20	Actresses (Ours All)	1885	£35.00	—
B12	Athletes	1881	£35.00	—
B8	Presidential Candidates & Actresses	1880	£40.00	—
B22	Presidents of the United States	1884	£15.00	—
25	Theatrical Types	1890	£20.00	£500.00

HARTLEY'S TOBACCO CO. (S. Africa)

L19	South African English Cricket Tour 1929	1929	£35.00	—

S. F. HESS & CO. (U.S.A.)

F?	Photographic Cards	1885	£4.00	—
55	Poker Puzzle Cards	1890	£30.00	—
25	Terms of Poker Illustrated	1890	£30.00	—

HILSON CO. (U.S.A.)

X25	Battleships & Signal Flags	1901	£12.00	£300.00
X25	National Types	1901	£10.00	£250.00

IMPERIAL CIGARETTE & TOBACCO CO. (Canada)

?24	Actresses	1900	£30.00	—

IMPERIAL TOBACCO CO. OF INDIA LTD. (India)

25	Indian Historical Views	1910	£1.00	£25.00
40	Nautch Girl Series (Pedro Cigs.)	1908	£1.00	£40.00
40	Nautch Girl Series (Railway Cigs.)	1908	£1.00	£40.00
52	Nautch Girl Series (P/C Inset, Pedro)	1908	£1.20	£62.50
52	Nautch Girl Series (P/C Inset, Railway)	1908	£1.20	£62.50
K52	Miniature Playing Cards	1933	60p	—
52	Playing Cards	1919	£1.25	

IMPERIAL TOBACCO CO. OF CANADA LTD. (Canada)

50	Actresses, Framed Border (Plain Back)	1910	£1.50	£75.00
L55/66	Aircraft Spotter Series (Packets)	1941	35p	£20.00
60	Animals (Millbank)	1916	50p	£30.00
L55	Animal With Flag (Silk)	1915	£1.60	£87.50
50	Arms of the British Empire	1911	£1.25	—
50	Around the World	1912	£2.50	—
50	Aviation Series	1910	£1.50	—

IMPERIAL TOBACCO CO. OF CANADA LTD. (Canada)—cont.

Qty		Date	Odds	Sets
90	Baseball Series	1912	£10.00	—
30	Beauties—Art Series (Plain Back)	1911	£5.00	—
25	Beauties—Girls in Costume	1904	£25.00	—
24	Beauties—Smoke Girls	1904	£25.00	—
M50	Birds, Beasts & Fishes	1924	£1.00	£50.00
30	Bird Series	1910	£1.00	£30.00
X100	Birds of Canada	1924	£1.50	—
X100	Birds of Canada (Western Canada)	1925	£2.50	—
50	Boy Scouts	1911	£2.00	£100.00
50	British Birds	1923	35p	£17.50
50	British Man of War Series (Plain Back)	1910	£5.00	£250.00
50	Buildings (Plain Back)	1902	£5.00	—
50	Butterflies & Moths	1911	£1.00	—
L24	Canada's Corvettes 1st Series	1943	£4.00	—
L24	Canada's Corvettes 2nd Series	1944	£4.00	—
50	Canadian Historical Portraits	1913	£2.00	—
48	Canadian History Series	1926	60p	£30.00
50	Canadian History Series (Anon)	1926	75p	—
P50	Canadian History Series (Silk)	1914	£6.00	—
M118	Canadian Miscellany (Silk)	1912	£2.50	—
50	Children of All Nations	1924	40p	£20.00
23	Dogs Series	1924	60p	£14.00
50	Dogs 2nd Series	1925	40p	£20.00
50	Famous English Actresses	1924	60p	£30.00
50	Film Favourites	1926	£2.00	—
50	Fish & Bait	1924	60p	£30.00
50	Fishes of the World	1924	60p	£30.00
50	Fish Series	1912	£1.00	—
50	Flower Culture in Pots	1925	35p	£17.50
50	Fowls, Pigeons & Dogs	1911	£1.50	—
30	Game Bird Series	1925	50p	£15.00
L55	Garden Flowers (Silk)	1913	£1.40	£75.00
G5	Garden Flowers (Silk)	1913	£10.00	—
50	Gardening Hints	1923	30p	£15.00
L25	Heraldic Signs & Their Origin	1925	60p	£15.00
45	Hockey Players	1912	£3.00	—
36	Hockey Series (coloured)	1911	£4.00	—
50	Hockey Series (blue)	1910	£4.00	—
50	How To Do It	1911	£1.50	£75.00
50	How to Play Golf	1925	£2.50	£125.00
50	Infantry Training	1915	£1.20	£60.00
100	Lacrosse Series Set 1	1910	£2.50	—
100	Lacrosse Series Set 2	1911	£2.50	—
50	Lacrosse Series Set 3	1912	£2.50	—
50	L'Histoire Du Canada	1914	75p	—
M48	Mail Carriers and Stamps	1903	£10.00	£480.00
50	Merchant Ships of the World	1924	40p	£20.00
25	Military Portraits	1914	£1.20	£30.00
50	Modern War Weapons	1915	£2.50	£125.00
56	Motor Cars	1921	75p	£40.00
50	Movie Stars	1925	60p	—
50	Musical Hall Artistes (Plain Back)	1911	£1.25	£62.50
50	Naval Portraits	1915	£1.20	£60.00

IMPERIAL TOBACCO CO. OF CANADA LTD. (Canada)—cont.

Qty		Date	Odds	Sets
25	Notabilities	1915	£1.20	£30.00
L55	Orders & Military Medals (Silk)	1915	£1.50	—
L50	Pictures of Canadian Life	1912	£4.00	—
52	Poker Hands	1924	50p	£26.00
25	Poultry Alphabet	1924	60p	£15.00
50	Prominent Men of Canada	1912	£2.00	—
50	Railway Engines	1924	50p	£25.00
L55	Regimental Uniforms of Canada (Silk)	1914	£1.60	—
P25	Rulers with Flags (Silk)	1910	£6.00	—
127	Smokers Golf Cards	1926	£1.50	—
50	The Reason Why	1924	60p	£30.00
25	The World's Dreadnoughts	1910	£1.20	—
50	Tricks and Puzzles	1911	£2.00	£100.00
50	Types of Nations	1910	£1.25	—
25	V.C. Heroes (Blue Back)	1915	£1.00	£25.00
L45	Views of the World	1912	£2.50	—
L25	Wild Animals of Canada	1912	£4.00	—
B144	World War I Scenes & Portraits	1916	£1.00	—
49	Yacht Pennants & Views (Silk)	1915	£2.00	£100.00

IMPERIAL TOBACCO CO. (NFLD.) LTD. (Canada)

B52	Playing Cards	1930	£4.00	—

JACK & JILL CIGARS (U.S.A.)

X25	Actresses "JAKE"	1890	£25.00	—

JAMAICA TOBACCO CO.

F?100	Miniature Post Card Series	1915	£3.50	—

KENTUCKY TOBACCOS (PTY.) LTD. (S. Africa)

L120	The March of Mankind	1940	75p	—

KEY WEST FAVORS (U.S.A.)

X50	Actresses "JAKE"	1892	£25.00	—

KHEDIVIAL COMPANY (U.S.A.)

B10	Aeroplane Series No. 103	1912	£8.00	—
B10	Prize Dog Series No. 102	1911	£8.00	—
M25	Prize Fight Series No. 101	1910	£7.00	—
M25	Prize Fight Series No. 102	1911	£7.00	—

WM. S. KIMBALL & CO. (U.S.A.)

?25	Actresses, Collotype	1887	£40.00	—
72	Ancient Coins	1888	£15.00	—
48	Arms of Dominions	1888	£10.00	—
50	Ballet Queens	1889	£10.00	£500.00
X20	Beautiful Bathers	1889	£15.00	—
52	Beauties, Playing Card Insets	1895	£10.00	£520.00
50	Butterflies	1888	£12.00	—
50	Champions of Games & Sports	1888	£12.50	—
50	Dancing Girls of the World	1889	£10.00	£500.00
50	Dancing Women	1889	£10.00	£500.00
50	Fancy Bathers	1889	£10.00	£500.00

WM. S. KIMBALL & CO. (USA)—cont.

Qty		Date	Odds	Sets
X25	French Novelties	1891	£20.00	—
X25	Gems of Beauty	1891	£20.00	—
50	Goddesses of the Greeks & Romans	1889	£12.00	—
X25	Household Pets	1891	£15.00	—
X15	National Flags	1887	£16.00	—
F?	Photographic Cards	1886	£1.50	—
XF?	Photographic Cards	1886	£2.50	—
X20	Pretty Athletes	1890	£15.00	—
50	Savage & Semi Barbarous Chiefs & Rulers ...	1890	£12.50	—
L?25	Wellstood Etchings	1887	*£50.00*	—

Printed Albums (exchanged for coupons)

	Ancient Coins	1888	—	£75.00
	Ballet Queens	1889	—	£60.00
	Champions of Games & Sports	1888	—	£75.00
	Dancing Girls of the World	1889	—	*£60.00*
	Dancing Women	1889	—	*£60.00*
	Fancy Bathers	1889	—	*£60.00*
	Goddesses of the Greeks & Romans	1889	—	*£60.00*
	Savage & Semi Barbarous Chiefs & Rulers ...	1890	—	*£75.00*

KINNEY BROS. (U.S.A.)

Qty		Date	Odds	Sets
25	Actresses "Set 1"	1891	£4.00	£100.00
25	Actresses "Set 2"	1891	£7.50	—
50	Actresses (Group 2)	1891	£3.00	—
50	Actresses (Group 3)	1892	£3.00	—
50	Actresses (Group 4, Coloured)	1893	£3.00	—
150	Actresses (Group 4, Sepia)	1893	£1.00	—
25	Animals	1890	£8.00	£200.00
10	Butterflies of the World (White)	1888	£8.00	£80.00
50	Butterflies of the World (Gold)	1888	£6.00	£300.00
25	Famous Gems of the World	1889	£8.00	£200.00
25	Famous Running Horses (American)	1890	£7.00	£175.00
25	Famous Running Horses (English)	1890	£6.00	£150.00
F45	Famous Ships	1887	*£5.00*	—
25	Great American Trotters	1890	£8.00	—
52	Harlequin Cards, 1st Series	1888	£8.00	£420.00
53	Harlequin Cards, 2nd Series	1888	£8.00	£420.00
L?4	Inaugural Types	1888	*£60.00*	—
X50	International Cards	1888	£17.50	—
K25	Jocular Oculars	1887	£25.00	—
25	Leaders	1889	£8.00	£200.00
50	Magic Changing Cards	1888	£10.00	—
622	Military Series	1887	£2.50	—
50	National Dances (white border)	1889	£7.00	£350.00
25	National Dances (no border)	1889	£8.00	£200.00
25	Naval Vessels of the World	1889	£10.00	£250.00
50	New Year 1890 Cards	1889	£10.00	—
K25	Novelties (Circular, Thick Cards)	1888	£12.50	—
K50	Novelties (Circular, Thin Cards)	1888	£5.00	£250.00
75	Novelties (Die Cut)	1888	£4.00	£300.00
14	Novelties (Oval)	1888	£15.00	—
45	Novelties (Rectangular)	1888	£6.00	£260.00
F?	Photographic Cards	1886	40p	—

KINNEY BROS. (U.S.A.)—cont.

Qty		Date	Odds	Sets
LF?	Photographic Cards	1886	£1.25	—
50	Surf Beauties	1889	£10.00	£500.00
1	Sweet Caporal Calendar	1890	—	£40.00
52	Transparent Playing Cards	1888	£8.00	£415.00
25	Types of Nationalities (Folders)	1890	£12.50	

Printed Albums (exchanged for coupons)

		Date	Odds	Sets
	Butterflies	1889	—	£60.00
	Celebrated American & English Running Horses	1890	—	*£60.00*
	Leaders	1889	—	£50.00
	Liberty Album	1889	—	£40.00
	National Dances	1889	—	*£60.00*
	Natural History	1890	—	£40.00
	Reigning Beauties	1889	—	£50.00
	Singers & Opera Houses	1889	—	£70.00
	Surf Beauties	1889	—	*£60.00*

KRAMERS TOBACCO CO. (PTY.) LTD. (S. Africa)

Qty		Date	Odds	Sets
50	Badges of South African Rugby Football Clubs ...	1933	£2.50	—

LA FAVORITA (Canary Islands)

Qty		Date	Odds	Sets
M30/58	Flags & Soldiers (Silk)	1915	35p	£10.50

LEWIS & ALLEN CO. (U.S.A.)

Qty		Date	Odds	Sets
X120	Views & Art Studies	1912	£3.00	—

LONE JACK CIGARETTE CO. (U.S.A.)

Qty		Date	Odds	Sets
25	Inventors & Inventions	1887	£35.00	—
50	Language of Flowers	1888	£15.00	—
F?	Photographic Cards	1886	£3.00	—

P. LORILLARD CO. (U.S.A.)

Qty		Date	Odds	Sets
25	Actresses (Coloured)	1888	£12.00	£300.00
B20	Actresses (Irregular Gold Frame)	1889	£12.50	—
B?150	Actresses (Fancy Surrounds)	1889	£12.00	—
B75	Actresses (Plain Surround)	1890	£8.00	—
X25	Actresses (Burdick 263)	1889	£12.00	£300.00
X25	Actresses (Burdick 264-1)	1890	£12.00	£300.00
X25	Actresses (Burdick 264-2)	1890	£12.00	—
X25	Actresses (Burdick 264-3, Grey Border) ...	1890	£12.00	—
X25	Actresses in Opera Roles	1892	£20.00	—
T25	Ancient Mythology Burlesqued	1893	£12.00	£300.00
T50	Beautiful Women	1893	£12.00	£600.00
X25	Boxing Positions & Boxers	1887	£25.00	—
M?10	Busts of Girls (Die Cut)	1886	*£50.00*	—
X25	Circus Scenes	1888	£30.00	—
X?10	Everyday Annoyances	1886	*£40.00*	—
25	National Flags	1888	£16.00	—
T52	Playing Card Inset Girls	1893	£14.00	—
X50	Prizefighters	1887	*£25.00*	—
X?15	Song Album	1887	*£30.00*	—
T25	Types of Flirtation	1892	£25.00	—
T25	Types of the Stage	1893	£12.00	£300.00

W. C. MACDONALD INC. (Canada)

Qty		Date	Odds	Sets
?350	Aeroplanes & Warships	1940	40p	—
53	Playing Cards (Many Printings)	1927	25p	—

B. & J. B. MACHADO (Jamaica)

25	British Naval Series	1916	£8.00	—
F50	Popular Film Stars	1926	£2.00	—
F52	Stars of the Cinema	1926	£2.00	—
50	The Great War—Victoria Cross Heroes	1916	£8.00	—
F50	The Royal Family at Home & Abroad	1927	£2.00	—
F50	The World of Sport	1928	£2.00	—

MACLIN–ZIMMER (U.S.A.)

X53	Playing Cards (Actresses)	1892	£15.00	—

H. MANDELBAUM (U.S.A.)

20	Comic Types of People	1890	£25.00	—
36	Flags of Nations	1890	£25.00	—

MASPERO FRERES LTD. (Palestine)

50	Birds, Beasts & Fishes	1925	£2.00	—

S. MATTINNO & SONS (Malta)

X36	Britain Prepared Series	1940	£1.50	—

P. H. MAYO & BROTHER (U.S.A.)

B25	Actresses (Fancy Frame)	1890	£12.00	£300.00
?25	Actresses (Sepia)	1886	£30.00	—
M25	Actresses (Black Border)	1890	£14.00	—
L12	Actresses (Diagonal)	1888	£35.00	—
?50	Actresses (Burdick 488)	1888	£16.00	—
X25	Actresses	1887	£25.00	—
28	Baseball Game (Die Cut)	1890	£30.00	—
40	Baseball Players	1892	£40.00	—
35	College Football Stars	1892	£20.00	—
20	Costumes & Flowers	1892	£16.00	—
19	Costumes of Warriors & Soldiers	1892	£16.00	—
25	Headdresses of Various Nations	1890	£20.00	—
?100	National Dances (Die Cut)	1890	£30.00	—
M25	National Flowers (Girl & Scene)	1891	£16.00	—
20	Naval Uniforms	1892	£16.00	—
F?	Photographic Cards	1887	£3.00	—
24	Presidents of U.S.	1888	£25.00	—
35	Prizefighters	1890	£15.00	—
20	Shakespeare Characters	1891	£16.00	£320.00
X12	The Seasons	1888	£35.00	—
X15	Wings of Birds of Plumage	1888	£35.00	—

M. MELACHRINO & CO. (Malta)

52	Peuples Exotiques "1 Serie"	1925	40p	£20.00
52	Peuples Exotiques "2 Serie"	1925	40p	£20.00
52	Peuples Exotiques "3 Serie"	1925	30p	£15.00

MIFSUD & AZZOPARDI (Malta)

Qty		Date	Odds	Sets
KF59	First Maltese Parliament	1922	£2.00	—

MRS. G. B. MILLER & CO. (U.S.A.)

X?	Actresses & Celebrities	1885	*£30.00*	—
X?	Alphabet Cards	1887	£30.00	—
22	Photographs of all the Presidents	1888	*£40.00*	—

L. MILLER & SONS (U.S.A.)

49	Animals & Birds	1900	*£35.00*	—
X25	Battleships	1900	£16.00	£400.00
X100	Beauties "THIBS"	1900	*£40.00*	—
X25	Generals & Admirals (Spanish War)	1900	£16.00	—
X24	Presidents of U.S.	1900	£12.50	£300.00
X50	Rulers of the World	1900	£12.50	£625.00

CHAS. J. MITCHELL (Canada)

26	Actresses "FROGA" (Brown Back)	1900	£15.00	—
26	Actresses "FROGA" (Green Back)	1900	£15.00	—

MOORE & CALVI (U.S.A.)

X53	Beauties, Playing Card Inset, Set 1	1888	£14.00	£750.00
X53	Beauties, Playing Card Inset, Set 2	1889	£12.00	£625.00
X53	Beauties, Playing Card Inset, Set 3	1890	£12.00	£625.00
X10	Rope Knots	1888	£30.00	—

MURAI BROS. (Japan)

50	Actresses "ALWICS"	1910	£4.00	£200.00
50	Beauties	1902	£6.00	£300.00
50	Dancing Girls of the World	1900	£15.00	—
32	Flowers	1900	£12.50	
26	Phrases and Advertisements	1900	£10.00	£260.00
50	World's Distinguished Personages	1900	£15.00	—
50	World's Smokers	1900	£12.50	—

NATIONAL CIGARETTE & TOBACCO CO. (U.S.A.)

25	National Types (Sailor Girls)	1890	£12.00	£300.00
F?	Photographic Cards	1888	£2.00	—

NATIONAL TOBACCO WORKS (U.S.A.)

GF?	Actresses, etc. (Newsboy)	1900	£7.50	—
G100	Actresses (Coloured)	1900	£15.00	—

OLD FASHION FINE CUT (U.S.A.)

FX?	Photographic Cards	1890	£4.00	—

OMEGA CIGARETTE FACTORY (Malta)

KF100	Cinema Stars	1936	65p	—

PENINSULAR TOBACCO CO. LTD. (India)

50	Animals and Birds	1910	£1.20	—
52	Birds of Brilliant Plumage (P/C Inset)	1916	£2.00	—
25	Birds of the East, 1st Series	1912	80p	£20.00
25	Birds of the East, 2nd Series	1912	80p	£20.00

PENINSULAR TOBACCO CO. LTD. (India)—cont.

Qty		Date	Odds	Sets
25	China's Famous Warriors	1912	80p	£20.00
50	Chinese Heroes	1913	£1.20	—
50	Chinese Modern Beauties	1912	£2.00	—
50	Chinese Trades Set 3	1912	£1.50	—
50	Chinese Trades Set 5	1913	£1.50	—
30	Fish Series	1916	£1.25	£37.50
25	Hindoo Gods	1909	£1.00	£25.00
37	Nautch Girl Series	1910	£3.00	—
25	Products of the World	1915	80p	£20.00

PIZZUTO (Malta)

50	Milton's "Paradise Lost"	1910	£3.00	—

THE PLANTERS STORES (India)

50	Actresses "FROGA"	1900	£12.50	—
25	Beauties "FECKSA"	1900	£15.00	—

POLICANSKY BROS. (South Africa)

M50	Birds, Beasts & Fishes (Nassa Cigs)	1924	£3.00	—
50	South African Fauna	1925	£3.00	—

RED MAN CHEWING TOBACCO (U.S.A.)

X40	American Indian Chiefs	1952	£3.50	£140.00

D. RITCHIE & CO. (Canada)

30	Actresses "RITAN"	1887	£20.00	£600.00
52	Beauties P/C Inset	1888	£15.00	—
52	Playing Cards	1888	£15.00	—

RITMEESTER CIGARS

X28	Austrian Cavalry (Cigar bands)	1976	40p	£12.50
X28	French Cavalry (Cigar bands)	1976	50p	£15.00
X28	German Cavalry (Cigar bands)	1976	35p	£10.00

D. E. ROSE & CO. (U.S.A.)

G28	Imperial Cards	1890	£20.00	£560.00

RUGGIER BROS. (Malta)

M50	Story of the Knights of Malta	1924	£2.00	£100.00

RUMI CIGARETTES (Germany)

B56	Beauties (Franks)	1901	£25.00	—

JOHN SCERRI (Malta)

147/150	Beauties & Children (Black & White)	1930	40p	£60.00
45	Beauties & Children (Coloured)	1930	50p	—
BF50	Beautiful Women	1931	75p	—
BF480	Cinema Artists	1931	75p	—
BF180	Cinema Stars	1931	75p	—
B50	Famous London Buildings	1934	£1.50	—
60	Film Stars (First Serie)	1931	75p	—
60	Film Stars (Second Serie)	1931	75p	—
52	Interesting Places of the World	1934	30p	£15.00
F25	International Footballers	1933	£2.00	£50.00
401	Malta Views	1928	30p	—

JOHN SCERRI (Malta)—cont.

Qty		Date	Odds	Sets
B51	Members of Parliament—Malta	1928	25p	£12.50
146	Prominent People	1930	50p	—
BF100	Scenes from Films	1932	60p	—
XF100	Talkie Stars	1932	75p	—
B100	World's Famous Buildings	1931	40p	£40.00

J. J. SCHUH TOBACCO CO. (Australia)

60	Australian Footballers A ($\frac{1}{2}$ Length)	1920	£2.00	£120.00
40	Australian Footballers B (Rays)	1921	£2.50	£100.00
60	Australian Footballers C (Oval Frame)	1922	£5.00	—
60	Australian Jockeys	1921	£2.00	£120.00
F72	Cinema Stars (Black & White)	1924	75p	£54.00
60	Cinema Stars (Coloured)	1924	75p	£45.00
L12	Maxims of Success	1917	£30.00	—
F72	Official War Photographs	1918	£1.50	£110.00
F96	Portraits of our Leading Footballers	1920	£1.50	£150.00

G. SCLIVAGNOTI (Malta)

50	Actresses & Cinema Stars	1923	80p	£40.00
MF71	Grand Masters of the Order of Jerusalem	1898	£3.50	—
F102	Opera Singers	1898	£3.50	—
M100	Opera Singers	1898	£3.50	—
B?47	Scenes with Girls	1905	£15.00	—

SINSOCK & CO. (China)

?50	Chinese Beauties	1905	£8.00	—

SNIDERS & ABRAHAMS PTY. LTD. (Australia)

31	Actresses	1905	£3.00	£100.00
20	Admirals & Warships of the USA	1908	£4.00	—
2	Advertisement Cards	1905	£10.00	—
60	Animals (Green, Descriptive Backs)	1912	£1.25	£75.00
60	Animals & Birds	1912	£1.00	£60.00
15	Australian Cricket Team	1905	£12.00	—
16	Australian Football—Incidents in Play ...	1906	£3.50	£55.00
74	Australian Footballers—Series A (Full Length) ...	1904	£5.00	—
76	Australian Footballers—Series B ($\frac{1}{2}$ Length) ...	1906	£4.00	—
76	Australian Footballers—Series C ($\frac{1}{2}$ Length) ...	1907	£4.00	—
56	Australian Footballers—Series D (Head/Shoulders)	1908	£3.00	£160.00
140	Australian Footballers—Series D (Head/Shoulders)	1909	£3.00	—
60	Australian Footballers—Series E (Head in Oval)	1910	£3.00	£180.00
60	Australian Footballers—Series F (Head in Rays)	1911	£3.00	—
60	Australian Footballers—Series G (With Pennant)	1912	£2.50	—
60	Australian Footballers—Series H (Head in Star)	1913	£2.00	—
60	Australian Footballers—Series I (Head in Shield)	1914	£2.00	—
56	Australian Footballers—Series J ($\frac{1}{2}-\frac{3}{4}$ Length) ...	1910	£4.00	—
48	Australian Jockeys (Blue Back)	1907	£1.50	£75.00
83	Australian Jockeys (Brown Back)	1908	£2.00	—
56	Australian Racehorses (Horizontal Back)	1906	£1.50	£85.00

ORIGINS

Cards originated in France in the mid 19th Century, as a development from the early tradesmen's cards. These were so popular that they began to be issued by many firms either advertising their own shop, like Bon Marche of Paris, or their products. The idea soon spread to the U.S.A., where shops and commodities issued these cards by the simple method of handing one over the counter to each customer.

One of the commodities so involved was tobacco, and around 1880 someone hit on the idea of printing a picture on the 'stiffener' inserted to protect the cigarettes in their paper pack. The idea took off rapidly, notably by firms such as Duke, and many fine sets of cards were issued in the U.S.A. before 1900.

There is evidence that Allen & Ginter started issuing insert cards in Britain around 1884, but it was not until some ten years after this that Wills started using cards, firstly the pure Advertising series, and shortly afterwards their Soldiers, Ships and Cricketers. Rival manufacturers took up the idea and cartophily was born.

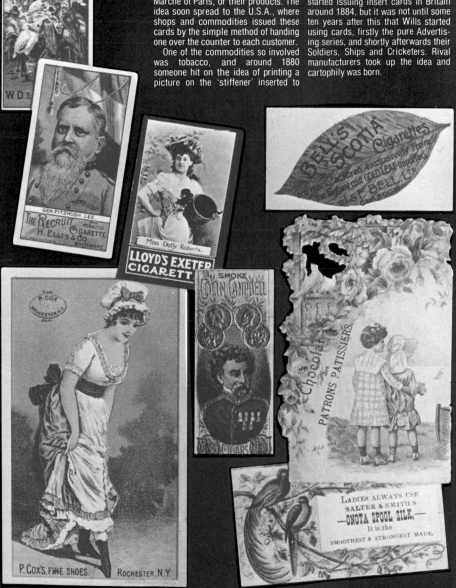

SILKS

In the world of cigarette card collecting silks is the name given to all items woven in, or printed on, fabrics of all sorts, including satin, canvas, blanket and leather.

Many tobacco and a few other trade firms issued silks in the early part of this century. The best known of these are Godfrey Phillips in Britain, mainly with their B.D.V. brand, the American Tobacco Co. in the U.S.A. and the British American Tobacco Co. in the Commonwealth, usually under the names of their subsidiaries such as the I.T.C. (Canada) or United Tobacco Co. (South Africa). Among trade issues the majority were given away with magazines such as Happy Home and My Weekly. Noteworthy however are the series of cabinet size silks given with each Christmas number of 'The Gentlewoman' between 1890 and 1915.

In some cases the subjects on silks are repeats of card issues, such as 'Best Dogs of their Breed', but the majority are new subjects, and cover a very wide range of interests. These include Flags, Regimental Badges and Colours, County Cricket Badges, Famous Queens, Paintings, Red Indians, Great War Leaders, Dogs, Flowers and even Automobile Pennants. Manufacturers encouraged the smokers to use the satin issues to make cushion covers and the like – I.T.C. of Canada issued large centrepieces for this purpose, and Godfrey Phillips even issued a set of CARDS entitled 'Prizes for Needlework'.

Silks are often thought of as a specialised subject, but the general collector should consider some of these as an attractive addition to his album. We can supply an illustrated book listing all known British silks for £3.00 (post paid).

DOROTHY ROSE

H.M.S. GRASSHOPPER
(TORPEDO BOAT DESTROYER)
923 Tons   12,000 H.P.

ENGLAND

Kensitas Cigarettes

BRITISH EMPIRE
RED DRAGON OF WALES

LANARKSHIRE YEOMANRY

Nº 28 G.P. TERRITORIAL BADGES

Le Chapeau de Paille
B.D.V. CIGARETTES

SNIDERS & ABRAHAMS PTY. LTD. (Australia)—cont.

Qty		Date	Odds	Sets
56	Australian Racehorses (Vertical Back)	1907	£1.50	—
40	Australian Racing Scenes	1911	£1.50	£60.00
132	Australian V.C.'s and Officers	1917	£2.50	—
12	Billiard Tricks	1908	£4.00	—
60	Butterflies & Moths (Captions in Capitals) ...	1914	75p	£45.00
60	Butterflies & Moths (Captions in Small Letters)	1914	75p	£45.00
60	Cartoons & Caricatures	1907	£3.00	—
12	Coin Tricks	1908	£3.50	—
64	Crests of British Warships	1915	£2.50	—
40	Cricketers in Action	1906	£15.00	—
12	Cricket Terms	1905	£6.00	£75.00
32	Dickens Series	1909	£2.00	£65.00
16	Dogs	1910	£3.00	£50.00
6	Flags (Shaped Metal)	1915	£1.50	—
6	Flags (Shaped Card)	1915	£1.50	—
60	Great War Leaders & Warships	1915	£1.50	£90.00
30	How to Keep Fit	1907	£3.00	£90.00
60	Jokes	1906	£1.50	£90.00
12	Match Puzzles	1908	£3.50	£42.00
48	Medals & Decorations	1915	£3.00	—
M45	Melbourne Buildings	1914	£4.00	—
25	Natives of the World	1904	£6.00	£150.00
12	Naval Terms	1905	£3.50	£42.00
30	Oscar Asche, Lily Brayton & Lady Smokers ...	1911	£3.00	£100.00
40	Shakespeare Characters	1909	£2.50	£100.00
30	Signalling Series	1916	£3.00	—
?14	Statuary	1905	£4.00	—
60	Street Criers in London, 1707	1914	£4.00	—
32	Views of Victoria in 1857	1906	£4.00	—
FS?200	Views of the World	1908	£1.50	—

SPAULDING & MERRICK (U.S.A.)

B24	Animals	1890	£15.00	—

STAR TOBACCO CO. (India)

?25	Beauties STARA	1898	£30.00	—
52	Beauties (P/C Inset)	1898	£15.00	—
52	Indian Native Types (P/C Inset)	1898	£15.00	—

SURBRUG CO. (U.S.A.)

B10	Aeroplane Series No. 103	1912	£8.00	—
B10	Prize Dog Series No. 102	1911	£8.00	—
M25	Prize Fight Series No. 101	1910	£7.00	—
M25	Prize Fight Series No. 102	1911	£7.00	—

TOBACCO PRODUCTS CORPORATION (Canada & U.S.A.)

?45	Canadian Sports Champions	1917	£4.00	—
60	Do You Know?	1918	£3.00	—
60	Hockey Players	1918	£4.00	—
220	Movie Stars	1915	£1.25	—
120	Movie Stars (Portrait in Oval)	1915	£1.25	—
L?50	Movie Stars	1915	£1.50	—
L?100	Movie Stars, Series No. 3	1916	£1.50	—
?180	Movie Stars, Series No. 4	1916	£1.50	—
L100	Movie Stars, Series No. 5	1916	£1.50	—

TUCKETT LTD. (Canada)

Qty		Date	Odds	Sets
B52	Aeroplane Series	1930	£2.00	£100.00
25	Autograph Series	1913	£17.50	—
?50	Beauties & Scenes	1910	*£2.50*	—
25	Boy Scout Series	1914	*£6.00*	—
7	British Gravures	1923	*£5.00*	—
L7	British Gravures	1923	*£5.00*	—
F100	British Views Plain backs	1912	£1.00	£50.00
F?250	British Views	1912	£1.00	—
F80	British Warships	1914	£3.50	—
F?100	Canadian Scenes	1912	£1.00	—
?50	Card Trick Series	1928	£3.00	—
B52	Tucketts Auction Bridge Series	1930	*£2.50*	—

U.S. TOBACCO CO. (U.S.A.)

X25	Actresses	1890	£25.00	—

UNITED CIGAR STORES (U.S.A.)

L25	The Aviators	1911	£8.00	£200.00

UNITED TOBACCO COMPANIES (SOUTH) LTD. (South Africa)

50	Aeroplanes of Today	1936	60p	£30.00
50	African Fish	1937	70p	£35.00
50	Animals & Birds	1923	£4.00	—
L24	Arms & Crests of Universities & Schools ...	1930	40p	£10.00
FS50	Beauties of Great Britain	1930	50p	—
L52	Boy Scout, Girl Guide & Voortrekker Badges ...	1932	80p	£40.00
B50	British Aeroplanes	1933	80p	£40.00
L20	British Butterflies (Silk)	1924	£5.00	—
L30	British Roses (Silk)	1924	£5.00	—
L62	British Rugby Tour of South Africa	1938	50p	£30.00
X25	Champion Dogs	1934	£1.50	—
50	Children of All Nations	1928	60p	£30.00
50	Cinema Stars (Flag Cigarettes)	1922	80p	—
60	Do You Know?	1930	35p	£21.00
50	Do You Know? 2nd Series	1930	40p	£20.00
50	Do You Know? 3rd Series	1931	40p	£20.00
30	Do You Know? (Different)	1933	40p	£12.00
50	Eminent Film Personalities	1930	80p	—
50	English Period Costumes	1932	60p	£30.00
L50	Exercises for Men & Women	1932	40p	£20.00
96	Fairy Tales	1926	50p	—
25	Famous Figures from South African History ...	1932	£1.00	—
L100	Famous Works of Art	1939	15p	£8.00
L120	Farmyards of South Africa	1934	20p	£24.00
L65	Flags of All Nations (Silk)	1910	£1.50	—
25	Flowers of South Africa	1932	80p	£20.00
FS52	Here There & Everywhere	1930	40p	£20.00
L50	Household Hints	1926	75p	—
B50	Humour in Sport	1929	£1.00	£50.00
25	Interesting Experiments	1930	60p	£15.00
L100	Medals & Decorations of the British Commonwealth of Nations	1941	35p	£35.00

Qty		Date	Odds	Sets
50	Merchant Ships of the World	1925	60p	£30.00
B52	Miniature Playing Cards (Flag)	1938	50p	—
50	Motor Cars	1928	£1.60	£80.00
FS48	Nature Studies	1930	50p	—
M25	Old Masters (Silk)	1926	£4.00	—
L100	Our Land	1938	15p	£8.00
B150	Our South African Birds	1942	16p	£25.00
L150	Our South African Birds	1942	15p	£16.00
B100	Our South African Flora	1940	15p	£8.00
L100	Our South African Flora	1940	15p	£7.50
B100	Our South African National Parks	1941	15p	£8.00
L100	Our South African National Parks	1941	15p	£7.50
L200	Our South Africa—Past & Present	1938	15p	£16.00
L24	Pastel Plates	1930	50p	£12.00
L88	Philosophical Sayings	1938	60p	—
L50	Pictures of South Africa's War Effort	1940	15p	£7.00
FS48	Pictures of the East	1930	30p	£15.00
25	Picturesque People of the Empire	1929	60p	£15.00
L50	Pottery Types (Silk)	1926	£3.00	—
M50	Pottery Types (Silk)	1926	£4.00	—
L50	Racehorses—South Africa (Set 1)	1929	60p	£30.00
L52	Racehorses—South Africa (Set 2)	1930	60p	£30.00
50	Regimental Uniforms	1937	70p	£35.00
50	Riders of the World	1931	70p	£35.00
50	Safety First	1936	40p	£20.00
B40	Ships of All Times	1931	80p	£32.00
25	South African Birds 1st Series	1927	60p	£15.00
25	South African Birds 2nd Series	1927	60p	£15.00
L52	South African Butterflies	1937	35p	£17.50
L52	South African Coats of Arms	1931	30p	£15.00
L17	South African Cricket Touring Team	1929	£7.00	£120.00
B100	South African Defence	1941	15p	£8.00
L52	South African Flora	1935	16p	£8.50
L100	South African Flowers (Silk)	1913	£2.00	—
L50	South African Places of Interest	1934	15p	£7.50
L65	South African Rugby Football Clubs	1933	40p	£26.00
L52	Sports & Pastimes of South Africa	1936	60p	£30.00
L47	Springbok Rugby & Cricket Teams	1931	£1.00	£47.00
FS50	Stereoscopic Photographs, Assorted Subjects	1928	50p	—
FS50	Stereoscopic Photographs of South Africa	1929	50p	—
25	Studdy Dogs (Bonzo)	1925	£2.00	—
B50	Tavern of the Seas	1939	30p	£15.00
50	The Story of Sand	1934	40p	—
50	The World of Tomorrow	1938	40p	£20.00
L40	Views of South African Scenery, 1st Series	1918	£3.00	—
L36	Views of South African Scenery, 2nd Series	1920	£3.00	—
25	Warriors of All Nations (Crossed Swords)	1937	60p	£15.00
25	What's This—Troublesome Things & Their Remedy	1929	80p	£20.00
50	Wild Animals of the World	1932	70p	£35.00
25	Wild Flowers of South Africa 1st Series	1925	60p	£15.00
25	Wild Flowers of South Africa 2nd Series	1926	60p	£15.00
B40	Wonders of the World	1931	60p	£24.00
B100	World Famous Boxers	1939	80p	—

UNIVERSAL TOBACCO CO. (India)

Qty		Date	Odds	Sets
F50	Actresses	1900	£12.50	—

UNIVERSAL TOBACCO CO. (PTY.) LTD. (S. Africa)

835	Flags of All Nations	1935	40p	—

S. W. VENABLE TOBACCO CO. (U.S.A.)

X?56	Actresses	1888	£15.00	—
X8	Baseball Scenes	1888	*£40.00*	—
X?2	Sea Shore Scenes	1888	*£40.00*	—

GEO. F. YOUNG (U.S.A.)

X?76	Actresses	1889	£15.00	—
X8	Baseball Scenes	1888	*£40.00*	—
X10	National Sports—Girls	1887	*£40.00*	—
X?	Photographic Cards	1886	£2.50	—
X2	Seashore Scenes	1888	*£40.00*	—

Part 3

NON-TOBACCO ISSUES

INDEX OF BRANDS (Non-Tobacco)

A-1 DAIRIES LTD. (Tea)

Qty		Date	Odds	Sets
25	Birds and Their Eggs	1965	—	£5.00
25	Butterflies & Moths	1964	—	£1.00
25	The Story of Milk	1967	—	£1.50

A-1 DOLLISDALE TEA

25	Do You Know About Shipping & Trees?	1963	—	£1.00

A. B. C. (Cinemas)

10	Animals	1952	80p	£8.00
10	An Adventure in Space	1950	£1.50	£15.00
10	Birds	1958	—	£4.00
10	Birds & Birdwatching	1953	£1.50	—
10	British Athletes	1955	—	£3.00
20	British Soldiers (Black Back)	1949	15p	—
20	British Soldiers (Brown Back)	1949	12p	£2.50
10	Colorstars 1st	1962	—	£1.50
10	Colorstars 2nd	1962	£1.25	—
10	Colorstars 3rd	1962	60p	—
10	Dogs	1957	—	£6.00
L15	Film Stars	1935	£2.50	—
10	Film Stars	1948	40p	£4.00
10	Horses	1958	—	£4.00
10	Interesting Buildings	1956	—	£3.00
10	Journey by Land	1954	£1.25	—
10	Journey by Water	1954	£1.25	—
10	Journey to the Moon	1955	—	£4.00
10	Parliament Buildings	1957	—	£4.00
10	Railway Engines	1951	£1.75	£17.50
10	Scenes from Films	1953	£1.00	—
10	Sea Exploration	1957	—	£3.50
10	Sea Scenes	1958	—	£3.50
10	Sports on Land	1956	—	£3.50
12	Star Series	1936	£2.50	—
10	Travel of the Future	1956	—	£3.00
10	Water Sports	1956	—	£3.00

A. H. C. (Confectionery)

25	Tropical Birds (Anon.)	1955	—	£1.00
25	Wonders of the Universe	1955	—	£1.00

A. & B. C. GUM
40 Page Illustrated Reference Book—£2.75

M120	All Sports Series	1954	£1.25	£150.00
P17	Banknotes	1971	£1.50	—
X55	Batman (Pink Back, Fan Club Panel)	1966	70p	£38.50
X55	Batman (Numbered Pink Back, no panel)	1966	50p	£27.50
X55	Batman (Numbered on Front)	1966	60p	£33.00
X44	Batman (1A-44A)	1966	50p	£22.00
X44	Batman (1B-44B)	1966	£1.00	£44.00
X38	Batman (Black Back)	1966	60p	£22.50
B1	Batman Secret Decoder	1966	—	£5.00
X38	Batman (Black Back, Dutch)	1966	£1.25	£47.50
X73	Battle Cards	1966	35p	£25.00
X66	Battle of Britain	1970	35p	£22.50
X60	Bazooka Joe and his Gang	1968	£2.25	—

A. & B. C. GUM—cont.

Qty		Date	Odds	Sets
X60	Beatles (Black & White)	1964	£1.25	£75.00
X45	Beatles, 2nd Series	1965	£2.50	—
X40	Beatles (Coloured)	1965	£2.50	—
K120	Car Stamps	1971	£2.00	—
X21	Car Stamps Albums	1971	£4.00	—
X45	Champions	1969	30p	£13.50
LS3	Christian Name Stickers	1967	*£1.25*	—
X15	Civil War Banknotes	1965	£1.50	£22.50
X88	Civil War News	1965	50p	£44.00
X43	Comic Book Foldees	1968	75p	£32.50
P24	Crazy Disguises	1970	£5.00	—
X48	Cricketers	1959	£1.00	£48.00
X48	Cricketers 1961 Test Series 94 x 68mm ...	1961	£1.25	£60.00
X48	Cricketers 1961 Test Series 90 x 64mm ...	1961	£1.40	£70.00
X66	Elvis Presley Series	1956	£3.00	—
X36	Exploits of William Tell	1960	40p	£15.00
22	Famous Indian Chiefs	1968	£1.25	—
X54	Fantastic Twisters	1972	£2.50	—
M48	Film & TV Stars	1953	£1.25	£60.00
M48	Film & TV Stars No. 2 Series (49-96) ...	1953	£1.25	—
M48	Film & TV Stars No. 3 Series (97-144) ...	1953	£1.25	—
X48	Film Stars (Plain Back)	1954	80p	£40.00
X73	Flags (cut-outs)	1971	25p	£18.00
L80	Flags of the World	1960	15p	£12.00
40	Flag Stickers	1966	*£2.50*	—
X80	Flags of the World	1959	12p	£10.00
X46	Footballers (Planet, 1-46)	1958	10p	£5.00
X46	Footballers (without "Planet" 1-46) ...	1964	60p	£27.50
X46	Footballers (Planet 47-92)	1958	£1.25	—
X46	Footballers (without "Planet" 47-92) ...	1964	£1.00	—
X49	Footballers (Football Quiz, 1-49)	1959	80p	£40.00
X49	Footballers (Football Quiz, 50-98) ...	1959	£1.25	—
X42	Footballers (Black Back, 1-42)	1960	50p	£20.00
X42	Footballers (Black Back, 43-84)	1960	75p	£30.00
XF64	Footballers (Plain Back)	1961	75p	£48.00
XF44	Footballers (Plain Back, Scottish)	1961	£2.50	—
X82	Footballers (Bazooka)	1962	£1.25	—
X55	Footballers (Make-A-Photo, 1-55)	1963	£1.00	—
X55	Footballers (Make-A-Photo, 56-110) ...	1963	£1.00	—
X81	Footballers (Make-A-Photo, Scottish) ...	1963	*£2.50*	—
X58	Footballers (Quiz, 1-58)	1964	75p	£45.00
X45	Footballers (Quiz, 59-103)	1964	£1.50	—
X46	Footballers (Quiz, 104-149)	1964	£2.50	—
X81	Footballers (Quiz, Scottish)	1964	£2.50	—
X55	Footballers (In Pairs, 1-110)	1966	75p	—
X55	Footballers (In Pairs, 111-220)	1966	£1.00p	—
X55	Footballers (In Pairs, Scottish) ...	1966	£1.50	—
X55	Footballers (Star Players)	1967	15p	£8.00
P12	Footballers	1967	£2.00	£24.00
X54	Footballers (Yellow, 1-54)	1968	60p	—
X47	Footballers (Yellow, 55-101)	1968	60p	£30.00
M20	Football Emblems	1968	£2.00	—
E26	Football Team Pennants	1968	£2.50	—
X65	Footballers (Football Facts, 1-64)	1969	40p	£26.00

Qty		Date	Odds	Sets
X54	Footballers (Football Facts, 65-117)	1969	30p	£15.00
X55	Footballers (Football Facts, 117-170)	1969	30p	£15.00
MF36	Footballers	1969	75p	—
X42	Footballers (Football Facts, Scottish, 1-41)	1969	£1.50	—
X35	Footballers (Football Facts, Scottish, 42-75)	1969	£2.50	—
MF15	Footballers (Scottish)	1969	£2.00	—
X84	Footballers (Orange Back, 1-84)	1970	10p	£7.00
X85	Footballers (Orange Back, 85-169)	1970	10p	£5.00
X86	Footballers (Orange Back, 170-255)	1970	25p	£20.00
72	Football Colour Transparencies	1970	£1.00	—
P14	Footballers, Pin-ups	1970	£1.25	£17.50
X85	Footballers (Green Back, Scottish, 1-85)	1970	50p	—
X86	Footballers (Green Back, Scottish, 86-171)	1970	50p	—
P28	Footballers, Pin-ups (Scottish)	1970	£2.00	—
X109	Footballers (Did You Know, 1-109)	1971	15p	£15.00
X110	Footballers (Did You Know, 110-219)	1971	15p	£16.50
X71	Footballers (Did You Know, 220-290)	1971	25p	£18.00
X73	Footballers (Did You Know, Scottish, 1-73)	1971	10p	£4.00
X71	Footballers (Did You Know, Scottish, 74-144)	1971	75p	—
23	Football Club Crests	1971	£1.00	—
16	Football Club Crests (Scottish)	1971	50p	£8.00
X109	Footballers (Orange/Red, 1-109)	1972	10p	£7.50
X110	Footballers (Orange/Red, 110-219)	1972	10p	£8.50
B22	Football Card Game	1972	25p	£5.50
M23	Footballers, Superstars	1972	£1.00	—
X89	Footballers (Rub Coin, Scottish, 1-89)	1972	60p	—
X89	Footballers (Orange/Red, Scottish, 90-179)	1972	80p	—
M32	Footballers (Autographed Photos)	1973	60p	£18.00
X131	Footballers (Blue Back, 1-131)	1973	10p	£13.00
X130	Footballers (Blue Back, 132-263)	1973	25p	—
X90	Footballers (Red Back, Scottish, 1-90)	1973	75p	—
X88	Footballers (Red Back, Scottish, 91-178)	1973	75p	—
E16	Football Giant Team Posters	1973	£1.50	—
X132	Footballers (Red Back, Rub Coin)	1974	10p	£13.00
X132	Footballers (Green Back, Scottish, Rub Coin)	1974	30p	£40.00
X40	Fotostars	1961	50p	£20.00
X66	Funny Greetings	1961	50p	£33.00
X66	Funny Valentines	1961	60p	£40.00
X36	Golden Boys (Matt)	1958	50p	£18.00
XF40	Golden Boys (Glossy)	1958	£1.00	—
L27	Grand Prix	1970	16p	£5.00
D200	Hip Patches	1968	£1.00	—
X55	Huck Finn	1968	20p	£11.00
X60	Kung Fu	1974	30p	£18.00
X55	Land of the Giants	1969	60p	£33.00
X55	Lotsa Laffs	1970	25p	£14.00
X84	Love Initials	1970	£1.25	—
X36	Magic	1967	30p	£11.00
L1	Magic Circle Club Application	1969	—	£3.50
X74	Man on the Moon	1969	40p	£30.00
X52	Mickey Takers	1970	£1.50	—
B24	Military Emblem Stickers	1966	£2.00	—
X55	Monkees (Black & White)	1967	40p	£22.00
X55	Monkees (Coloured)	1967	40p	£22.00

A. & B. C. GUM—cont.

Qty		Date	Odds	Sets
X30	Monkees Hit Songs	1967	50p	£15.00
X49	Nutty Initial Stickers	1968	£1.50	—
E16	Olympic Posters	1972	£2.00	—
X36	Olympics	1972	£1.00	£36.00
X55	Partridge Family	1972	20p	£11.00
X120	Planes	1960	30p	£36.00
X44	Planet of the Apes	1968	40p	£17.50
X33	Put-on Stickers	1969	£1.50	—
X48	Railway Quiz	1958	35p	£17.50
X72	Railway Quiz	1959	75p	£48.00
M24	Royal Portraits	1953	£1.50	£36.00
M34	Silly Stickers	1966	£1.50	—
X25	Sir Francis Drake	1961	80p	£20.00
X88	Space Cards	1958	50p	£44.00
X44	Stacks of Stickers	1971	£1.25	£55.00
X55	Star Trek	1969	£1.75	—
X66	Superman in the Jungle	1968	60p	£40.00
X16	Superman in the Jungle (Jig-saw)	1968	£1.25	£20.00
X25	The Girl from UNCLE	1965	60p	£15.00
X36	The High Chaparral	1969	40p	£15.00
X54	The Legend of Custer	1968	50p	£27.00
X55	The Man from UNCLE	1965	50p	£27.50
X40	The Rolling Stones	1965	£2.50	—
X50	Top Stars	1964	£1.00	£50.00
X40	Top Stars (different)	1964	£1.00	£40.00
X56	TV Westerns	1959	60p	£33.00
X44	Ugly Stickers	1967	£1.00	£44.00
P88	Wacky Plaks	1962	£1.00	£88.00
E16	Wanted Posters	1968	£3.00	—
X70	Who–Z–At Star?	1958	60p	£42.00
X55	Winston Churchill Cards	1965	12p	£6.50
X37	World Cup Footballers	1970	80p	£30.00
30	World Cup Football Stickers	1966	£2.00	—
E16	World Cup Posters	1966	£2.00	—
X66	You'll Die Laughing (Creature Feature)	1974	12p	£8.00
X48	You'll Die Laughing (Purple back)	1967	20p	—

ABBEY GRANGE HOTEL

15	Fighting Vessels	1986	—	£2.00

P. A. ADOLPH ("Subbuteo")

24	Famous Footballers 1st	1954	—	£3.00
24	Famous Footballers 2nd	1954	—	£3.00

A. W. ALLEN LTD. (Confectionery, Australia)

32	Bradman's Records	1931	£10.00	—
72	Butterflies & Moths	1920	75p	—
36	Cricketers (Brown front)	1932	£5.00	£180.00
36	Cricketers (Brown front, different)	1933	£6.00	—
36	Cricketers (Flesh tinted, frame back)	1934	£4.00	£150.00
36	Cricketers (Flesh tinted, no frame)	1936	£4.00	£150.00
36	Cricketers (coloured)	1938	£3.50	£125.00
M24	Fliers	1926	£3.00	—
144	Footballers (striped colours)	1933	75p	—

A. W. ALLEN LTD. (Confectionery, Australia)—cont.

Qty		Date	Odds	Sets
72	Footballers (pennants)	1934	75p	—
49	Kings & Queens of England	1937	75p	£37.50
36	Medals	1938	75p	—
36	Soldiers of the Empire	1938	75p	—
36	Sports & Flags of Nations	1936	£1.00	£36.00
M24	Wrestlers	1926	£2.50	£60.00

ALMA CONFECTIONERY

48	James Bond 007 Moonraker	1980	60p	£30.00

JAMES ALMOND (Confectionery)

25	Sports and Pastimes	1925	£5.00	—

AMALGAMATED PRESS LTD.

24	Aeroplanes (Plain Back)	1933	£1.50	—
32	Aeroplanes & Carriers	1932	£1.50	—
M32	Australian & English Cricket Stars	1932	£4.00	£125.00
M12	Catchy Tricks & Teasers	1933	£1.00	£12.00
M16	England's Test Match Cricketers	1928	£4.00	£64.00
M22	English League (Div. 1) Footer Captains	1926	£1.00	£22.00
M16	Exploits of the Great War	1929	75p	£12.00
16	Famous Aircraft	1927	£1.50	£24.00
M16	Famous Australian Cricketers	1929	£4.00	£64.00
16	Famous Film Stars	1927	£2.50	£40.00
M24	Famous Footer Internationals	1926	£1.00	£24.00
M22	Famous Shipping Lines	1926	£2.00	£45.00
M32	Famous Test Match Cricketers	1926	£2.00	£65.00
24	Famous Trains & Engines	1932	£1.25	£30.00
16	Fighting Planes of the World	1934	£1.50	—
32	Football Fame Series	1936	£1.00	£32.00
M16	Great War Deeds	1927	75p	£12.00
M32	Great War Deeds (Different)	1928	75p	£24.00
M16	Heroic Deeds of the Great War	1927	75p	£12.00
32	Makes of Motor Cars & Index Marks	1923	80p	£25.00
32	Mechanical Wonders of 1935	1935	£1.50	—
32	Modern Motor Cars	1926	£2.50	—
24	Motors (Plain Back)	1933	£1.50	—
24	Ships of the World (Champion)	1924	£1.25	£30.00
33	Ships of the World (Different, Anonymous) ...	1935	£1.50	—
BF66	Sportsmen	1922	25p	£16.50
32	Sportsmen of the World	1934	60p	£20.00
M12	Sports Queeriosities	1933	£1.50	£18.00
M24	The Great War 1914-1918	1928	75p	£18.00
M16	The Great War 1914-1918 New Series	1929	75p	£12.00
M16	The R.A.F. at War (Plain Back)	1940	£2.00	—
M32	Thrilling Scenes from the Great War	1927	75p	£24.00
M16	Thrills of the Dirt Track	1929	£2.00	£32.00
M16	Tip Top Tricks and Teasers	1927	£1.25	£20.00
M14	V.C.'s & Their Deeds of Valour (Plain Back) ...	1928	£2.00	—
M24	Wonderful London	1926	£2.00	£48.00

AMARAN TEA

25	Coins of the World	1964	—	£2.00
25	Dogs' Heads	1965	—	£1.00
25	Do You Know?	1969	—	£1.50

AMARAN TEA—cont.

Qty		Date	Odds	Sets
25	Flags & Emblems	1964	—	£2.00
25	Naval Battles	1971	—	£3.00
25	Old England	1969	—	£1.25
25	Science in the 20th Century	1966	—	£1.25
25	The Circus	1966	—	£1.50
25	Veteran Racing Cars	1965	—	£3.50

AMPOL (Oil, Australia)

M32	Cars of To-day	1958	—	£6.00

THE ANGLERS MAIL (Periodical)

E3	Terminal Tackle Tips	1976	—	£1.25

ANGLO-AMERICAN CHEWING GUM LTD.

L36	Kidnapped (Thriller Chewing Gum)	1935	£1.50	—
X66	The Horse	1966	—	£5.00
40	Underwater Adventure	1966	—	£2.00
50	Zoo Stamps of the World	1966	30p	£15.00

ANGLO CONFECTIONERY LTD.

X66	Captain Scarlet & The Mysterons	1968	£1.25	£80.00
L12	Football Hints (Folders)	1970	35p	£4.25
X84	Football Quiz	1969	35p	£30.00
X66	Joe 90	1968	£1.00	£66.00
L66	National Team Colours	1970	£1.50	£100.00
X84	Railway Trains & Crests	1974	40p	£35.00
X66	Space	1967	25p	£16.50
X66	Tarzan	1967	12p	£8.00
X66	The Beatles—Yellow Submarine	1968	£2.00	£130.00
X66	The Horse	1966	50p	—
X56	The New James Bond	1970	£1.50	—
X64	U.F.O.	1971	30p	£20.00
M24	Vintage Cars Series	1970	£2.00	£48.00
X78	Walt Disney Characters	1971	£1.25	£100.00
X66	Wild West	1970	30p	£20.00
X48	World Cup 1970	1970	65p	£32.00

ANONYMOUS

K24	Animal Jungle Game	1965	—	£2.50
50	Animals of the World	1954	—	£1.75
50	Aquarium Fish	1957	—	£2.00
25	Aquarium Fish (Plain backs)	1961	—	£1.00
25	Aviary and Cage Birds	1960	—	£1.50
25	Bandsmen of the British Army	1960	—	£3.00
25	Bridges of the World	1958	—	£1.00
25	British Uniforms of the 19th Century	1957	—	£1.00
20	Budgerigars	1960	16p	£3.25
25	Cacti	1961	—	£1.00
25	Careless Moments	1922	—	£5.00
25	Castles of Britain	1962	—	£1.25
25	Children of All Nations	1958	—	£1.00
25	Dogs	1958	—	£1.50
25	Do You Know	1963	—	£1.00
25	Evolution of the Royal Navy	1957	—	£1.00
25	Family Pets	1964	—	£1.50

ANONYMOUS—cont.

Qty		Date	Odds	Sets
25	Flags & Emblems	1961	—	£1.25
25	Flowers	1971	—	£1.75
25	Football Clubs & Badges	1962	—	£1.00
25	Jockeys and Owners Colours	1963	—	£3.00
50	Mars Adventure	1958	—	£15.00
25	Medals of the World	1959	—	£1.00
100	Miscellaneous Subjects (Gum)	1965	—	£5.00
25	Modern Aircraft	1958	—	£1.00
X12	Motor Cycles (Collectors Series)	1987	—	£2.00
25	Musical Instruments	1971	—	£1.25
25	Pigeons	1971	—	£2.50
25	Pond Life	1963	—	£1.00
M24	R.A.F. Badges	1985	—	£2.50
1	Soldier Bugler	1965	—	£1.00
25	Sports of the Countries	1967	—	£2.00
25	The Circus	1966	—	£1.50
25	The Wild West	1960	—	£1.25
1	Venice in London	1965	—	15p

BELGIAN ISSUES
X100	Famous Men	1938	—	£6.00

U.S. ISSUES
X30	Aeroplanes & Insignia	1945	—	£10.00
M48	America at War (101-148)	1942	—	£30.00
M48	America at War (501-548)	1943	—	£40.00
M48	America at War (601-648)	1943	—	£40.00
10	Boxers "A"	1926	—	£7.50
10	Boxers "B"	1926	—	£7.50
10	Boxers "C"	1926	—	£7.50
10	Boy Scouts	1926	—	£7.50
M48	Disney Characters	1942	£1.25	£60.00
10	Film Stars "A"	1926	—	£6.00
10	Film Stars "B"	1926	—	£6.00
10	Film Stars "C"	1926	—	£6.00
M60	Pinocchio (Bread Issue)	1950	—	£7.50
10	Presidents "A"	1926	—	£6.00
10	Presidents "B"	1926	—	£6.00
10	Western Pioneers	1926	—	£7.50

SPANISH ISSUES
X32	Footballers (P/C Backs)	1930	50p	£16.00

APLIN & BARRETT (Cheese)
X25	Whipsnade	1937	50p	£12.50

ARBUCKLE COFFEE CO. (U.S.A.)
P50	Animals	1890	£3.00	£150.00
P50	Cooking Subjects	1890	£3.00	—
P100	General Subjects (Unnumbered)	1890	£4.00	—
P50	General Subjects (51-100)	1890	£3.50	—
P50	History of Sports & Pastimes of the World ...	1893	£3.00	£150.00
P50	History of United States & Territories ...	1890	£2.50	£125.00
P50	Illustrated Atlas of U.S.	1890	£2.50	£125.00
P50	Illustrated Jokes	1890	£3.50	—
P50	Principal Nations of the World	1890	£2.50	£125.00
P50	Views from a Trip around the World	1890	£2.50	£125.00

ARDMONA (Tinned Fruit, Australia)

Qty		Date	Odds	Sets
X50	International Cricket Series III	1980	—	£6.00

ARMITAGE BROS. LTD. (Pet Foods)

25	Animals of the Countryside	1964	—	£1.00
25	Country Life	1968	—	£1.00

ARROW CONFECTIONERY Co.

12	Conundrums	1904	£20.00	—
12	Shadowgraphs	1904	£20.00	—

ASKEY'S (Biscuits)

25	People & Places	1971	—	£2.00
25	Then & Now	1971	—	£2.00

AUSTIN MOTOR CO. LTD.

M13	Famous Austin Cars	1953	£2.00	—

AUSTRALIAN DAIRY CORPORATION

X63	Kanga Cards (Cricket)	1985	—	£6.00
X50	Super Cricket Card Series 1982-3	1983	—	£6.00
X50	Super Cricket Card Series 1983-4	1984	—	£6.00

AUSTRALIAN LICORICE PTY LTD. (Australia)

?27	Australian Cricketers	1930	£5.00	—
24	Australian Cricketers	1931	£5.00	£120.00
24	English Cricketers (Blue Back)	1928	£5.00	£120.00
24	English Cricketers (Brown Back)	1930	£5.00	—
18	English Cricketers ("18 in set")	1932	£5.00	—
12	South African Cricketers	1931	£5.00	£60.00

AUTOBRITE (Car Polish)

25	Vintage Cars	1965	—	£3.00

AUTOMATIC MACHINE CO.

25	Modern Aircraft	1958	—	£2.00

AUTOMATIC MERCHANDISING CO.

X25	Adventure Twins & The Treasure Ship	1958	—	£10.00

AVON RUBBER CO. LTD.

30	Leading Riders of 1963	1963	—	£15.00

B.B.B. PIPES

25	Pipe History	1926	£3.50	—

B.T. LTD. (Tea)

25	Aircraft	1961	—	£3.00
25	British Locomotives	1961	—	£4.00
25	Do You Know	1967	—	£3.50
25	Holiday Resorts	1963	—	£1.00
25	Modern Motor Cars	1962	—	£6.00
25	Occupations	1962	—	£3.50
25	Pirates & Buccaneers	1961	—	£3.50
25	The West	1964	—	£2.00

BADSHAH TEA CO.

25	British Cavalry Uniforms of the 19th Century ...	1963	—	£4.00
25	Butterflies & Moths	1971	—	£1.00

BADSHAH TEA CO.—cont.

Qty		Date	Odds	Sets
25	Fish & Bait	1971	—	£1.00
25	Fruits of Trees & Shrubs	1965	—	*£2.00*
25	Garden Flowers	1963	—	£3.00
25	Naval Battles	1971	—	£3.00
25	People & Places	1970	—	£1.00
25	Regimental Uniforms of the Past	1971	—	£1.50
25	Romance of the Heavens	1968	—	£15.00
25	Wonders of the World (Series of 50)	1970	—	£1.25

BAILEY'S (Toffee)

25	War Series (Ships)	1916	£7.50	—

J. BAINES (Commerical)

L200	Football Cards (Shaped)	1897	£3.50	—

BAKE-A-CAKE LTD.

56	Motor Cars	1952	£1.75	£100.00

BARBERS TEA LTD.

1	Advertising Card – Cinema & Television Stars ...	1955	—	50p
1	Advertising Card—Dogs	1956	—	25p
1	Advertising Card—Railway Equipment	1958	—	60p
25	Aeroplanes	1956	—	£3.50
24	Cinema & Television Stars	1955	—	£7.50
24	Dogs	1961	—	£1.25
5	Ferry to Hong Kong	1957	£3.50	—
25	Locomotives	1956	—	£7.50
24	Railway Equipment	1958	—	£4.00

JOHN O. BARKER (IRELAND) LTD. (Gum)

X24	Circus Scenes	1970	—	£7.50
X24	Famous People	1970	—	£7.50
25	The Wild West	1970	*£1.50*	—

BARRATT & CO. LTD. (Confectionery)

M30	Aircraft (Varnished)	1941	£1.50	—
M30	Aircraft (Unvarnished)	1943	£2.00	—
25	Animals in the Service of Man	1964	—	£1.00
16	Australian Cricketers, Action Series	1926	£6.00	£100.00
15	Australian Test Players	1930	£8.00	—
25	Birds	1960	—	£3.00
50	Botany Quest	1966	£1.00	£50.00
25	British Butterflies	1965	£1.40	£35.00
25	Butterflies & Moths	1969	—	£1.00
25	Cage & Aviary Birds	1960	—	£3.00
50	Captain Scarlet & The Mysterons	1967	—	£15.00
50	Cars of the World	1965	80p	£40.00
B122	Characters from Film Cartoons	1940	£3.00	—
4	Coronation & Jubilee Medallions	1902	£15.00	—
25	Coronation, 1911	1911	£10.00	—
20	Cricket Team Folders	1933	£7.00	—
?260	Cricketers, Footballers & Football Teams ...	1925	£4.00	—
L60	Disneyland "True Life"	1956	50p	£30.00
L50	F.A. Cup Winners	1935	£3.50	—
25	Fairy Stories	1926	£1.20	£30.00
12	Famous British Constructions, Aircraft Series ...	1925	£12.50	—

BARRATT & CO. LTD. (Confectionery)—cont.

Qty		Date	Odds	Sets
B?240	Famous Cricketers (Various Series)	1936	£5.00	—
35	Famous Film Stars	1961	75p	£26.00
B248	Famous Footballers (Various Series)	1936	£1.75	—
B79	Famous Footballers (Non-Descriptive)	1947	£1.75	—
B50	Famous Footballers, New Series	1950	£1.50	—
B50	Famous Footballers, New Series (Different)	1952	£1.50	—
B50	Famous Footballers Series A1	1953	£1.20	£60.00
B50	Famous Footballers Series A2	1954	£1.20	£60.00
B50	Famous Footballers Series A3	1955	£1.20	—
60	Famous Footballers Series A4	1956	80p	£48.00
60	Famous Footballers Series A5	1957	80p	£48.00
60	Famous Footballers Series A6	1958	80p	£48.00
60	Famous Footballers Series A7	1959	80p	£48.00
50	Famous Footballers Series A8	1960	80p	£40.00
50	Famous Footballers Series A9	1961	80p	£40.00
50	Famous Footballers Series A10	1962	40p	£20.00
50	Famous Footballers Series A11	1963	80p	£40.00
50	Famous Footballers Series A12	1964	80p	£40.00
50	Famous Footballers Series A13	1965	80p	£40.00
50	Famous Footballers Series A14	1966	75p	£37.50
50	Famous Footballers Series A15	1967	—	£3.00
32/50	Famous Sportsmen	1971	—	£2.00
B45	Fastest on Earth	1953	70p	£30.00
32	Felix Pictures	1930	£12.50	—
25	Fish & Bait	1962	—	£3.00
12	Football Action Caricatures	1928	£5.00	—
100	Football Stars	1930	£5.00	—
50	Football Stars	1974	*£1.00*	—
?69	Football Team Folders	1933	£3.50	—
B66	Football Teams—1st Division	1930	£3.50	—
48	Giants in Sport	1959	£1.25	£60.00
C12	Gold Rush (packets)	1960	£3.00	—
25	Headdresses of the World	1962	—	£3.50
25	Historical Buildings	1960	—	£2.00
48	History of the Air	1959	60p	£30.00
32	History of the Air	1959	£1.50	—
25	History of the Air	1960	—	£4.00
25	Interpol	1964	£1.60	£40.00
50	Leaders of Sport	1927	£3.50	—
35	Magic Roundabout	1968	—	£2.50
25	Merchant Ships of the World (Black Back)	1962	—	£5.00
25	Merchant Ships of the World (Blue Back)	1962	—	£2.00
L40	Modern Aircraft	1957	75p	£30.00
B45	Modern British Aircraft	1959	£1.25	—
13	National Flags	1914	£12.50	—
64	Natural History (Plain Back)	1940	£2.50	—
B24	Naval Ships (Plain Back)	1939	£4.00	—
B6	Our King & Queen (Plain Back)	1940	£5.00	—
25	People & Places	1965	—	£1.00
25	Pirates & Buccaneers	1960	—	£1.50
P25	Pop Stars	1980	—	£5.00
12	Prominent London Buildings	1912	£10.00	—
30	Robin Hood	1961	80p	£24.00
36	Sailing into Space	1959	£1.25	—

STORAGE

The main problem regarding the storage of cigarette cards lies in the effort to strike a balance between being able to maintain them in as good condition as possible and yet being able to examine them. If the reader is simply an investor there is no problem – he can wrap each set carefully in paper, put it into a box, and thence into a bank vault. But the only way to **enjoy** cigarette cards is to look at them. The modern method is to house cards in transparent pages, which can accommodate most sizes of cards and can be stored in loose leaf binders. The entire card may be viewed, both back and front, yet will not deteriorate through sticky fingers or spilt coffee. Care should be taken to use a page made from a suitable material – there are on the market now many apparently cheap pages which contain large amounts of plasticiser, a substance which could adversely affect certain cards. Full details of our own Nostalgia and Hendon albums are given on pages 16 and 148 of this book.

Another method of storage which is becoming more popular is to mount cards in frames, which can then be hung on a suitable wall. Several framing systems are now available which hold the cards in position without harming them, and enable the backs to be examined, as well as accommodating complete sets of 50 cards.

TRADE CARDS

Although the hobby of cartophily is more popularly known as cigarette card collecting, and tobacco cards tend to be regarded as the elite, there has recently been a noticeable increase in the interest in other trade cards – or simply 'trade cards'. One of the reasons is that since the War it has been mainly the issue of trade cards that has kept the encyclopaedia of cartophily updated, while more important is the realisation that there are many attractive cards produced by manufacturers such as Brooke Bond, Barratt, Cadbury and Church & Dwight.

Apart from the more obvious confectionery and periodical issues it is amazing how much variety there is among the issuers. Many are associated with groceries and household goods, such as the tea, coffee, jam and margarine issues, as well as bleach, toothpaste, hairgrips and even toilet rolls. Cards can also be found issued with Blakey's Boot Protectors, Carter's Little Liver Pills and Singer Sewing Machines. One series of War Portraits was issued by over 40 different firms, some of them tobacco, but also including cinemas, a draper, and Dr. Bow-er-man's Dental Surgery.

BARRATT & CO. LTD. (Confectionery)—cont.

Qty		Date	Odds	Sets
50	Soccer Stars	1973	60p	£30.00
50	Soldiers of the World	1966	—	£5.00
16	South African Cricketers	1929	£7.50	—
25	Space Mysteries	1965	—	£2.50
L20	Speed Series	1930	£4.00	—
50	Tarzan	1967	—	£6.00
35	Test Cricketers Series A	1956	£2.00	£70.00
48	Test Cricketers Series B	1957	£3.50	—
50	The Secret Service	1970	—	£10.00
24	The Wild West	1961	—	£2.00
25	The Wild West (Different)	1963	—	£2.00
50	The Wild Wild West	1969	—	£20.00
25	The Young Adventurer	1965	£1.50	£37.50
50	Thunderbirds	1967	£1.25	£62.50
50	Thunderbirds 2nd Series	1968	50p	£25.00
50	Tom & Jerry	1970	—	£4.00
50	Trains	1970	—	£4.00
50	Trains of the World	1964	—	£6.00
35	T /'s Huckleberry Hound & Friends	1961	£1.00	£35.00
35	TV's Sea Hunt	1961	£1.25	£45.00
35	TV's Yogi Bear	1969	£1.20	£42.00
35	TV's Yogi Bear & Friends	1971		£1.00
70	U.F.O.	1971	—	£12.50
1	Victory V Sign	1940	—	£5.00
B35	Walt Disney Characters	1956	80p	£28.00
50	Walt Disney Characters, 2nd Series	1957	80p	£40.00
36	Walt Disney's Robin Hood	1957	80p	£28.00
35	Walt Disney's True Life	1962	80p	£28.00
25	Warriors Through the Ages	1962	—	£2.50
25	What Do You Know?	1964	—	£1.00
X72	Wild Life	1972	30p	£22.00
M50	Wild Animals by George Cansdale	1954	80p	£40.00
36	Wild West Series No. 1	1959	£1.00	£36.00
25	Willum	1961	£3.00	£75.00
50	Wisecracks	1970	—	£1.75
50	Wisecracks 2nd Series	1970	—	£4.00
50	Wisecracks 3rd Series	1971	—	£5.00
50	Wonders of the World	1962	—	£1.75
25	World Locomotives	1961	—	£5.00
50	Wunders Der Welt	1968	—	£2.50
50	Zoo Pets	1964	80p	£40.00

GEO. BASSETT & CO. LTD. (Confectionery)

Qty		Date	Odds	Sets
25	Motor Cars—Vintage & Modern	1968	—	£2.50
25	Nursery Rhymes	1966	—	£1.25
25	Popular Dogs	1967	—	£1.50
25	Victoria Cross Heroes in Action	1970	—	£1.75

BARRATT DIVISION

Qty		Date	Odds	Sets
50	Age of the Dinosaurs	1979	20p	—
40	Ali-Cat Magicards	1978	20p	—
50	Asterix in Europe	1977	10p	£2.00
50	Athletes of the World	1980	10p	£4.00
48	Bananaman	1986	10p	£2.50

GEO. BASSETT & CO. LTD. (Confectionery)—cont.

Qty		Date	Odds	Sets
M20	Battle (Packets)	1985	50p	£10.00
50	Cricket	1978	£1.50	—
50	Cricket, 2nd Series	1979	£1.00	£50.00
50	Disney—Health & Safety	1977	—	£2.00
50	Football Action	1977	35p	—
50	Football Action	1978	35p	—
50	Football 1978-79	1979	30p	£15.00
50	Football 1979-80	1980	10p	£4.00
50	Football 1980-81	1981	—	£4.00
50	Football 1981-82	1982	10p	£5.00
50	Football 1982-83	1983	15p	—
50	Football 1983-84	1984	10p	£2.50
50	Football 1984-85	1985	10p	£2.50
48	Football 1986-87	1986	10p	£4.00
50	Football Stars	1974	—	£5.00
50	Football Stars—1975-6	1975	30p	—
48	Hanna Barbera's Cartoon Capers	1984	10p	—
24	Holograms	1986	15p	£6.00
50	House of Horror	1982	20p	£10.00
40	Knight Rider	1987	10p	£5.00
50	Living Creatures of Our World	1979	10p	£4.00
50	Play Cricket	1980	12p	£6.00
25	Pop Stars	1974	—	£1.00
35	Secret Island 1st Series	1976	20p	—
40	Secret Island 2nd Series	1976	—	£1.50
M20	Sky Fighters (Packets)	1986	—	£6.00
50	Space 1999	1976	10p	£5.00
50	Super Heroes	1984	—	£5.00
50	Survival on Star Colony 9	1979	10p	£2.50
40	Swim and Survive	1983	10p	£4.00
B20	The A Team	1986	—	£6.00
50	The Conquest of Space	1980	20p	—
50	Tom & Jerry	1974	30p	—
70	U.F.O.	1974	—	£2.00
50	World Cup Stars	1974	—	£1.75
50	World of the Vorgans	1978	20p	—
50	World Record Breakers	1983	—	£10.00
49/50	Yogi's Gang	1976	—	£3.00

BATTLEAXE TOFFEE

24	British and Empire Uniforms	1915	£15.00	—

BATTLE PICTURE WEEKLY

80	Weapons of World War II	1975	—	£12.50

BAYTCH BROS. (Commercial)

64	Fighting Favourites	1951	£2.00	—

BEANO LTD. (Gum)

1	Bang-o-Spacesuit Coupon	1950	—	25p
25	Fascinating Hobbies	1950	—	*£15.00*
50	Modern Aircraft (Beano)	1951	—	£12.50
50	Modern Aircraft (British Educational)	1951	—	£2.00
50	Ships of the Royal Navy	1955	—	£2.50
50	The Conquest of Space	1956	—	£2.00

BEANO LTD. (Gum)—cont.

Qty		Date	Odds	Sets
50	This Age of Speed No. 1 (Aeroplanes)	1954	—	£5.00
50	This Age of Speed No. 2 (Buses & Trams)	1954	—	£10.00
50	Wonders of Modern Transport (Aircraft)	1955	—	£15.00
25	Wonders of the Universe (Foto Gum)	1960	—	£1.00

S. N. BEATTIE & CO. (Commercial)

24	Safety Signs	1955	£1.00	£24.00

J. J. BEAULAH (Canned Goods)

1	Boston Stump	1953	—	25p
25	Coronation Series	1953	—	£20.00
24	Marvels of the World	1954	—	£1.00
24	Modern British Aircraft	1953	—	£1.50

THE BEEHIVE STORES

25	British Uniforms of the 19th Century	1959	—	£7.00

BELLS SCOTCH WHISKY

?41	Other Famous Bells (Shaped)	1975	25p	£10.00

J. BELLAMY & SONS LTD. (Confectionery)

25	Vintage & Modern Trains of the World	1975	—	£3.00

VAN DEN BERGHS LTD. (Margarine etc.)

60	Countryside Cards	1975	35p	—
L24	Pirates	1965	£1.25	£30.00
M12	Recipes From Round the World	1958	80p	—
M12	Regional Recipes	1958	80p	—
L24	This Modern World	1965	£1.00	£24.00

DE BEUKELAER (Biscuits)

KF100	All Sports	1932	15p	£12.50
KF1000	Film Stars (1-1000)	1932	35p	—
KF100	Film Stars (1001-1100)	1937	40p	—
KF100	Film Stars (B1-100)	1935	35p	—
132	Film Stars (Gold Background)	1939	20p	£26.00
K160	Film Stars (Gold background)	1936	60p	—
M100	Pinocchio Series	1940	40p	—
M60	Sixty Glorious Years	1940	75p	—
M100	Snow White Series	1940	30p	£30.00

J. BIBBY & SONS LTD. (Cooking Fat)

L25	Don't You Believe It	1955	60p	£15.00
L25	Good Dogs	1955	£1.60	£40.00
L25	How What and Why	1955	60p	£15.00
L25	Isn't it Strange	1955	60p	£15.00
L25	They Gave it a Name	1955	£1.60	£40.00
L25	This Wonderful World	1955	80p	£20.00

ALFRED BIRD & SONS (Custard)

K48	Happy Families	1938	50p	£24.00

BIRDSEYE FROZEN FOODS

T12	England's Football Team	1980	—	£12.00

BIRKUM (Cheese, Denmark)

Qty		Date	Odds	Sets
25	Motor Cars	1956	—	£7.00

BISHOPS STORTFORD DAIRY FARMERS (Tea)

25	Dogs' Heads	1967	—	£2.50
25	Freshwater Fish	1964	—	*£5.00*
25	Historical Buildings	1964	—	£3.00
25	History of Aviation	1964	—	£5.00
25	Passenger Liners	1965	—	£1.50
25	Pond Life	1966	—	£1.00
25	Science in the 20th Century	1966	—	£1.00
25	The Story of Milk	1966	—	£1.50

BLAKEY BOOT PROTECTORS

72	War Series	1916	£3.50	—

BLUE BAND SERIES (Stamps)

24	History of London's Transport	1954	—	£4.00
24	History of London's Transport 2nd Series	1955	£1.25	£30.00
16	See Britain by Coach	1954		£1.25

BLUE BIRD STOCKINGS

P12	Exciting Film Stars	1963	—	£4.00
24	Star Cards	1963	£1.75	—

BLUE CAP LTD. (Cheese)

PACKAGE SERIES

12	Animal Series D	1953	60p	—
8	Animal Series E	1953	£1.00	—
12	Farm Series A	1953	30p	£4.00
12	Farm Series B	1953	30p	£4.00
12	Farm Series C	1953	30p	£4.00
K144	Flixies	1952	35p	—
12	Sports Series D	1953	75p	—
8	Sports Series E	1953	£1.50	—

E. H. BOOTH & CO. LTD. (Tea)

25	Badges & Uniforms of Famous British Regiments & Corps	1967	—	£1.00
25	Ships & Their Workings	1971	—	£2.00

BOW BELLS (Periodical)

BF6	Handsome Men on the British Screen	1922	£1.50	£9.00

BOYS CINEMA (Periodical)

BF6	Famous Film Heroes	1922	£1.50	£9.00
M24	Famous Heroes	1922	£1.00	£24.00
F7	Film Stars (Anon)	1930	£1.50	
MF8	Film Stars (Brown Front)	1930	£1.50	£12.00
MF8	Film Stars (Black Front)	1931	£1.50	£12.00

BOYS COMIC LIBRARY

4	Heroes of the Wild West	1910	£7.50	

BOYS FRIEND (Periodical)

3	Famous Boxers Series	1911	£3.50	£10.50
3	Famous Flags Series	1911	£3.50	£10.50

BOYS FRIEND (Periodical)—cont.

Qty		Date	Odds	Sets
3	Famous Footballers Series	1911	£3.50	£10.50
3	Famous Regiments Series	1911	£3.50	£10.50
BF4	Footballers ($\frac{1}{2}$ Length)	1923	£1.25	£5.00
BF5	Footballers (2 Per Card)	1922	£1.20	£6.00
BF15	Rising Boxing Stars	1922	80p	£12.00

BOYS MAGAZINE (Periodical)

M8	Boxers	1922	£2.50	£20.00
B8	Coloured Studies of Famous Internationals	1922	£2.00	£16.00
M10	Cricketers	1922	£5.00	£50.00
F10	Famous Cricketers Series	1929	£3.50	£35.00
F12	Famous Footballers Series	1929	£1.50	£18.00
BF10	Football Series	1922	£1.00	£10.00
M30	Footballers (Picture 49 x 39 mm)	1922	£1.50	—
B64	Footballers & Sportsmen (Picture 56 x 35)	1922	£2.00	—
12	Zat Cards (Cricketers)	1930	£4.00	£50.00
M11	Zat Cards (Cricketers)	1930	£5.00	£55.00

BOYS REALM (Periodical)

BF15	Famous Cricketers	1922	£1.50	£22.50
BF9	Famous Footballers	1922	£1.25	£11.50

C. & T. BRIDGEWATER LTD. (Biscuits)

KF48	Coronation Series	1937	15p	£3.50
KF96	Film Stars 1st (CE over No.)	1932	15p	£15.00
KF96	Film Stars 2nd (E below No.)	1933	15p	£15.00
KF96	Film Stars 3rd (Black & White)	1934	20p	£20.00
KF48	Film Stars 4th	1935	15p	£6.00
KF48	Film Stars 5th	1937	30p	—
KF48	Film Stars 6th (F before No.)	1938	30p	—
F48	Film Stars 7th	1939	30p	£15.00
KF48	Film Stars 8th	1940	15p	£4.00
KF48	Radio Stars 1st (Black & White)	1935	25p	£12.50
KF48	Radio Stars 2nd (Coloured)	1936	15p	£5.00

JOHN M. BRINDLEY & ASSOCIATES (Printers)

30	Australian Cricketers	1986	—	£7.50
20	Car Badges & Emblems	1987	—	£3.00
30	Cricketers, A Series	1985	—	£8.00
30	Cricketers, 2nd Series	1985	—	£10.00
X16	Cricketers, Howzat, 3rd Series	1985	—	£8.00
30	Cricketers, 4th Series	1986	—	£7.50
X20	Cricketers, 5th Series (sketches)	1986	—	£7.50
25	Cricketing Greats	1987	—	£3.00
30	Cricket, The Old School	1987	—	£7.50
20	Golfers	1987	—	£5.00
20	Locos	1987	—	£2.50
30	London, Brighton & South Coast Railway	1986	—	£5.00
20	Military	1987	—	£2.50
25	Old Golfing Greats	1987	—	£3.00
20	Racing Series	1987	—	£3.00

BRITISH AUTOMATIC CO. (Weight)

24	British Aircraft	1950	40p	£10.00
24	British Birds	1950	50p	£12.00

BRITISH AUTOMATIC CO. (Weight)—cont.

Qty		Date	Odds	Sets
24	British Locomotives	1948	20p	£5.00
36	British Motor Cars	1954	£1.25	£45.00
44	Coronation Information	1953	75p	—
32	Dogs 1st Series	1953	12p	£4.00
32	Dogs (A Series, no "weigh Daily", as 2nd)	1953	50p	£16.00
32	Dogs 2nd Series	1953	35p	£11.00
24	Famous Trains of the World 1st Series	1952	30p	£7.00
24	Famous Trains of the World 2nd Series	1952	30p	£7.00
30	Fortunes, 1st Series	1950	50p	—
32	Fortunes, 2nd Series	1953	15p	£5.00
32	Fortunes, 3rd Series	1954	50p	—
24	Freshwater Fish	1950	50p	£12.00
24	History of Transport	1948	10p	£1.50
44	Jokes	1951	25p	£11.00
24	Olympic Games	1952	£1.00	—
37	Quotations	1951	50p	—
24	Racing & Sports Cars	1957	75p	£18.00
24	Space Travel	1955	75p	£18.00
24	Speed	1949	12p	£3.00
24	Sportsmen	1955	75p	£18.00
20	Twenty Questions	1952	75p	£15.00
24	Warships of the World	1954	10p	£2.00
1	Watch Your Weight	1950	—	40p

BRITISH TELECOM

T11	Football Clubs	1987	—	£2.00

BROOKE BOND & CO. LTD. (Tea)
(Special albums available for many series—ask for quote)

50	Adventurers & Explorers	1973	10p	£2.00
50	African Wild Life	1962	10p	£2.00
50	Asian Wild Life	1962	10p	£2.00
50	Bird Portraits (no address)	1957	50p	£25.00
50	Bird Portraits (with address)	1957	20p	£10.00
20	British Birds	1954	40p	£8.00
50	British Butterflies	1963	10p	£2.50
50	British Costume	1967	10p	£2.00
50	British Wild Life (Brooke Bond Great Britain Ltd.)	1958	40p	£20.00
50	British Wild Life (Brooke Bond Tea Ltd.)	1958	12p	£6.00
50	British Wild Life (Brooke Bond & Co. Ltd.)	1958	40p	£20.00
50	Butterflies of the World	1964	10p	£2.50
12	Chimp Stickers	1986	16p	£2.00
50	Famous People	1969	10p	£2.00
50	Features of the World	1984	10p	£2.00
L25	Features of the World (Double Cards)	1984	25p	—
50	Flags & Emblems of the World	1967	10p	£2.00
50	Freshwater Fish	1960	10p	£2.50
50	History of Aviation	1972	10p	£2.00
50	History of the Motor Car	1968	10p	£2.00
40	Incredible Creatures (last line Sheen Lane) ...	1985	12p	£4.00
40	Incredible Creatures (last line Walton...) ...	1986	12p	£4.00
40	Incredible Creatures (last line PO Box...) ...	1986	10p	£2.50
40	Incredible Creatures (thick cards, stickers) ...	1987	75p	—
40	Incredible Creatures (green, back, Irish) ...	1986	13p	£5.00

BROOKE BOND & CO. LTD. (Tea)—cont.

Qty		Date	Odds	Sets
L20	Incredible Creatures (Double, Sheen Lane) ...	1986	40p	—
L20	Incredible Creatures (Double, Walton)	1986	30p	—
L20	Incredible Creatures (Double, PO Box)	1986	50p	—
50	Inventors and Inventions	1975	10p	£2.00
40	Olympic Greats	1979	10p	£2.00
50	Out Into Space (Issued with . . .)	1956	£1.50	—
50	Out Into Space (Issued in . . .)	1958	30p	£15.00
40	Play Better Soccer	1976	10p	£2.00
40	Police File	1977	10p	£2.00
X10	Poly Filla Modelling Cards	1974	20p	£2.00
50	Prehistoric Animals	1972	10p	£2.00
50	Queen Elizabeth I—Queen Elizabeth II	1982	10p	£2.00
L25	Queen Elizabeth I-II (Double Cards)	1982	25p	—
40	Small Wonders	1981	10p	£2.00
50	The Race into Space	1971	10p	£2.00
50	The Saga of Ships	1970	10p	£2.00
50	The Sea—Our Other World	1974	10p	£2.00
50	Transport Through the Ages	1966	10p	£2.00
50	Trees In Britain	1966	10p	£2.00
50	Tropical Birds	1961	10p	£2.50
40	Unexplained Mysteries of the World	1987	10p	—
40	Vanishing Wildlife	1978	10p	£2.00
50	Wild Birds in Britain	1965	10p	£2.00
50	Wild Flowers 1st Series	1955	80p	£40.00
50	Wild Flowers 2nd Series (with issued by) ...	1959	10p	£2.00
50	Wild Flowers 2nd Series (no issued by) ...	1959	50p	£25.00
50	Wild Flowers 3rd Series	1964	10p	£2.00
50	Wild Life in Danger	1963	10p	£2.00
50	Wonders of Wildlife	1976	10p	£2.00
40	Woodland Wildlife	1980	10p	£2.00

BLACK BACK REPRINTS

Qty		Date	Odds	Sets
50	African Wild Life	1973	—	£1.75
50	British Butterflies	1973	—	£1.75
50	British Costume	1973	—	£1.75
50	Famous People	1973	—	£1.75
50	Flags & Emblems of the World	1973	—	£4.00
50	Freshwater Fish	1973	—	£1.75
50	History of the Motor Car	1974	—	£1.75
50	The Race Into Space	1974	—	£1.75
50	The Saga of Ships	1973	—	£1.75
50	Transport Through the Ages	1973	—	£4.00
50	Trees in Britain	1973	—	£1.75
50	Tropical Birds	1974	—	£1.75
50	Wild Birds in Britain	1973	—	£1.75
50	Wild Flowers Series 2	1973	—	£1.75
50	Wild Life in Danger	1973	—	£1.75

CARD GAMES BASED ON REGULAR SERIES

Qty		Date	Odds	Sets
L36	British Costume Card Game	1974	—	£2.00
L36	Flags & Emblems Snap Game	1974	—	£2.00
L36	Motor History Snap Game	1974	—	£2.00

CANADIAN ISSUES

Qty		Date	Odds	Sets
48	African Animals	1964	—	£2.50
48	Animals & Their Young	1972	—	£2.50

BROOKE BOND & CO. LTD. (Tea)—cont.

Qty		Date	Odds	Sets
48	Animals of North America	1960	—	£20.00
48	Birds of North America	1962	—	£15.00
48	Butterflies of North America	1965	—	£7.50
48	Canadian/American Songbirds	1966	—	£15.00
48	Dinosaurs	1963	—	£40.00
48	Exploring the Oceans	1971	—	£2.50
48	Indians of Canada	1974	—	£2.50
48	North American Wildlife in Danger	1970	—	£2.50
48	Songbirds of North America (Red Rose/ Blue Ribbon)	1959	—	£40.00
48	Songbirds of North America (Red Rose only, "Album available")	1959	£1.25	—
48	Songbirds of North America (Red Rose only, "Mount Your Collection")	1959	£1.25	—
48	The Arctic	1973	—	£2.50
48	The Space Age	1969	—	£2.50
48	Transportation Through the Ages (top line black)	1967	—	£7.50
48	Transportation Through the Ages (top line red)	1967	£1.50	—
48	Trees of North America	1968	—	£7.50
48	Tropical Birds (top line black)	1964	—	£10.00
48	Tropical Birds (top line red)	1964	£1.25	—
48	Wild Flowers of North America	1961	—	£17.50

RHODESIAN ISSUES

Qty		Date	Odds	Sets
50	African Birds	1965	75p	—
50	African Wild Life	1963	£1.00	£50.00
50	Asian Wild Life	1963	75p	£37.50
50	Butterflies of the World	1966	80p	£40.00
50	Tropical Birds	1962	80p	£40.00
50	Wildlife in Danger	1964	£1.00	—

SOUTH AFRICAN ISSUES

Qty		Date	Odds	Sets
50	Our Pets	1967	70p	£35.00
50	Out Into Space	1966	60p	£30.00
50	Wild Van Afrika (Bilingual)	1965	80p	£40.00
50	Wild Van Afrika (one language)	1965	£1.50	—

U.S.A. ISSUES

Qty		Date	Odds	Sets
48	Animals of North America	1960	£2.00	—
48	Birds of North America	1962	£2.00	—
48	Butterflies of North America	1964	£1.50	—
48	Canadian/American Song Birds	1966	80p	£40.00
48	Dinosaurs	1963	£2.00	—
48	Tropical Birds	1964	£1.50	—
48	Wild Flowers of North America	1961	£1.50	—

BROOK MOTORS

Qty		Date	Odds	Sets
G12	Motor Cycles (cut from calendars)	1975	—	£3.00
P12	Steam Engines	1973	—	£6.00
P12	Steam Engines (different)	1970	—	£20.00
P12	The Traction Engine	1972	—	£10.00
P12	Veteran Cars	1961	—	£7.50

DAVID BROWN (Tractors)

Qty		Date	Odds	Sets
XF3	Is Your Slip Showing?	1954	—	£2.00

BROWN & POLSON (Custard)

Qty		Date	Odds	Sets
X25	Recipe Cards	1925	£2.00	—

BROWNE BROS. LTD. (Tea)

Qty		Date	Odds	Sets
25	Birds	1964	—	£4.00
25	British Cavalry Uniforms of the 19th Century ...	1964	—	£5.00
25	Garden Flowers	1965	—	£10.00
25	History of the Railways 1st	1964	—	£4.00
25	History of the Railways 2nd	1964	—	£5.00
25	Passenger Liners	1966	—	£10.00
25	People & Places	1965	—	£1.00
25	Tropical Birds	1966	—	£1.00
25	Wonders of the Deep	1965	—	£1.25
25	Wonders of the World	1970	—	£3.50

BOUCHERE'S FIRM

Qty		Date	Odds	Sets
50	War Portraits	1916	£17.50	—

BUBBLES INC. (Gum)

Qty		Date	Odds	Sets
X55	Mars Attacks	1965	£6.00	£330.00
X55	Mars Attacks (reprints, U.S.A.)	1984	—	£12.00
X50	Outer Limits	1966	£1.00	£50.00

BUCHANAN'S (Jam)

Qty		Date	Odds	Sets
24	Birds and Their Eggs	1924	£4.00	—

JOHNNY BUNNY (Medicines)

Qty		Date	Odds	Sets
25	Football Clubs and Badges	1958	—	£15.00

BUNSEN CONFECTIONERY CO.

Qty		Date	Odds	Sets
?100	Famous Figures Series	1925	£6.00	—

BURDALL & BURDALL (Gravy Salt)

Qty		Date	Odds	Sets
30	Wild Animals	1924	£3.00	—

BURGER KING (Restaurants, U.S.A.)

Qty		Date	Odds	Sets
X36	The Empire Strikes Back	1981	—	£5.00

BURTONS WAGON WHEELS (Biscuits)

Qty		Date	Odds	Sets
25	Indian Chiefs	1972	—	£1.00
L7	Pictures of the Wild West	1983	70p	£5.00
25	The West	1972	—	£1.00
25	Wild West Action	1972	—	£1.00

BUTTAPAT DAIRIES

Qty		Date	Odds	Sets
?24	People of the World	1915	£10.00	—

K. F. BYRNES (U.S.A.)

Qty		Date	Odds	Sets
X22	Firemen	1981	—	£3.50
X22	Firemen	1982	—	£3.50
X22	Firemen	1983	—	£3.50

CBS IRONMONGERY LTD.

Qty		Date	Odds	Sets
30	Glamorgan Cricketers	1984	—	£10.00

C. & G. CONFECTIONERY LTD.

Qty		Date	Odds	Sets
25	Box of Tricks 1st Series	1965	75p	—
25	Box of Tricks 2nd Series	1965	75p	—

CADBURY BROS. LTD. (Chocolate)

Qty		Date	Odds	Sets
T12	Antarctic Series	1913	£10.00	—
X6	Bay City Rollers	1975	—	£1.25
L12	Birds in Springtime	1983	—	£2.50
6	Bournville Series B	1906	£8.00	£48.00
P3	Bournville Views (script at side)	1906	£1.00	£3.00
P6	Bournville Views (block at side)	1906	£2.00	£12.00
P6	Bournville Views (white borders)	1906	£2.00	£12.00
P8	Bournville Views (gravure)	1906	£2.00	—
6	Bournville Village Series	1906	£8.00	—
P25	British Birds (Reward Cards)	1910	£5.00	—
12	British Birds & Eggs	1910	£4.00	—
P12	British Birds & Their Eggs (Reward Cards) ...	1910	£4.00	—
P32	British Butterflies & Moths (Reward Cards) ...	1910	£3.00	£100.00
6	British Colonies, Maps & Industries	1908	£7.50	£45.00
120	British Marvels	1936	35p	—
120	British Marvels Series 2	1936	40p	—
12	British Trees Series	1911	£3.00	£36.00
80	Cadbury's Picture Making	1936	75p	—
12	Cathedral Series	1913	£3.00	£36.00
6	Colonial Premiers Series	1908	£8.00	£48.00
12	Constellations Series	1912	£4.00	£48.00
24	Copyright (Inventors) Series	1914	£6.00	—
1	Coronation	1911	—	£12.50
48	Dangerous Animals	1970	—	£4.00
6	Dog Series	1908	£12.00	—
C12	English Industries	1908	£15.00	—
25	Fairy Tales	1924	£1.00	£25.00
27	Famous Steamships	1923	£1.00	£27.00
12	Fish	1910	£6.00	—
P6	Fish & Bait Series	1909	£12.50	—
12	Flag Series	1912	£1.00	£12.00
C6	Flag Series (Joined Pairs)	1912	£2.00	£12.00
C12	Flag Series (different)	1910	£10.00	—
X12	Flight (Birds)	1982	40p	£5.00
32	Happy Families	1950	£1.00	—
1	Largest Steamers in the World	1907	—	£8.00
6	Locomotive Series	1906	£12.50	—
12	Match Puzzles	1906	£15.00	—
6	Old Ballad Series	1906	£10.00	—
X6	Panama Series	1910	£10.00	—
X5	Pop Stars	1975	25p	£1.25
1	Poster Series	1910	—	£15.00
X8	Prehistoric Monsters	1975	—	£1.25
P6	Rivers of the British Isles (Reward Cards) ...	1910	£8.00	£48.00
24	Shadow Series	1914	£6.00	—
6	Shipping Series (4 Sizes)	1910	£5.00	—
T6	Sports Series	1906	*£15.00*	—
24	Strange But True	1970	—	£1.00
12	The Age of the Dinosaur	1971	—	£1.00
25	Transport	1925	15p	£3.50
L6	Wildlife Stickers	1986	—	£1.50

CADET SWEETS ("C.S.")

Qty		Date	Odds	Sets
25	Arms & Armour	1961	—	£1.00
50	Buccaneers	1957	—	£3.00
50	Buccaneers (Different)	1959	—	£5.00
25	Daktari	1969	—	£2.00
50	Doctor Who and the Daleks	1965	£1.20	£60.00
25	Dogs 1st Series	1958	—	£2.00
25	Dogs 2nd Series	1958	—	£2.00
25	Evolution of the Royal Navy	1959	—	£1.00
B22	Famous Explorers (packets)	1960	£3.50	—
50	Fifty Years of Flying	1953	—	£17.50
50	Footballers	1956	—	£3.00
50	Footballers (Different) large wording	1959	—	£2.50
50	Footballers (different) small wording	1959	—	£3.00
50	Footballers & Club Colours	1963	—	£2.50
25	How?	1969	—	£1.75
50	Motor Cars	1954	—	£5.00
25	Prehistoric Animals	1961	—	£4.00
50	Railways of the World (Cadet)	1956	—	£2.50
50	Railways of the World (Paramount Laboratories)	1956	—	£6.00
50	Railways of the World (Paramount Sweets)	1956	—	£4.00
50	Record Holders of the World	1956	—	£2.00
25	Record Holders of the World (Different)	1962	—	£1.00
25	Ships Through the Ages 1st Series	1963	—	£1.00
25	Ships Through the Ages 2nd Series	1963	—	£1.00
50	Stingray	1965	—	£6.50
48	The Adventures of Rin Tin Tin	1960	—	£3.00
50	The Conquest of Space	1957	—	£2.50
25	Treasure Hunt	1964	—	£1.00
50	UNCLE	1966	—	£7.50
25	What Do You Know?	1965	—	£7.50

A. J. CALEY & SON (Confectionery)

Qty		Date	Odds	Sets
K24	Film Stars	1930	£3.00	—
10	Passenger Liners	1939	£3.50	—
48	Wisecracks (Mickey Mouse Weekly)	1932	£1.50	—

CALTEX OIL (Australia)

Qty		Date	Odds	Sets
X6	Stargazer (Haley's Comet)	1986	—	75p

F. C. CALVERT & CO. LTD. (Toothpaste)

Qty		Date	Odds	Sets
25	Dan Dare Series	1954	—	£10.00

CANDY GUM

Qty		Date	Odds	Sets
M50	Autosprint	1975	—	£2.50
M30	Autosprint, 2nd Series	1975	—	£2.50
M30	Autosprint, 2nd Series (Plain Back)	1975	—	£3.00

CANDY NOVELTY CO.

Qty		Date	Odds	Sets
B25/50	Dog Series—A1 Set	1953	—	£1.00

CANNINGS (Jam)

Qty		Date	Odds	Sets
25	Types of British Soldiers	1914	£8.00	—

F. CAPERN (Bird Seed)

Qty		Date	Odds	Sets
?10	British Birds	1925	£6.00	—
P54	Cage Birds	1926	£1.00	—
24	Picture Aviary	1964	—	*£6.00*
1	Picture Aviary Introductory Card	1964	—	10p

CAPEZIO (Ballet Shoes, U.S.A)

XF12	Famous Dancers Gallery	1950	—	£10.00

CARD INSERT LTD.

1	Famous Footballers	1953	—	£1.00

CARR'S BISCUITS

M20	Animals of the World	1930	£4.00	—
E20	Cricketers	1967	£1.00	£20.00

CARSONS CHOCOLATE

72	Celebrities	1902	£8.00	—

CARTERS LITTLE LIVER PILLS

28	Dominoes	1911	60p	£16.00

F. C. CARTLEDGE (Razor Blades)

X48	Epigrams "A"	1939	15p	£5.00
X64	Epigrams "B"	1939	15p	£6.50
X96	Epigrams "C"	1939	15p	£15.00
50	Famous Prize Fighters	1938	20p	£10.00

CASH & CO. (Shoes)

20	War Series	1916	£5.00	£100.00

CASSELLS (Periodical)

M6	British Engines	1923	£5.00	£30.00
B12	Butterflies & Moths Series	1923	£3.00	£36.00

CASTROL OIL

X18	Famous Riders	1958	£1.00	£18.00
X24	Racing Cars	1958	75p	£18.00

CAVE AUSTIN & CO. LTD. (Tea)

20	Inventors Series	1923	£6.00	—

CEDE LTD.

25	Coins of the World	1956	—	£1.50

CENTRAL ELECTRICITY AUTHORITY

B10	Interesting Careers	1961	—	75p

CEREBOS (Salt)

100	Sea Shells	1925	75p	£75.00

CEYLON TEA CENTRE

24	The Island of Ceylon	1955	—	£1.00

H. CHAPPEL & CO. (Confectionery)

10	British Celebrities	1905	£17.50	—

CHARTER TEA & COFFEE CO. LTD.

Qty		Date	Odds	Sets
25	Prehistoric Animals 1st Series	1962	—	£10.00
25	Prehistoric Animals 2nd Series	1962	—	£10.00
25	Strange But True 1st Series	1961	—	£3.00
25	Strange But True 2nd Series	1961	—	£3.00
25	Transport Through the Ages 1st Series	1961	—	£4.00
25	Transport Through the Ages 2nd Series	1961	—	£4.00

CHEF & BREWER

L20	Historic Pub Signs	1984	—	£5.00

CHIVERS & SONS LTD. (Preserves)

L125	Firm Favourites	1932	£1.25	—
P6	Studies of English Fruits Series 1	1924	£3.00	£18.00
P6	Studies of English Fruits Series 2	1924	£3.00	£18.00
24	Wild Wisdom	1964	£1.00	—
48	Wild Wisdom in Africa	1964	75p	—
48	Wild Wisdom, River and Marsh	1964	75p	—

PACKAGE ISSUES

L15	Children of Other Lands	1952	40p	£6.00
L15	Chivers British Birds	1951	40p	£6.00
L20	On Chivers Farms	1951	40p	£8.00

CHIX CONFECTIONERY CO. LTD.

X50	Famous Footballers	1960	£1.00	£50.00
X48	Famous Footballers No. 1 Series	1953	60p	£30.00
X48	Famous Footballers No. 2 Series	1956	50p	£25.00
X48	Famous Footballers No. 3 Series	1958	75p	—
X50	Famous Last Words	1970	40p	—
X24	Footballers (Portrait & Action) 1-24	1952	—	£1.00
X24	Footballers (Portrait & Action) 25-48	1952	—	£1.00
L50	Funny Old Folk	1970	—	£7.00
L50	Happy Howlers	1970	40p	£20.00
L50	Krazy Kreatures from Outer Space	1970	—	£15.00
L50	Military Uniforms	1970	—	£8.50
L50	Moon Shot	1966	70p	—
X50	Popeye	1960	£1.50	—
X50	Scottish Footballers	1960	£2.50	—
X50	Ships of the Seven Seas	1968	£1.00	—
X50	Soldiers of the World	1962	50p	£25.00
X50	Sports through the Ages	1968	£1.25	—
96	TV & Radio Stars	1954	75p	—
X50	Wild Animals	1960	£1.00	—

CHUMS (Periodical)

BF23	Cricketers	1923	£1.75	£40.00
BF20	Football Teams	1922	75p	£15.00
F8	Football Teams New Series	1923	£1.00	£8.00
X10	Real Colour Photos (Footballers)	1922	£2.50	—

CHU-BOPS (U.S.A.)

L8	Elvis Record Covers	1980	—	£6.00

CHURCH & DWIGHT (Baking Soda, U.S.A.)

Qty		Date	Odds	Sets
M60	Beautiful Birds, New Series	1899	£1.75	£105.00
M60	Beautiful Birds of America	1898	£2.50	£150.00
M60	Beautiful Flowers	1899	£1.50	£90.00
X10	Birds of Prey	1976	—	£1.50
M30	Champion Dog Series	1902	£3.00	—
M30	Dairy Animals	1905	£2.50	—
M30	Fish Series	1900	£1.75	£52.50
M30	Game Bird Series	1904	£2.00	£60.00
M60	Interesting Animals	1903	£2.00	£120.00
M30	Mother Goose Series	1900	£3.00	—
M30	New Series of Birds	1908	£1.25	£37.50
M30	New Series of Dogs	1910	£3.00	—
M30	Useful Birds of America	1915	£1.50	£45.00
M30	Useful Birds of America, 2nd Series	1918	£1.50	£45.00
M30	Useful Birds of America, 3rd Series	1922	£1.50	£45.00
M30	Useful Birds of America, Series 4	1924	£1.50	£45.00
M15	Useful Birds of America, Series 5	1924	£1.20	£18.00
M15	Useful Birds of America, Series 6	1924	£1.20	£18.00
M15	Useful Birds of America, Series 7	1924	£1.20	£18.00
M15	Useful Birds of America, Series 8	1924	£1.20	£18.00
M15	Useful Birds of America, Series 9	1926	25p	£3.75
M15	Useful Birds of America, Series 10	1926	30p	£4.50

CLEVEDON CONFECTIONERY LTD.

Qty		Date	Odds	Sets
50	British Aircraft	1958	£1.00	—
25	British Orders of Chivalry & Valour	1960	£1.25	—
50	British Ships	1959	£1.00	—
B50	British Trains & Engines	1958	£1.75	—
25	Dan Dare	1961	£1.60	—
40	Did You Know?	1963	£1.25	—
40	Famous Cricketers	1959	£4.00	—
25	Famous Cricketers	1962	£4.00	—
50	Famous Football Clubs	1964	60p	£30.00
50	Famous Footballers	1961	£1.50	—
50	Famous International Aircraft	1963	60p	£30.00
B50	Famous Screen Stars	1959	£1.25	—
40	Film Stars	1958	£1.25	—
50	Football Club Managers	1959	£2.00	—
50	Hints on Association Football	1961	£1.00	—
50	Hints on Road Safety	1962	£1.00	—
50	International Sporting Stars	1960	60p	£30.00
B50	Regimental Badges	1959	£1.25	—
X25	Sporting Memories	1962	£2.00	—
50	The Story of the Olympics	1961	60p	—
50	Trains of the World	1962	70p	£35.00
B30	Wagon Train	1963	£1.50	—

CLEVELAND (Petrol)

Qty		Date	Odds	Sets
P20	Golden Goals	1970	—	£12.50

CLOVER DAIRIES LTD.

Qty		Date	Odds	Sets
25	Animals & Reptiles	1970	—	£1.00
25	British Rail	1973	—	£1.00
25	People & Places	1972	—	£1.00

CLOVER DAIRIES LTD.—cont.

Qty		Date	Odds	Sets
25	Prehistoric Animals	1965	—	£1.00
25	Science in the 20th Century	1971	—	£1.00
25	Ships & Their Workings	1971	—	£1.00
25	The Story of Milk	1970	—	£1.50
25	Transport Through the Ages	1971	—	£1.00

COCA COLA (Drinks)

M100	Our Flower Paradise (S. Africa)	1960	—	£12.00
X96	The World of Nature (U.S.A.)	1960	—	£8.50

CECIL COLEMAN LTD. (Confectionery)

24	Film Stars	1935	£3.00	—

COLGATE-PALMOLIVE (Toiletries)

D24	Famous Sporting Trophies	1979	—	£3.00
P4	Royal Britain	1951	£1.25	£5.00

COLINVILLE LTD. (Gum)

M56	Look'n See	1958	£2.00	—
L25	Prairie Pioneers	1959	£1.50	£37.50
L28	Space Fantasy 1st Series (1-28)	1959	£1.50	—
L28	Space Fantasy 2nd Series (29-56)	1959	£1.50	—

COLLECTABLES OF SPALDING (SHOP)

25	British Cavalry Uniforms	1987	—	£3.75
25	Military Maids	1987	—	£3.75
25	Warriors through the Ages	1987	—	£3.75

COLLECTOR & HOBBYIST (Periodical)

25	Fascinating Hobbies	1950	—	£1.00

COLLECTORS SHOP

25	Bandsmen of the British Army	1960	—	£6.00
3	Bonus Cards	1961	60p	—
2	Bonus Cards 1961-62	1961	—	£1.00
25	Butterflies & Moths	1961	—	£5.00

COLT 45 (Drink)

X5/6	Advertising Slogans (Silk)	1976	£2.00	£10.00
X4	American Scenes (Beer Mats)	1975	—	£2.00

COMET SWEETS

25	A. & M. Denis on Safari 1st Series	1961	—	£1.00
25	A. & M. Denis on Safari 2nd Series	1961	—	£1.00
25	Modern Wonders (black back)	1961	—	£1.00
25	Modern Wonders (blue back)	1961	—	£7.50
25	Olympic Achievements 1st Series	1960	—	£1.50
25	Olympic Achievements 2nd Series	1960	—	£1.50
M22	Olympic Achievements (package)	1960	£3.50	—

COMIC LIFE (Periodical)

BF4	Sports Champions	1922	£1.75	£7.00

COMMODEX (Gum)

Qty		Date	Odds	Sets
L88	Operation Moon	1969	60p	£50.00
L120	Super Cars	1970	30p	£36.00

COMMONWEALTH SHOE & LEATHER CO. (U.S.A.)

M12	Makes of Planes	1930	£1.25	£15.00

COMO CONFECTIONERY PRODUCTS LTD.

L25	History of the Wild West 1st	1963	75p	—
L25	History of the Wild West 2nd	1963	—	£4.00
50	Lenny's Adventures	1961	50p	—
50	Noddy & His Playmates	1962	—	£5.00
L25	Noddy's Adventures 1st Series	1958	40p	—
L25	Noddy's Adventures 2nd Series	1958	60p	—
25	Noddy's Budgie & Feathered Friends 1st ...	1964	60p	—
25	Noddy's Budgie & Feathered Friends 2nd ...	1964	40p	—
L50	Noddy's Friends Abroad	1959	50p	—
L50	Noddy's Nursery Rhyme Friends	1959	40p	—
L50	Sooty's Adventures	1960	50p	—
L50	Sooty's New Adventures 2nd	1961	—	£4.00
50	Sooty's Latest Adventures 3rd	1963	50p	—
25	Speed 1st Series	1962	75p	—
25	Speed 2nd Series	1962	—	£2.00
25	Supercar 1st Series	1962	£1.25	—
25	Supercar 2nd Series	1962	—	£16.00
25	Top Secret 1st Series	1965	75p	—
25	Top Secret 2nd Series	1965	75p	—
L26	XL5 1st Series	1965	£5.00	—
L26	XL5 2nd Series	1966	£5.00	—

COMPTON'S GRAVY SALT

22	Footballers Serie A (Black)	1924	£3.50	—
22	Footballers Serie A (Coloured)	1924	£4.00	—
22	Footballers Serie B (Black)	1924	£3.50	—
22	Footballers Serie B (Coloured)	1924	£5.00	—
22	Footballers Serie C	1924	£5.00	—
22	Footballers Serie D	1924	£5.00	—

COOPER & CO. LTD. (Tea)

50	Do You Know?	1962	—	£1.50
25	Inventions & Discoveries 1st Series	1962	50p	£12.50
25	Inventions & Discoveries 2nd Series	1962	—	£12.50
25	Mysteries & Wonders of the World 1st Series ...	1961	—	£1.50
25	Mysteries & Wonders of the World 2nd Series ...	1961	—	£1.00
25	Prehistoric Animals 1st Series	1962	—	£10.00
25	Prehistoric Animals 2nd Series	1962	—	£10.00
25	Strange But True 1st Series	1961	—	£1.00
25	Strange But True 2nd Series	1961	—	£1.00
24	The Island of Ceylon	1955	£1.00	—
25	Transport Through the Ages 1st Series	1961	—	£3.00
25	Transport Through the Ages 2nd Series	1961	—	£2.50

CO-OPERATIVE SOCIETIES (Shops)

B48	World Cup Teams & Players. *Complete with Poster*	1982	—	£2.50
D306	Espana '82. *Complete with Album*	1982	—	£6.00
—	Special Poster for above (only if ordered at same time)	1982	—	50p

THE TOBACCO WAR

MURAI'S CIGARETTES
are the BEST and CHEAPEST

CIRCASSIAN

In 1890 five of the leading American tobacco manufacturers combined to form the American Tobacco Company. They expanded rapidly, absorbed many other firms in the U.S.A., and in order to extend further they turned their attention to overseas markets. In September 1901 they acquired the British firm of Ogdens, and used it to pursue an aggressive sales policy, in the best American traditions. Because of the danger to them, 13 of the leading British Companies reacted immediately by forming the Imperial Tobacco Company in November of the same year. A short battle developed, and this inevitably resulted in a peace formula between the two generals. Under this Ogdens was transferred to Imperial, each pulled out of the other's home territories, and the rest of the world was left to a new, jointly owned firm, British American Tobacco Co.

Cigarette cards formed a substantial part of the ammunition in this War. Both sides produced many attractive series to promote their image. Most of the A.T.C. cards with the Old Gold brand backs were issued in Britain; Ogden Tabs at one stage bore the slogan 'British made by British Labour' in order to allay fears; and I.T.C. replied with several fine series of cards, the set of Wills Locomotives and Rolling Stock being a splendid example.

Player's Cigarettes

WILLS'S Cigarettes

ENGLAND, ROWING

THESE PICTURES are packed IN THE BRANDS OF CIGARETTES MANUFACTURED BY BRITISH-AMERICAN TOBACCO CO. LTD.

PEDRO Cigarettes

BRITISH-AMERICAN TOBACCO CO. LTD. SUCCESSOR TO W DUKE SONS & CO

PEDRO CIGARETTES.
British-American Tobacco Co., Ltd.

TRY THE CELEBRATED OLD GOLD TOBACCO IMPORTED FROM AMERICA BY THE AMERICAN TOBACCO CO.

CODE NAMES

When cigarette cards first became popular in this country the most prolific subjects were actresses and militaria – since virtually all cigarette smokers were men! In the golden age around the turn of the century many manufacturers including many of the largest issued some of the same sets as their competitors. In order to distinguish the many similar series a coding system has been developed for series of Actresses and Boer War subjects that in general do not have a series title of their own. This is based on the first letter (or letters) of the names of some of the leading issuers of the particular set.

Thus Beauties PAC were issued by Pritchard & Burton, Adkin and Cope, and Beauties HOL by Harris, Ogden & Lambert & Butler. Actresses HAGG were issued by Hill, Anonymous, Gabriel and Glass (as well as Baker and Bell), while Boer War Celebrities CLAM is taken from Churchman, Lambert & Butler, Anonymous and Muratti. The most popular set of this type must surely have been Actresses FROGA, which includes four sets all similar in appearance and was issued by more than 25 different companies, including Dunn's Hats in Britain, and tobacco issuers in Canada and India.

It is fortunate that so many of the series had an Anonymous version, allowing the frequent use of the letter 'A', and hence some sort of pronounceable acronyms.

As a general rule in British issues Actress series are those in which the subject's name is printed, while the unidentified ladies are known as Beauties.

JOHN COURAGE (Brewers)

Qty		Date	Odds	Sets
X6	Sporting Heroes (Beer Mats)	1975	—	£3.00

COW & GATE (Baby Food)

X24	Advertisement Cards	1928	£1.00	£24.00
X48	Happy Families	1928	—	£17.50

COWANS (Confectionery, Canada)

24	Dog Pictures	1930	£3.00	—
24	Horse Pictures	1930	£2.50	—
24	Learn to Swin	1929	£2.50	—
24	Noted Cats	1930	£3.00	£72.00

CRESCENT CONFECTIONERY CO.

100	Sportsmen	1928	£7.50	—

CROMWELL STORES

25	Do You Know?	1963	—	£3.00
25	Racing Colours	1963	—	£3.00

CROSBIE (Preserves)

K54	Miniature Playing Cards	1938	40p	

JOSEPH CROSFIELD & SONS LTD. (Soap)

36	Film Stars	1924	£3.00	—

CRYSELCO ELECTRIC LAMPS

X25	Beautiful Waterways	1939	40p	£10.00
X25	Buildings of Beauty	1938	50p	£12.50
X12	Interesting Events of 60 Years Ago	1955	—	£12.50

D. CUMMINGS & SON (Commercial)

64	Famous Fighters	1947	—	£12.50

DAILY EXPRESS (Newspaper)

X59	Car Cards	1971	—	£1.50

DAILY HERALD (Newspaper)

32	Cricketers	1954	£1.50	—
32	Footballers	1954	50p	—
32	Turf Personalities	1955	12p	£2.50

DAILY ICE CREAM CO.

24	Modern British Locomotives	1954	—	£6.00

DAILY MAIL (Newspaper)

P176	War Photographs	1916	75p	—

DAILY MIRROR (Newspaper)

M100	Star Soccer Sides	1966	20p	£20.00

DAILY SKETCH (Newspaper)

40	World Cup Souvenir	1970	60p	£24.00

DAINTY NOVELS

Qty		Date	Odds	Sets
10	World's Famous Liners	1912	£6.00	£60.00

DANDY GUM

Qty		Date	Odds	Sets
K50	Bird Series (transfers)	1950	£1.00	—
M160	Cars and Bikes	1977	30p	—
M200	Birds (F1-200)	1968	—	£25.00
M100	Film & Entertainment Stars (Serie G)	1968	25p	£25.00
M116	Flag Parade	1965	—	£15.00
M160	Flag Parade	1978	—	£20.00
M55	Football World Cup (P/C Inset)	1986	—	£6.00
B72	Motor Cars	1966	35p	—
B53	Our Modern Army (P/C Inset)	1958	—	£25.00
B43/53	Our Modern Army (P/C Inset)	1958	10p	£5.00
B53	Pin Ups (P/C Inset)	1956	£1.00	—
B53	Pin Ups (P/C Inset, Different)	1978	—	£5.00
M70	Pop Stars (Serie P)	1977	16p	£12.00
M56	Rock Stars (Playing Card Inset)	1987	—	£6.00
M100	Soldier Parade	1970	—	£20.00
M72	Veteran & Vintage Cars	1966	50p	£36.00
M100	Wild Animals (H1-100)	1969	—	£15.00
M200	Wonderful World	1978	—	£25.00

LIAM DEVLIN & SONS LTD. (Confectionery)

Qty		Date	Odds	Sets
M36	Coaching Gaelic Football	1960	£3.00	—
48	Corgi Toys	1971	—	£25.00
50	Do You Know?	1964	—	£1.75
B50	Famous Footballers (New Series)	1952	£2.50	—
B50	Famous Footballers (A1)	1953	£2.00	—
B50	Famous Footballers (A2)	1954	£2.00	—
50	Famous Footballers (A3)	1955	£2.00	£100.00
B54	Famous Speedway Stars	1960	£4.00	—
B45	Fastest on Earth	1953	£1.50	—
36	Flags of the Nations	1960	£1.25	—
48	Gaelic Sportstars	1960	£2.50	—
48	Irish Fishing	1962	—	£6.00
50	Modern Transport	1966	—	£2.50
48	Our Dogs	1963	£2.00	—
48	Right or Wrong?	1963	£2.00	—
B35	Walt Disney Characters	1956	£2.00	—
B48	Wild Animals by George Cansdale	1954	£1.50	—
48	Wild Wisdom	1970	£1.25	—
50	Wonders of the World	1972	—	£1.75
100	World Flag Series	1970	£2.50	—

DICKSON ORDE & CO. LTD. (Confectionery)

Qty		Date	Odds	Sets
50	Footballers	1960	—	£1.75
25	Ships Through the Ages	1961	60p	—
25	Sports of the Countries	1962	—	£1.50

DINKIE PRODUCTS LTD. (Hair Grips)

Qty		Date	Odds	Sets
L24	Films (Plain backs)	1952	£1.00	—
L20	Gone with the Wind (Series 5)	1948	£1.00	—
X20	M.G.M. Films (Series 3)	1948	—	£12.00

DINKIE PRODUCTS LTD (Hair Grips)—cont.

Qty		Date	Odds	Sets
L24	M.G.M. Films (Series 7)	1949	—	£12.00
L24	M.G.M. Films (Series 9)	1950	—	£12.00
L24	M.G.M. Films (Series 10)	1951	£2.00	—
L24	M.G.M. Films (Series 11)	1951	£2.00	—
L24	Paramount Pictures (Series 8)	1950	—	£12.00
X24	Stars & Starlets (Series 1)	1947	—	£12.00
X20	Stars & Starlets (Series 2)	1947	—	£12.00
L24	Warner Bros. Artistes (Series 4)	1948	—	£12.00
L24	Warner Bros. Films (Series 6)	1949	—	£12.00

DIRECT TEA SUPPLY CO.

25	British Uniforms of the 19th Century	1958	—	£10.00

DISNEY MAGAZINE

P8	Disney Characters	1987	—	£3.00

F. M. DOBSON (Confectionery)

100	Newcastle & Sunderland's 100 Greatest Footballers	1982	—	£3.00
2	Error Cards	1982	—	50p

A. & J. DONALDSON (Commercial)

?500	Sports Favourites	1953	£2.50	—

DONRUSS (Gum, U.S.A.)

X59	B.M.X. Card Series	1984	—	£5.00
X66	Disneyland	1965	—	£12.00
X66	Elvis	1978	—	£5.00
X66	Freddie and the Dreamers	1965	—	£12.50
X66	Kiss, 1st Series	1978	—	£5.00
X66	Kiss, 2nd Series	1978	—	£5.00
X55	Knight Rider	1983	—	£4.00
X66	Magnum P.I.	1983	—	£5.00
X66	M.A.S.H.	1982	—	£5.00
X99	Moonraker	1979	—	£8.00
X66	1980 P.G.A. Tour	1981	—	£7.50
X66	1981 P.G.A. Tour	1982	—	£7.50
X66	Rock Stars	1978	—	£3.00
X99	Rocky II	1981	—	£4.00
X22	Rocky II Stickers	1981	—	£3.50
X63	Saturday Night Fever	1977	—	£4.00
X66	Sgt. Peppers Lonely Hearts Club Band	1978	—	£5.00
X66	Space 1999	1976	—	£4.00
X78	The Dark Crystal	1982	—	£5.00
X74	Tron	1983	—	£4.00
X66	Voyage to the Bottom of the Sea	1964	—	£15.00
X63	Zero Heroes	1983	—	£4.00

DOUBLE DIAMOND (Beer)

P5	Puzzle Pictures (beer mats)	1976	—	£1.00

DRYFOOD LTD. (Confectionery)

50	Animals of the World	1956	—	£1.75
K50	Zoo Animals	1955	—	£1.75

DUCHESS OF DEVONSHIRE DAIRY CO. LTD.

Qty		Date	Odds	Sets
L25	Devon Beauty Spots	1936	£3.00	£75.00

DUNHILLS (Confectionery)

25	Ships & Their Workings	1962	—	£3.00

DUNKIN (Confectionery, Spain)

X88	Martial Arts	1976	—	£15.00
M50	Motor Cycles of the World	1976	—	£20.00

DUNNS (Chocolate)

60	Animals	1924	£3.00	—

DUTTON'S BEER

12	Team of Sporting Heroes	1981	—	75p

THE EAGLE (Periodical)

M12	Marvels of this Modern Age (with album)	1965	—	£3.00
16	Wallet of Soccer Stars	1965	—	£2.50

EAST KENT NATIONAL BUS CO.

L8	British Airways Holidays	1984	—	65p

J. EDMONDSON & CO. LTD (Confectionery)

26	Actresses FROGA	1901	£30.00	—
4	Aeroplane Models	1939	£6.50	—
?40	Art Picture Series	1914	£7.50	—
15	Birds & Eggs	1924	£4.00	—
?20	Boy Scout Proficiency Badges	1924	£7.50	—
20	British Ships	1925	80p	£16.00
20	Dogs	1924	£3.50	—
20	Famous Castles	1925	£3.00	—
40	Flags of All Nations	1923	£3.00	—
24	Pictures from the Fairy Stories	1930	£2.50	—
24	Popular Sports	1930	£3.50	—
25	Sports & Pastimes Series	1916	£6.00	—
12	Throwing Shadows on the Wall	1937	£1.50	£18.00
25	War Series	1916	£7.50	—
12	Woodbine Village	1936	£1.50	£18.00
26	Zoo Alphabet	1935	£3.50	—

EDWARDS & SONS (Confectionery)

27	Popular Dogs	1954	£1.50	—
12	Products of the World	1957	—	75p
25	Transport Present & Future (Descriptive) ...	1956	—	£1.00
25	Transport Present & Future (Non-Descriptive) ...	1955	—	£1.25
25	Wonders of the Universe	1956	—	£1.00

ELKES BISCUITS LTD.

25	Do You Know?	1964	—	£1.50

ELY BREWERY CO. LTD.

B24	Royal Portraits	1953	£1.00	£24.00

EMPIRE MARKETING BOARD

Qty		Date	Odds	Sets
12	Empire Shopping	1926	£1.25	£15.00

H. E. EMPSON & SONS LTD. (Tea)

25	Birds	1962	—	£2.50
25	British Cavalry Uniforms of the 19th Century ...	1963	—	£6.00
25	Garden Flowers	1966	50p	£12.50
25	History of the Railways 1st Series	1966	50p	—
25	History of the Railways 2nd Series	1966	50p	—
25	Passenger Liners	1964	40p	£10.00
25	Tropical Birds	1966	40p	£10.00
25	Wonders of the Deep	1965	—	£1.00

ENGLISH & SCOTTISH C.W.S. (Shops)

50	British Sports Series	1904	£20.00	—
25	Humorous Peeps into History (1-25)	1927	£1.20	£30.00
25	Humorous Peeps into History (26-50)	1928	£2.50	—
25	In Victoria's Days	1930	£1.20	£30.00
X12	The Rose of the Orient Film Series	1925	25p	£3.00
X12	The Rose of the Orient 2nd Film Series	1925	30p	£3.50
X12	The Story of Tea (Blue Back)	1925	35p	£4.25
X12	The Story of Tea (Brown Back)	1925	30p	£3.50

ESKIMO FOODS

P4	The Beatles	1965	—	£16.00

JOHN E. ESSLEMONT LTD. (Tea)

25	Before Our Time	1966	—	£1.50
25	Into Space	1966	—	£2.00

ESSO PETROLEUM CO.

M16	Squelchers (Football)	1970	60p	£10.00

ESTA MEDICAL LABORATORIES INC. (U.S.A.)

E6	Curiosa of Conception	1960	—	£3.00

EVERSHED & SON LTD. (Soap)

25	Sports and Pastimes	1914	£7.50	—

EVERY GIRL'S PAPER

BF17	Film Stars	1924	£1.50	£25.00

EWBANKS LTD.

25	Animals of the Farmyard	1960	—	£1.00
25	British Uniforms	1956	—	£1.25
25	Miniature Cars & Scooters	1960	—	£1.25
50	Ports & Resorts of the World	1960	—	£2.00
25	Ships Around Britain	1961	—	£1.00
25	Sports & Games	1958	—	£1.25
25	Transport Through the Ages (black back)	1957	—	£1.00
25	Transport Through the Ages (blue back)	1957	—	£7.50

EXPRESS WEEKLY (Periodical)

Qty		Date	Odds	Sets
25	The Wild West (No Overprint)	1958	—	£1.25
25	The Wild West (Red Overprint)	1958	—	£1.00

FACCHINO'S CHOCOLATE WAFERS

100	Cinema Stars	1936	16p	£16.00
50	How or Why	1937	20p	£10.00
50	People of All Lands	1937	80p	—
50	Pioneers	1937	80p	£40.00

FAITH PRESS (Commercial)

10	Boy Scouts (LCC)	1928	£2.00	£20.00

FAMILY STAR (Periodical)

K52	Fortune Telling Cards	1952	—	£7.50

FARM TO DOOR SUPPLIES (Luton) LTD.

25	Castles of Great Britain	1965	£2.00	—
25	Cathedrals of Great Britain	1964	£2.00	—

FARROWS (Sauces)

50	Animals in the Zoo	1925	£3.00	—

ALEX FERGUSON (Confectionery)

41	V.C. Heroes	1916	£10.00	—

JOHN FILSHILL LTD. (Confectionery)

24	Birds & Their Eggs	1924	£3.00	—
25	Footballers	1924	£4.00	—

FINDUS (Frozen Foods)

20	All About Pirates	1967	—	£2.00

FINE FARE TEA

25	Inventions & Discoveries 1st Series	1965	—	£2.00
25	Inventions & Discoveries 2nd Series	1965	—	£2.00
12	Your Fortune in a Tea-cup	1966	—	£1.50

FISH MARKETING BOARD

18	Eat More Fish	1930	£1.25	—

FIZZY FRUIT (Confectionery)

25	Buses and Trams	1959	—	£8.00

FLEER GUM INC. (U.S.A.)

X60	CB Talk	1982	—	£4.00
X44	Crazy Magazine Covers 3rd	1981	—	£3.50
X66	Gomer Pyle, U.S.M.C.	1965	—	£8.00
X72	Here's Bo!	1980	—	£3.50
E12	Here's Bo Posters	1980	—	£2.50
X66	McHale's Navy	1965	—	£8.00

FLEETWAY PUBLICATIONS LTD.

X72	Adventures of Sexton Blake	1968	30p	£22.50
P28	Football Teams	1959	75p	£21.00
P2	Pop Stars (Roxy)	1961	—	60p
50	Star Footballers of 1963	1963	30p	£15.00

FLORENCE CARDS (Commercial)

Qty		Date	Odds	Sets
24	Luton Corporation Tramways	1983	—	£1.00
T20	Tramway Scenes	1985	—	£1.25

FORD MOTOR CO. LTD.

Qty		Date	Odds	Sets
M50	Major Farming	1955	£2.50	—

FOSTER CLARK PRODUCTS (Malta)

Qty		Date	Odds	Sets
50	The Sea—Our Other World	1974	—	£12.50

A. C. W. FRANCIS (Confectionery, Grenada)

Qty		Date	Odds	Sets
25	Football Clubs & Badges	1967	—	£5.00
25	Pond Life	1967	—	£3.50
25	Sports of the Countries	1967	—	£4.00

LES FRERES (Shop)

Qty		Date	Odds	Sets
25	Aircraft of World War II	1964	—	£3.00

J. S. FRY & SONS LTD. (Confectionery)

Qty		Date	Odds	Sets
3	Advertisement Cards	1910	£12.00	—
50	Ancient Sundials	1924	£1.25	£62.50
50	Birds & Poultry	1912	£1.00	£50.00
24	Birds & Their Eggs	1912	£1.60	£40.00
15	China & Porcelain	1907	£5.00	£75.00
P2	Coronation Postcards	1911	£5.00	—
25	Days of Nelson	1906	£3.50	£87.50
25	Days of Wellington	1906	£3.50	£87.50
25	Empire Industries	1924	£2.50	—
50	Exercises for Men & Women	1926	£2.50	—
48	Film Stars	1934	£1.00	—
50	Fowls, Pigeons & Dogs	1908	£1.50	£75.00
P12	Fun Cards	1972	—	75p
25	Match Tricks	1921	*£15.00*	—
15	National Flags	1908	£2.50	£37.50
50	Nursery Rhymes	1917	£1.20	£60.00
50	Phil May Sketches	1905	£1.50	£75.00
25	Red Indians	1927	£2.50	—
25	Rule Britannia	1915	£3.00	£75.00
50	Scout Series	1912	£3.00	£150.00
48	Screen Stars	1928	£1.50	—
120	This Wonderful World	1935	75p	—
50	Time & Money in Different Countries	1908	£1.50	£75.00
50	Tricks & Puzzles (Black Back)	1924	£1.20	£60.00
50	Tricks & Puzzles (Blue Back)	1918	£1.20	£60.00
6	War Leaders (Campaign Packets)	1915	£12.50	—
25	With Captain Scott at the South Pole	1913	£3.50	£87.50

CANADIAN ISSUES

Qty		Date	Odds	Sets
50	Children's Nursery Rhymes	1912	£6.00	—
25	Radio Series	1912	£4.00	—
50	Scout Series—Second Series	1913	£5.00	—
50	Treasure Island Map	1912	£3.50	—

GAUMONT CHOCOLATE BAR

Qty		Date	Odds	Sets
F50	Film Stars	1936	£1.00	—

GAYCON PRODUCTS LTD. (Confectionery)

Qty		Date	Odds	Sets
25	Adventures of Pinky & Perky 1st Series	1961	75p	—
25	Adventures of Pinky & Perky 2nd Series	1961	75p	—
50	British Birds & Their Eggs	1961	—	£1.75
25	British Butterflies	1962	—	£7.50
25	Do You Know? 1st Series	1964	75p	—
25	Do You Know? 2nd Series	1964	75p	—
50	Flags of All Nations	1963	60p	—
25	History of the Blue Lamp 1st Series	1962	—	£5.00
25	History of the Blue Lamp 2nd Series	1962	—	£5.00
30	Kings & Queens	1961	—	£1.00
25	Modern Motor Cars	1959	£1.00	—
25	Modern Motor Cars of the World 1st Series	1962	£1.25	—
25	Modern Motor Cars of the World 2nd Series	1962	£1.25	—
25	Red Indians 1st Series	1960	—	£2.50
25	Red Indians 2nd Series	1960	—	£2.50
25	Top Secret 1st Series	1963	£1.00	—
25	Top Secret 2nd Series	1963	£1.00	—

GEES FOOD PRODUCTS

Qty		Date	Odds	Sets
30	Kings & Queens	1961	—	£5.00
16	See Britain by Coach	1959	—	£1.00

GEM LIBRARY (Periodical)

		Date	Odds	Sets
BF4	Footballers—Autographed Action Series	1923	£1.25	£5.00
BF6	Footballers—Autographed Real Action Photo Series	1922	£1.25	£7.50
BF15	Footballers—Special Action Photo	1922	£1.20	£18.00
L16	Marvels of the Future	1929	£1.25	£20.00

ALFRED GERBER (Cheese)

		Date	Odds	Sets
M143	Glorious Switzerland	1952	60p	—

GIRLS FRIEND (Periodical)

		Date	Odds	Sets
B6	Actresses (Silk)	1913	£6.00	£36.00

GIRLS MIRROR (Periodical)

		Date	Odds	Sets
BF10	Actors & Actresses	1922	£1.25	£12.50

GIRLS WEEKLY

		Date	Odds	Sets
12	Flower Fortune Cards	1912	£7.50	—

GLAMOUR

		Date	Odds	Sets
F52	Pop Singer Card Game	1957	40p	£20.00

GLENGETTIE TEA

Qty		Date	Odds	Sets
25	Animals of the World	1964	—	£1.00
25	Birds & Their Eggs	1970	—	£2.50
25	British Locomotives	1959	—	£1.50
25	Do You Know?	1970	—	£1.00
25	Historical Scenes	1968	—	£1.00
25	History of the Railways 1st Series	1974	—	£1.00
25	History of the Railways 2nd Series	1974	—	£1.00
25	International Air Liners	1963	—	£1.00
25	Medals of the World (Black Back)	1959	—	£1.00

GLENGETTIE TEA—cont.

Qty		Date	Odds	Sets
25	Medals of the World (Blue Back)	1959	—	£6.00
25	Modern Transport (Black Back)	1963	—	£6.00
25	Modern Transport (Blue Back)	1963	—	£7.50
25	Naval Battles	1971	—	£1.00
25	Rare British Birds	1967	—	£1.50
25	Sovereigns, Consorts & Rulers of G.B. 1st	1970	—	£6.00
25	Sovereigns, Consorts & Rulers of G.B. 2nd	1970	—	£6.00
25	The British Army (Black Back)	1976	—	£1.00
25	The British Army (Blue Back)	1976	—	£1.00
25	Trains of the World	1966	—	£1.00
25	Veteran & Vintage Cars	1966	—	£10.00
25	Wild Flowers	1961	—	£1.25

GLENTONS LTD. (Shop)

Qty		Date	Odds	Sets
24	World's Most Beautiful Butterflies	1910	£3.00	—

J. GODDARD & SONS LTD. (Metal Polish)

Qty		Date	Odds	Sets
L4	Cleaning a Silver Teapot	1928	£1.50	—
L3	Four Generations	1923	50p	£1.50
L12	London Views	1925	35p	£4.25
L12	Old Silver	1924	50p	£6.00
L9	Old Silver at the Victorian & Albert Museum	1933	£1.00	£9.00
L12	Ports of the World	1928	£1.00	£12.00
L12	Present Day Silverware	1937	75p	£9.00
L4	Silverware with Flowers I	1928	£1.00	£4.00
L8	Silverware with Flowers II	1933	£1.25	£10.00
L2	Use & Cleaning of Silverware I	1926	25p	50p
L6	Use & Cleaning of Silverware II	1937	£2.00	—
L8	Views of Leicester	1934	£1.50	£12.00
L12	Views of Old Leicester	1928	£1.50	—

GOLDEN FLEECE (Australia)

Qty		Date	Odds	Sets
X36	Pedigree Dogs	1972	—	£7.50

GOLDEN GRAIN TEA

Qty		Date	Odds	Sets
25	Birds	1970	—	£5.00
25	British Cavalry Uniforms of the 19th Century	1964	—	£2.50
25	Garden Flowers	1971	—	£1.00
25	Passenger Liners	1970	—	£1.00

GOLDEN WONDER (Potato Crisps)

Qty		Date	Odds	Sets
24	Soccer All Stars	1978	—	£1.00
14	Space Cards (round corners)	1979	—	75p
14	Space Cards (square corners)	1979	—	75p
24	Sporting All Stars	1979	—	£1.00
24	TV All Stars	1979	—	£1.00
36	World Cup Soccer All Stars	1978	—	£1.25

GOODIES LTD. (Confectionery)

Qty		Date	Odds	Sets
25	Flags & Emblems	1961	—	£1.50
25	Indian Tribes	1975	80p	£20.00
25	Mini Monsters	1975	70p	£17.50
24	Olympics	1972	80p	£20.00

GOODIES LTD.—cont.

Qty		Date	Odds	Sets
25	Pirates	1976	80p	£20.00
25	Prehistoric Animals	1969	80p	—
25	Robbers & Thieves	1976	80p	—
25	The Monkees 1st Series	1967	—	£5.00
25	The Monkees 2nd Series	1968	£1.25	—
25	Vanishing Animals	1977	80p	£20.00
25	Weapons Through the Ages	1974	70p	£17.50
25	Wicked Monarchs	1973	70p	£17.50
25	Wide World/People of Other Lands	1968	70p	£17.50
25	Wild Life	1977	80p	£20.00
25	World Cup '74	1974	80p	£20.00

D. W. GOODWIN & CO. (Flour)

Qty		Date	Odds	Sets
36	Careers for Boys & Girls	1930	£5.00	—
24	Extra Rhymes, 2nd Series	1930	£6.00	—
36	Flags of All Nations	1930	£4.00	—
?30	Jokes Series	1930	£5.00	—
?30	Optical Illusions	1930	£4.00	—
?30	Ships Series	1930	£5.00	—
?36	World Interest Series	1930	£4.00	—

WILLIAM GOSSAGE & SONS LTD. (Soap)

Qty		Date	Odds	Sets
48	British Birds & Their Eggs	1924	£1.00	£50.00
48	Butterflies & Moths	1924	75p	£36.00

GOWERS & BURGONS (Tea)

Qty		Date	Odds	Sets
25	British Birds & Their Nests	1970	—	£3.00
25	Family Pets	1964	—	£1.00
25	People & Places	1970	—	£1.00
25	Prehistoric Animals	1969	—	£7.50
25	Sailing Ships Through the Ages	1971	—	£7.50
25	The Circus	1964	—	£10.00
25	Veteran and Vintage Cars	1965	—	£6.00
25	Veteran Racing Cars	1964	40p	—

GRANGERS NO. "1"

Qty		Date	Odds	Sets
12	Dr Mabuse Series	1926	£5.00	£60.00

GRANOSE FOODS LTD.

Qty		Date	Odds	Sets
M48	Adventures of Billy the Buck	1956	—	£1.25
M16	Air Transport	1957	—	£1.00
M16	Animal Life	1957	—	75p
25	Animals in the Service of Man	1965	£1.50	—
M16	Aquatic & Reptile Life	1957	—	75p
M48	King of the Air	1956	20p	—
M48	Life Story of Blower the Whale	1956	25p	—
M48	Lone Leo the Cougar	1955	25p	—
L20	150 Years of British Locomotives	1981	30p	—
M16	Out Winged Friends	1957	25p	—
M16	Plant Life	1957	50p	—
M48	Silver Mane, the Timber Wolf	1955	—	£2.50
M16	Space Travel	1957	—	£2.50
M48	Tippytail the Grizzly Bear	1956	—	£1.75
M16	Water Transport	1957	—	75p
M16	World Wide Visits	1957	—	75p

GREGG (Jelly, New Zealand)

Qty		Date	Odds	Sets
B48	Aquatic Birds	1974	—	£5.00
B40	Land Birds of New Zealand	1974	—	£6.00
B35	Rare and Endangered Birds	1974	—	£6.00
B40	Remarkable Birds of the World	1974	—	£6.00

HALPINS (Tea)

25	Aircraft of the World	1958	—	£1.00
L20	Aircraft of the World (Double, as Above)	1958	—	£4.00
25	Nature Studies	1958	—	£2.00

HAMPSHIRE CRICKET CLUB

24	Sunday League Era	1987	—	£4.50

HAPPY HOME (Periodical)

B8	Child Studies (Silk)	1912	£6.00	—
M9	Flags (Silk)	1914	£3.50	£31.50
B9	Our Lucky Flowers (Silk)	1912	£7.50	—
K14	The Happy Home Silk Button (Silk)	1914	£4.00	£56.00
M12	Women on War Work (Silk)	1915	£4.00	£48.00

HARDEN BROS. & LINDSAY LTD. (Tea)

50	Animals of the World	1960	—	£5.00
50	British Birds & Their Eggs	1960	—	£10.00
50	National Pets	1961	—	£1.75

HARRISON (Pomade)

25	Beauties	1902	£15.00	—

JOHN HAWKINS & SONS LTD. (Cotton)

LF30	The Story of Cotton	1925	£3.00	£90.00

HEINEKEN (Beer)

P12	The Heineken Story (beer mats)	1976	—	£2.00

HEINZ (Foods)

E1	Australian Cricket Team	1964	—	£1.25

HERALD ALARMS

10	Feudal Lords	1986	—	£5.00
X10	Feudal Lords	1986	—	£5.00

HERON PETROL

K16	Holidays	1960	60p	—

HERTFORDSHIRE POLICE FORCE

X12	Postage Stamps	1985	—	£3.00

JOHN HINDHAUGH & CO. (Bread)

25	Railway Engines	1913	£20.00	—

HITCHMAN'S DAIRIES LTD.

Qty		Date	Odds	Sets
25	Aircraft of World War II	1966	—	£4.00
25	Animals of the World	1964	—	£4.00
25	British Birds & Their Nests	1970	50p	£12.50
25	British Railways	1971	—	£1.25
25	Buses & Trams	1966	—	£1.50
25	Merchant Ships of the World	1970	—	£4.00
25	Modern Wonders	1962	—	£5.00
25	Naval Battles	1971	—	£1.25
25	People & Places	1971	—	£1.50
25	Regimental Uniforms of the Past	1973	—	£1.00
25	Science in the 20th Century	1966	—	£1.25
25	The Story of Milk	1965	—	£7.50
25	Trains of the World	1970	—	£7.50

HOADLEY'S CHOCOLATES LTD.—(Australia)

Qty		Date	Odds	Sets
50	British Empire Kings & Queens	1940	60p	£30.00
?33	Cricketers (black fronts)	1928	£6.00	—
36	Cricketers (brown fronts)	1933	£5.00	£180.00
50	Early Australian Series	1938	60p	£30.00
50	Empire Games and Test Teams	1932	£4.00	—
40	Test Cricketers	1936	£5.00	—
B36	Test Cricketers (different)	1938	£6.00	—
50	The Birth of a Nation	1938	75p	£37.50
50	Victorian Footballers (Heads, 1-50)	1938	£1.00	£50.00
50	Victorian Footballers 51-100	1938	£1.00	£50.00
50	Victorian Footballers (Action)	1938	£1.00	£50.00
50	Wild West Series	1938	50p	£25.00

HOBBYPRESS GUIDES (Books)

Qty		Date	Odds	Sets
20	Preserved Railway Locomotives	1983	—	£1.25
20	Preserved Steam Railways 1st	1983	—	£1.00
20	Preserved Steam Railways 2nd	1984	—	£1.00
20	The World's Great Cricketers	1984	—	£3.00

THOMAS HOLLOWAY LTD. (Pharmaceutics)

Qty		Date	Odds	Sets
X39	Natural History Series (Animals Heads)	1900	£3.50	£140.00
X39	Natural History Series (Birds)	1900	£3.50	£140.00
X60	Natural History Series (Full Length)	1900	£3.00	£180.00
X50	Pictorial History of the Sports and Pastimes of all Nations	1900	£4.00	£200.00

HOME & COLONIAL STORES LTD.

Qty		Date	Odds	Sets
26	Advertising Alphabet	1914	£3.50	—
M100	Flag Pictures	1916	£1.75	—
M40	War Heroes	1916	£2.00	£80.00
M40	War Pictures	1916	£2.00	£80.00
100	War Pictures (Different)	1916	£1.75	£175.00

HOME COUNTIES DAIRIES TEA

Qty		Date	Odds	Sets
25	Country Life	1964	—	£1.00
25	International Air Liners	1965	—	£1.00
25	The Story of Milk	1965	—	£1.50

HOME MIRROR (Periodical)

Qty		Date	Odds	Sets
M4	Cinema Star Pictures (Silk)	1919	£6.00	—

HOME WEEKLY (Periodical)

12	Little Charlie Cards	1920	£10.00	—

GEORGE W. HORNER & CO. LTD. (Confectionery)

P24	Wireless Cards	1926	£5.00	—

HORNIMAN (Tea)

P10	Boating Ways	1910	£8.00	—
P12	British Birds & Eggs	1910	£7.50	—
48	Dogs	1961	—	£1.75
P10	Naval Heroes	1910	£8.00	—
48	Pets	1960	—	£1.75
48	Wild Animals	1958	—	£1.75

HORSLEY'S STORES

25	British Uniforms of the 19th Century	1968	—	£4.00
25	Castles of Britain	1968	—	£5.00
25	Family Pets	1968	—	£3.50

VAN HOUTEN (Chocolate)

M4	Dutch Costumes (Wrappers)	1953	—	£2.00
P12	How Nature Protects the Weak	1908	£5.00	£60.00

HULL CITY FOOTBALL CLUB

X20	Footballers	1950	£1.75	£35.00

HUNT CROP & SONS (Vedast)

15	Characters from Dickens	1912	£5.00	£75.00

HUNTLEY & PALMER (Biscuits)

P12	Animals	1900	£4.00	£48.00
P12	Aviation	1900	*£25.00*	—
P12	Biscuits in Various Countries	1900	£3.50	£42.00
P6	Biscuits with Travellers	1900	£4.00	£24.00
P12	Children of Nations I (Gold Border)	1900	£3.50	£42.00
P12	Children of Nations II (White Border)	1900	£3.50	£42.00
P12	Children at Leisure & Play	1900	£4.00	£48.00
P12	Harvests of the World	1900	£10.00	—
P12	Hunting	1900	£5.00	—
P8	Inventors	1900	£10.00	—
X12	Rhondes Enfantines	1900	£12.50	—
P12	Scenes with Biscuits	1900	£3.50	£42.00
X8	Shakespearian Series	1900	£4.00	£32.00
P12	Soldiers of Various Countries	1900	£7.50	£90.00
P12	Sports (Semi-Circular Background)	1900	£4.00	£50.00
P12	Sports (Plain Background)	1900	£4.00	£50.00
P12	The Seasons	1900	£5.00	—
P12	Travelling During the 19th Century	1900	£7.50	—
P12	Views of Italy & the French Riviera	1900	£4.00	—
P12	Warships of Nations	1900	£7.50	—
P8	Watteau	1900	£4.00	£32.00
P8	Wonders of the World	1900	£7.50	—

HUSTLER SOAP

Qty		Date	Odds	Sets
20	Animals 1st Series	1925	40p	£8.00
20	Animals 2nd Series	1925	50p	£10.00
20	Animals 3rd Series	1925	40p	£8.00
30	Regimental Nicknames	1924	£1.00	£30.00

R. HYDE & CO. LTD. (Bird Seed)

80	British Birds	1928	60p	£48.00
80	Cage Birds	1930	60p	£48.00
80	Canary Culture	1930	50p	£45.00
M10	Cartoons	1908	£7.50	—
M24	Modern Wonders	1924	£5.00	£120.00

I.P.C. MAGAZINES LTD.

M25	Lindy's Cards of Fortune	1975	—	£2.00

JOHN IRWIN SONS & CO. LTD. (Tea)

6	Characters from Shakespeare	1912	£12.50	—

JACOB & CO. (Biscuits)

D24	Banknotes That Made History (With Album)	1975	—	75p
D32	Famous Picture Cards From History (With Album)	1978	—	£1.00
25	Vehicles of All Ages	1924	£1.40	£35.00
25	Zoo Series (Brown Back)	1924	60p	£15.00
25	Zoo Series (Green Back)	1924	40p	£10.00

JESK (Confectionery)

25	Buses & Trams	1959	—	£6.00

JIBCO (Tea)

28	Dominoes	1956	£2.00	—
K53	Miniature Playing Cards	1956	£2.00	—
K50	Puzzle Cards	1955	£2.00	—
K25	Screen Stars	1955	£1.00	—
K25	Screen Stars, 2nd Series	1956	—	£1.25

R. L. JONES & CO. LTD. (Drink)

24	Jet Aircraft of the World	1956	—	£1.00

JUBBLY (Drink)

50	Adventurous Lives	1967	—	£1.75

JUNIOR PASTIMES (Commercial)

52	Popular English Players	1951	£1.00	—
52	Popular Players (Footballers)	1951	£1.00	—
52	Popular Railway Engines	1951	£1.00	—
L80	Star Pix	1951	60p	—

JUST SEVENTEEN (Magazine)

T17	Posters	1986	—	75p

K.P. NUTS & CRISPS

12	Sports Adventure Series	1978	—	£5.00
20	Wonderful World of Nature	1983	30p	—

KANE PRODUCTS LTD. (Confectionery)

Qty		Date	Odds	Sets
36	ATV Stars (Packets)	1957	£1.00	—
50	British Birds & Their Eggs	1960	—	£12.50
25	Cricket Clubs & Badges	1957	—	£1.50
L50	Disc Stars	1960	30p	£15.00
X50	Disc Stars	1960	—	£10.00
50	Dogs	1955	75p	£37.50
X72	Film Stars (Plain Back)	1955	50p	£36.00
50	Flags of All Nations	1959	—	£4.00
25	Football Clubs & Colours	1956	—	£1.00
50	Historical Characters	1957	—	£2.00
25	International Football Stars	1957	—	£3.50
30	Kings & Queens	1959	—	£2.50
X30	Kings & Queens	1959	—	£4.00
25	Modern Motor Cars	1959	—	£4.00
50	Modern Racing Cars	1954	—	£2.00
25	National Pets Club 1st Series	1958	—	£2.00
25	National Pets Club 2nd Series	1958	£1.00	£25.00
25	1956 Cricketers 1st Series	1956	—	£2.50
25	1956 Cricketers 2nd Series	1956	—	£4.00
25	Red Indians 1st Series	1957	—	£2.00
25	Red Indians 2nd Series	1957	—	£1.50
25	Roy Rogers Colour Series	1958	20p	£5.00
25	Roy Rogers Series	1957	60p	£15.00
50	Space Adventure	1955	—	£15.00
50	20th Century Events	1955	60p	£30.00
K50	Wild Animals	1954	—	£1.75

KARDOMAH (Tea)

K?500	General Interest (various series)	1900	£2.00	—

M. & S. KEECH

15	Australian Cricket Team 1905	1986	—	£2.50
15	English Cricketers of 1902	1987	—	£2.50

KEILLER (Confectionery)

LF18	Film Favourites	1926	£4.00	—
25	Scottish Heritage	1976	—	£5.00

KELLOGG LTD. (Cereals)

16	A History of British Military Aircraft	1963	10p	£1.50
16	Animals (3D)	1968	£1.25	£20.00
12	Famous Firsts	1963	—	75p
12	International Soccer Stars	1963	—	£1.25
40	Motor Cars	1950	£1.00	£40.00
40	Motor Cars (Coloured, as above)	1951	£1.25	£50.00
X56	Playing Cards	1986	—	£3.00
16	Ships of the British Navy	1962	30p	£5.00
12	The Story of the Bicycle	1964	£1.50	£18.00
16	The Story of the Locomotive 1st Series	1963	30p	£5.00
16	The Story of the Locomotive 2nd Series	1963	30p	£5.00
16	Veteran Motor Cars	1962	20p	£3.00

CANADIAN ISSUES

M150	General Interest 1st Set	1940	75p	—
M150	General Interest 2nd Set	1940	75p	—
M150	General Interest 3rd Set	1940	75p	—

KENT COUNTY CRICKET CLUB

Qty		Date	Odds	Sets
50	Cricketers of Kent	1986	—	£6.00

KIDDYS FAVOURITES LTD. (Commercial)

Qty		Date	Odds	Sets
52	New Popular Film Stars	1950	75p	—
52	Popular Boxers	1950	70p	—
52	Popular Cricketers	1950	£1.75	—
65	Popular Film Stars	1950	75p	—
52	Popular Footballers	1950	£1.00	—
52	Popular Olympics	1950	75p	—
75	Popular Players (Hearts on Front)	1950	75p	—
52	Popular Players (Shamrocks on Front)	1950	£1.00	—
52	Popular Speedway Riders	1950	£1.50	—

KINGS LAUNDRIES LTD. (Walthamstow, E. London)

Qty		Date	Odds	Sets
25	Famous Railway Engines	1953	£1.50	—
25	Modern British Warplanes	1953	£1.25	—
25	Modern Motor Cycles	1953	£1.25	—
25	Radio & Television Stars	1953	£1.25	—

KINGS OF YORK (Laundry)

Qty		Date	Odds	Sets
25	Flags of All Nations (Silk)	1954	£1.00	£25.00
30	Kings & Queens of England	1954	—	£1.00

KINGS SPECIALITIES (Food Products)

Qty		Date	Odds	Sets
26	Alphabet Rhymes	1915	£6.00	—
25	"Dont's" or Lessons in Etiquette	1915	£4.00	—
25	Great War Celebrities	1915	£5.00	—
25	Heroes of Famous Books	1915	£4.00	—
25	King's "Discoveries"	1915	£4.00	—
25	King's "Servants"	1915	£4.00	—
25	Proverbs	1915	£4.00	—
37	Unrecorded History	1915	£4.00	—
100	War Pictures	1915	£5.00	—
25	Where King's Supplies Grow	1915	£4.00	—

KNOCKOUT (Periodical)

Qty		Date	Odds	Sets
20	Super Planes of Today	1956	—	£1.00

KNORR (Cheese)

Qty		Date	Odds	Sets
T6	Great Trains of Europe	1983	80p	£5.00

KRAFT CHEESE

Qty		Date	Odds	Sets
12	Historic Military Uniforms	1971	—	75p

LACEY'S CHEWING GUM

Qty		Date	Odds	Sets
50	Footballers	1923	£5.00	—
?24	Uniforms	1923	£10.00	—

F. LAMBERT & SONS LTD. (Tea)

Qty		Date	Odds	Sets
25	Before Our Time	1961	—	£1.00
25	Birds & Their Eggs	1962	—	*£3.00*
25	Butterflies & Moths	1960	—	£1.00
25	Cacti	1962	—	£1.00
25	Car Registration Numbers 1st Series	1959	—	£2.50
25	Car Registration Numbers 2nd Series	1960	—	£5.00

LIEBIG

The Liebig Extract of Meat Co. Ltd. was formed in 1856 and was acquired by Brooke Bond in 1971. In Britain their product was renamed Oxo, which it is known as today. In a period of 100 years from 1872 the Company issued a large number of sets of cards, including postcards, menus, calendars, place cards and other novelty issues. The first series were issued in France, but eventually cards could be obtained all over Europe, in languages such as Danish, Czech, Spanish and even Russian. Many series were printed in English, including the Oxo insert series, and issued in Britain and the U.S.A.

In all the Company issued 2,000 different sets of cards. These covered an enormous variety of subjects, including the Trans-Siberian Railway, Shadowgraphs, Gulliver, Fans, Education in Ancient Greece, and the Left Bank of the Po. There is even a set showing the life of Justus von Liebig, founder of the firm, and another showing how the cards themselves are prepared and printed.

Because of the size of the subject a separate Catalogue is available (price £3.00) listing all the issues, and a small selection of series is listed on page 193.

MODERN CARDS

The Second World War resulted in the virtual disappearance of Cigarette Cards, and it has only been in the last three or four years that some companies have started to issue series with brands of cigars such as Doncella, Grandee and Tom Thumb. The keen collector has however been fortunate in the considerable number of trade cards issued since the War.

Most prominent among these have been the issues with tea, and foremost of these is Brooke Bond. Their first set (British Birds) was issued in 1954, and since then they have been responsible for 39 sets in Britain as well as 17 in Canada. Other companies such as Horniman and Lyons also issued sets, but with limited success.

Another product responsible for many series is confectionery (including bubble gum). Barratt, later to become Bassett, issued many series with their sweet cigarettes. A. & B.C. Gum, a subsidiary of Topps, also issued many series, including the celebrated 'Mars Attacks', which had to be withdrawn because it was considered too horrific.

Periodicals are another product issuing many series, with Fleetway Publications and Thomson maintaining the tradition of the pre-war issues. But a keen eye at the local supermarket will over a period of time observe many card series, by firms such as Jacob's Biscuits, Bell's Whisky and Shelley's Ice Cream.

F. LAMBERT & SONS LTD. (Tea)—cont.

Qty		Date	Odds	Sets
25	Football Clubs & Badges	1958	—	£1.00
25	Game Birds & Wild Fowl	1964	—	£3.00
25	Historic East Anglia	1961	—	£1.00
25	Interesting Hobbies	1965	—	£6.00
25	Passenger Liners	1965	—	£6.00
25	Past & Present	1964	—	£1.00
25	People & Places	1966	—	*£3.00*
25	Pond Life	1964	—	£5.00
25	Sports & Games	1964	—	£1.00

LANCASHIRE CONSTABULARY

24	Cop-a-cards	1987	—	£5.00
X12	Motor Cars	1987	—	£3.50

LANCASTER REPRINTS

45	Hockey Players (I.T.C. Canada)	1987	—	£7.50
36	Hockey Series (I.T.C. Canada)	1987	—	£7.50

HERBERT LAND (Cycles)

30	Army Pictures, Cartoons, etc.	1915	£20.00	—

LEAF BRANDS INC. (Confectionery)

X50	Cliff Richard	1960	50p	£25.00
X50	Do You Know?	1961	10p	£3.00
X90	Famous Artistes	1960	60p	—
X50	Famous Discoveries & Adventures	1962	75p	—
X50	Footballers	1961	16p	£8.00
X40	The Flag Game	1960	20p	£8.00
X50	Totem Pole Talking Signs	1962	30p	£15.00

LETRASET

12	Star Wars	1978	—	£3.50

LEVER BROS. (Soap)

20	British Birds & Their Nests	1961	—	£1.00
F150	Celebrities	1900	£2.00	—
L39	Celebrities	1901	£3.00	£120.00

LIEBIG CATALOGUE IN ENGLISH (3rd EDITION)

The most comprehensive Liebig catalogue ever! And the first in English!

*** Titles and prices of all normal series—over 1800.

*** Lists of all menus and table cards, including some hitherto unrecorded.

*** Lists of all Oxo series, Brooke Bonds, and other Liebig/Lemco issues.

*** Cross reference to Fada and Sanguinetti Catalogues.

*** Comprehensive thematic index.

65 pages, including illustrations. Price (inc. Postage) **£3.00**.

LIEBIG EXTRACT OF MEAT CO. (see also Oxo)

This firm issued nearly 2,000 different sets throughout Europe between 1872 and 1974. Because inclusion of all these in this volume would be impracticable we have produced a separate catalogue of Liebig Cards. See separate announcement for details. Some recent Italian issues are included below as a sample of the scope of these series.

Qty		Date	Odds	Sets
X6	1839 Ancient Cavalry	1970	—	£2.00
X6	1840 Ancient Helmets	1970	—	£1.50
X6	1799 Antique Pistols	1964	—	£2.00
X6	1837 Astronomy 1st Series	1970	—	£1.00
X6	1838 Astronomy 2nd Series	1970	—	£1.00
X6	1856 Beethoven	1973	—	£1.25
X6	1848 Bullfighting 1st Series	1970	—	£1.00
X6	1849 Bullfighting 2nd Series	1970	—	£1.00
X6	1825 Carabinieri (Military Police)	1968	—	£5.00
X6	1833 Chess Pieces	1969	—	£2.00
X6	1844 Conquest of the Moon 1st Series	1971	—	£1.00
X6	1851 Conquest of the Moon 2nd Series	1972	—	£1.00
X6	1818 Cradles	1967	—	£1.00
X6	1842 Dangerous Occupations 1st Series	1970	—	£1.00
X6	1843 Dangerous Occupations 2nd Series	1970	—	£1.00
X6	1824 Early Aviation	1968	—	£2.00
X6	1812 Ecumenical Councils	1966	—	£1.00
X6	1852 Famous Duels	1972	—	£1.00
X6	1819 Famous Places from "The Promised Bride"	1967	—	£2.00
X6	1841 Giovanni Pascoli	1970	—	£1.00
X6	1817 History of Photography	1965	—	£2.00
X6	1854 History of Typewriters	1972	—	£1.25
X6	1855 How Animals See 1st Series	1973	—	£1.00
X6	1858 How Animals See 2nd Series	1973	—	£1.00
X6	1832 Italian Aviation	1969	—	£2.00
X6	1836 Life & Works of Rossini	1969	—	£1.00
X6	1820 Life of Massimo D'Azeglio	1967	—	£1.00
X6	1795 Lithographic Art	1964	—	£2.00
X6	1834 Locomotives	1969	—	£2.00
X6	1831 Modern Aviation	1969	—	£2.00
X6	1828 Old Uniforms 1st Series	1968	—	£1.00
X6	1829 Old Uniforms 2nd Series	1968	—	£1.00
X6	1830 Old Uniforms 3rd Series	1968	—	£2.00
X6	1826 Philosophy & Science	1968	—	£2.00
X6	1764 Pinocchio	1962	—	£2.50
X6	1835 Principal Middle East States	1969	—	£2.00
X6	1801 Protected Birds	1964	—	£1.00
X6	1853 Resurrection (Paintings)	1972	—	£2.00
X6	1857 Search for Microbes 1st Series	1973	—	£1.00
X6	1860 Search for Microbes 2nd Series	1973	—	£1.00
X6	1850 Self Portraits	1972	—	£1.00
X6	1783 Story of Guns 1st Series	1962	—	£5.00
X6	1790 Story of Guns 2nd Series	1963	—	£2.00
X6	1859 Story of the Circus 1st Series	1973	—	£1.25
X6	1861 Story of the Circus 2nd Series	1974	—	£1.25
X6	1846 Symbols of Power 1st Series	1971	—	£2.00
X6	1847 Symbols of Power 2nd Series	1972	—	£1.00
X6	1863 The Animal Kingdom	1974	—	£1.00
X6	1862 Warships	1974	—	£2.00
X6	1771 World's Motorways	1962	—	£2.00

LIFEGUARD PRODUCTS (Soap)

Qty		Date	Odds	Sets
25	British Butterflies	1955	—	75p

JOSEPH LINGFORD & SON LTD. (Baking Powder)

36	British War Leaders	1949	—	£20.00

LIPTON LTD. (Tea)

60	Flags of the World	1967	—	£4.00
50	The Conquest of Space	1962	—	£2.50

LODGE SPARK PLUGS

T24	Cars	1960	£5.00	—

LONDESBORO' THEATRE

50	War Portraits	1916	£20.00	—

LONGLEAT HOUSE

25	Longleat House	1967	—	£1.00

LOT-O-FUN (Periodical)

BF4	Champions	1922	£2.00	£8.00

G. F. LOVELL & CO. LTD. (Confectionery)

36	British Royalty Series	1910	£15.00	—
36	Football Series	1910	£15.00	—
25	Photos of Football Stars	1926	£4.00	—

J. LYONS & CO. LTD. (Ice Cream & Tea)

40	All Systems Go	1968	50p	£20.00
48	Australia	1959	10p	£1.75
25	Birds & Their Eggs	1962	—	£1.50
40	British Wildlife	1970	40p	£16.00
L16	Catweazle Magic Cards	1971	—	£1.25
X12	Did You Know?	1983	75p	—
40	European Adventure	1969	60p	—
40	Famous Aircraft	1965	12p	£5.00
40	Famous Cars	1966	60p	£24.00
40	Famous Locomotives	1964	£1.00	£40.00
48	Famous People	1966	30p	£15.00
32	HMS 1902-1962	1962	10p	£1.25
32	HMS 1902-1962 (non descriptive)	1962	—	£1.50
L35	Illustrated Map of the British Isles	1959	30p	£10.50
40	International Footballers	1972	60p	£24.00
40	Into the Unknown	1969	50p	£20.00
15	Jubilee	1977	60p	£9.00
50	100 Years of Motoring	1964	50p	—
40	On Safari	1970	40p	£16.00
40	Pop Scene	1971	50p	—
40	Pop Stars	1970	50p	£20.00
K24	Puzzle Series	1955	20p	£5.00
40	Soccer Stars	1971	60p	£24.00
40	Space Age Britain	1968	50p	£20.00
40	Space Exploration	1963	50p	£20.00
25	Space 1999	1976	60p	—

J. LYONS & CO. LTD. (Ice Cream & Tea)—cont.

Qty		Date	Odds	Sets
25	Star Trek	1979	£1.25	—
50	Train Spotters	1962	25p	£12.50
K100	Tricks & Puzzles	1926	£1.00	—
40	Views of London	1967	65p	£26.00
48	What Do You Know?	1957	10p	£1.75
24	Wings Across the World	1962	10p	£1.00
24	Wings Across the World (non descriptive)	1961	—	£2.50
24	Wings of Speed (Non descriptive))	1961	—	£1.25
24	Wings of Speed (Descriptive Back)	1961	10p	£1.00

MACFISHERIES (Shops)

L12	Gallery Pictures	1924	40p	£5.00
L14	Japanese Colour Prints	1924	50p	£7.00
L12	Poster Pointers	1925	40p	£5.00
L12	Sporting Prints	1923	50p	£6.00

MACGIRR & CO. (Tea)

24	Birds & their Eggs	1912	£3.00	—

MACROBERTSON (Confectionery, Australia)

24	Flags of all Nations	1916	£2.50	—
24	Naval & Military Decorations	1916	£3.00	—
24	Sons/Allies of the Empire	1916	£4.00	—
50	Sports of the World	1916	£1.00	£50.00

MADISON CONFECTIONERY PRODUCTIONS LTD.

X31	Christmas Greeting Cards	1957	£1.00	—
X48	Disc Jockey 1st Series	1957	40p	£20.00
X48	Disc Jockey 2nd Series	1958	50p	£25.00
X50	Recording Stars	1958	40p	£20.00

MAGNET LIBRARY (Periodical)

BF15	Footballers	1922	£1.00	£15.00
BF6	Football Teams	1922	£1.25	£7.50
BF4	Football Teams	1923	£1.25	£5.00

MANCHESTER EVENING NEWS

L30	Footballers	1976	—	£5.00

MAPLE LEAF GUM

K90	Motor Car & Motor Cycle Badges (Metal)	1960	50p	—
K75	National Flags (Metal)	1960	35p	—

R. MARCANTONIO LTD. (Ice Lollies)

50	Interesting Animals	1953	—	£1.75

MARS CONFECTIONS LTD.

25	Ceremonies of the Coronation (brown back)	1937	40p	£10.00
25	Ceremonies of the Coronation (blue back)	1937	£2.00	—
50	Famous Aeroplanes, Pilots & Airports	1938	40p	£20.00
50	Famous Escapes	1937	35p	£17.50
50	Famous Film Stars	1939	40p	£20.00
25	Wonders of the Queen Mary	1936	40p	£10.00

JAMES MARSHALL (GLASGOW) LTD. (Food)

30	Colonial Troops	1900	£15.00	—
1	Marshall's Products Illustrated	1926	—	£2.50
40	Recipes	1926	£2.50	—

MASTER VENDING CO. LTD. (Gum)

Qty		Date	Odds	Sets
X25	A Bombshell for the Sheriff	1959	40p	£10.00
X50	Cardmaster Football Tips	1958	30p	£15.00
X16	Cricketer Series—New Zealand 1958	1958	40p	£6.50
X50	Did You Know? (Football)	1959	12p	£6.00
X100	Jet Aircraft of the World (German text)	1958	50p	—
X100	Jet Aircraft of the World	1958	35p	£35.00
X25	Taxing the Sheriff	1959	20p	£5.00
X36	Tommy Steele	1958	65p	£23.50

J. JOHN MASTERS & CO. (Matches)

X12	Food from Britain	1987	—	60p

MATCH (Periodical)

X31	F.A. Cup Fact File	1986	—	£2.00

MAXILIN MARKETING CO.

25	Motor Cars	1951	—	£1.00

MAYNARDS LTD. (Confectionery)

12	Billy Bunter Series	1926	£8.00	—
?20	Football Clubs	1926	£6.00	—
18	Girl Guide Series	1921	£6.00	—
50	Girls of All Nations	1921	£2.00	£100.00
12	Strange Insects	1935	£2.50	£30.00
8	The European War Series	1916	£10.00	£80.00
12	Wonders of the Deep	1935	£2.50	£30.00
12	World's Wonder Series (Numbered)	1930	£2.50	—
10	World's Wonder Series (Unnumbered)	1930	£3.00	£30.00

MAYPOLE (Grocers)

25	War Series	1915	£3.00	£75.00

MAZAWATTEE (Tea)

X39	Kings and Queens	1902	£2.50	£100.00

McVITIE & PRICE (Food)

8	The European War Series	1916	£10.00	—

MEADOW DAIRY CO.

50	War Series	1915	£3.50	—

J. F. MEARBECK (Printer)

30	Army Pictures, Cartoons, etc	1915	£20.00	—

MELLINS FOOD

K2	Diamond Jubilee Coins	1897	£5.00	£10.00

MELOX (Dog Food)

L50	Famous Breeds of Dogs	1937	£2.00	—
M32	Happy Families (Dogs)	1935	£3.00	—

MERRYSWEETS LTD.

X48	Telegum TV Stars	1958	15p	£7.50
X48	Tracepiks	1960	£3.00	—
X48	World Racing Cars	1959	60p	£30.00

GEOFFREY MICHAEL PUBLISHERS LTD.

Qty		Date	Odds	Sets
40	Modern Motor Cars	1953	—	£5.00

MILK MARKETING BOARD

25	Prehistoric Animals	1963	—	£1.25

MILLERS (Tea)

25	Animals & Reptiles	1962	—	£1.00

MILLER

MF20	Film Stars	1958	—	£3.00

ROBERT R. MIRANDA LTD. (Confectionery)

50	150 Years of Locomotives	1956	—	£1.75
50	100 Years of Motoring	1955	—	£1.75
25	Ships Through the Ages	1957	—	*£5.00*
50	Strange Creatures	1961	—	£2.00

MISTER SOFTEE LTD. (Ice Cream)

M12	Beautiful Butterflies	1977	25p	£3.00
B20	County Badge Collection	1976	10p	£2.00
L12	Did You Know?	1976	25p	—
M24	Kings of the Road	1977	20p	£5.00
15	Moon Mission	1962	—	£5.00
M24	Pop Discs	1972	50p	—
M10	Pop Stars (Shaped)	1975	60p	£6.00
M20	Stamp in a Million	1976	50p	—
L10	Steam Power	1978	—	£2.50
P12	Top Ten (Blue Back)	1964	—	£1.50
20	Top Twenty	1963	20p	£4.00
25	TV Personalities	1962	75p	—
P12	Your World	1963	—	£1.00

MITCHAM FOODS LTD.

25	Aircraft of Today	1955	—	£2.00
25	Aquarium Fish 1st Series	1957	—	£10.00
25	Aquarium Fish 2nd Series	1957	—	£1.00
50	Butterflies & Moths	1959	70p	£35.00
25	Footballers	1956	—	£1.50
50	Mars Adventure	1958	£1.25	—
25	Motor Racing	1960	—	£5.00

MIZZ MAGAZINE

P4	The Seasons	1986	—	75p

MOBIL OIL CO. LTD.

M30	Football Club Badges (Silk)	1983	70p	£21.00
P40	Footy Photos 1965 (Australia)	1965	—	£8.00
X36	The Story of Grand Prix Motor Racing	1971	—	£1.25
25	Veteran & Vintage Cars	1962	—	£7.50
24	Vintage Cars	1966	—	£1.50

MOFFAT (B. & G. LTD.)

D102	Money That Made History	1981	—	£3.50

THE MOLASSINE CO. (Dog Food)

Qty		Date	Odds	Sets
50	Dogs (Full Length)	1963	30p	£15.00
50	Dogs (Heads)	1964	70p	£35.00
25	Dogs at Work	1970	—	£1.50
12	Dogs of All Countries	1925	£4.00	£50.00
50	Puppies	1967	70p	£35.00

MONTAGUE MOTOR MUSEUM

M24	Veteran & Vintage Cars	1965	—	£30.00

MONTY GUM

M98	Bruce Lee	1980	—	£3.00
L50	Elvis	1978	—	£8.00
L72	Flag Parade	1972	—	£5.00
M100	Flags of all Nations	1980	—	£3.00
L56	Footballers (P/C Inset)	1970	75p	£40.00
M54	Hitmakers (P/C Inset)	1978	—	£7.50
M72	Kojak	1975	15p	£10.00
M54	Kojak (P/C Inset)	1976	—	£7.50
L72	International Football Teams	1970	—	£20.00
L56	Motor Cars (P/C Inset)	1956	—	£35.00
M200	Olympics	1984	—	£8.00
M100	The Cops 1st Series	1976	8p	£8.00
M124	The High Chaparral	1970	—	£10.00

MORNING FOODS LTD.

1	Advertisement Card	1953	—	50p
F25	British Planes (numbered)	1978	£1.00	—
F25	British Planes (unnumbered)	1953	—	£4.00
F50	British Trains	1952	£1.75	—
25	British Uniforms	1954	—	£1.00
50	Modern Cars	1954	—	£3.00
50	Our England	1955	—	£2.00
25	Test Cricketers	1953	—	£5.00
12	The Cunard Line (Black Back)	1957	—	£1.00
12	The Cunard Line (Blue Back)	1957	—	£2.00
25	World Locomotives (Black Back)	1954	—	£1.00
25	World Locomotives (Blue Back)	1954	—	£4.00

E. D. L. MOSELEY (Confectionery)

B25	Historical Buildings	1954	—	£1.25

V. MUHLENEN & CO. (Cheese)

B6	Swiss Views, Series III	1955	—	£3.50
B6	Swiss Views, Series IV	1955	—	£4.00

MURCO PETROLEUM

P28	English Counties	1986	—	£2.50
B50	World's Airlines	1978	—	£2.50

MUSEUM OF BRITISH MILITARY UNIFORMS

25	British Cavalry Uniforms	1987	—	£3.75
25	Military Maids	1987	—	£3.75
25	Warriors through the Ages	1987	—	£3.75

MUSGRAVE BROS. LTD. (Tea)

Qty		Date	Odds	Sets
25	Birds	1961	—	£1.25
20	British Birds	1960	£2.50	—
50	British Wild Life	1962	£2.50	—
50	Butterflies of the World	1964	£1.50	—
25	Into Space	1961	—	£1.00
25	Modern Motor Cars	1962	—	£3.50
25	Pond Life	1963	—	£4.00
25	Products of the World	1961	—	£1.00
50	Transport through the Ages	1966	£1.00	£50.00
25	Tropical Birds	1964	—	£1.00
25	Wild Flowers	1961	—	£1.00

MYERS & METREVELI (Gum)

KF48	Film Stars	1953	£1.00	—
X48	Film Stars & Biographies	1953	£2.00	—
X60	Holywood Peep Show	1953	£1.75	—
L50	Spot the Planes	1953	£2.00	—

MY WEEKLY (Periodical)

M9	Battle Series (Silk)	1916	£4.00	£36.00
M12	Floral Beauties (Silk)	1914	£3.00	£36.00
M15	Language of Flowers (Silk)	1914	£3.00	£45.00
M54	Lucky Emblems (Silk)	1912	£5.00	—
M6	Lucky Flowers (Silk)	1913	£7.50	—
M12	Our Soldier Boys (Silk)	1915	£4.00	£48.00
M14	Soldiers of the King (Silk)	1915	£4.00	£56.00
M6	Sweet Kiss Series (Silk)	1913	£3.50	£21.00
M6	War Heroes (Silk)	1916	£4.00	£24.00

NABISCO FOODS LTD.

B5	Aces in Action	1980	—	£7.00
M24	Action Shots of Olympic Sports	1980	50p	£12.00
12	British Soldiers	1971	—	75p
P20	Champions of Sport	1961	75p	£15.00
P8	England's Soccer Stars Tactic Cards	1980	£1.00	£8.00
12	E.T.	1983	—	£3.00
L24	Footballers	1970	40p	£10.00
L10	History of Aviation	1970	80p	£8.00
P10	Motor Show	1960	£1.50	£15.00
L6	World Superstars & Sporting Trophies	1980	£1.25	—

AUSTRALIAN ISSUES

32	Leading Cricketers (Crispies etc.)	1948	£1.60	£50.00
M66	Popular Pets	1962	—	£7.00
L24	United Nations in Action	1968	—	£5.00

EDWARD NASSAR & CO. LTD. (Coffee, Gold Coast)

25	Transport, Present & Future	1955	—	£1.50

NATIONAL SPASTICS SOCIETY

24	Famous County Cricketers (Booklet)	1958	—	£12.50
24	Famous Footballers	1959	—	£1.50

NEEDLER'S (Confectionery)

12	Military Series	1916	£15.00	—

Trade Issues 1970s

They Gave Their Names. Wand Conf.

BRYAN ROBSON
Newcastle

105

Football Swap Cards. The Sun

Krazy Kreatures. Primrose

Naval Battles. Amalgamated Tobacco,
Badshah, Glengettie, Sweetule

RED-SHOULDERED HAWK

©1975 BY CHURCH & DWIGHT CO., INC.

Birds of Prey. Church & Dwight

Age of the Dinosaur. Cadbury

Trade Issues 1980s

COLLECTORS CARDS
EAST KENT
a **NATIONAL** bus company

"Series No 1"

Holidays. East Kent Bus Co.

SIMON DE MONTFORT
Earl of Leicester

HERALD ALARMS
CARDIFF

Feudal Lords. Herald Alarms

Bruce Lee. Monty Gum

ET. Nabisco

Woodland Wildlife. Brooke Bond

Athletes of the World. Bassett

K. S. Ranjitsinji

Cricketers. Brindley

Trade Issues 1940s, 1950s

Medals of the World.
Glengettie Tea, Anonymous

Weapons of Defence.
Sweetule, Amalgamated Tobacco

Bird Portraits.
Brooke Bond

The Cunard Line.
Morning Foods

150 Years of Locomotives.
Miranda

Footballers (Portraits & Action).
Chix

Trade Issues 1960s

Cycles & Motor Cycles. Priory Tea

Stingray. Cadet Sweets

Noddy. Como Conf

Wild Flowers. Typhoo

Moon Fleet. Walls

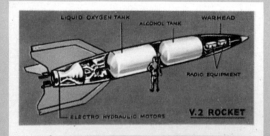

Weapons of World War II.
Northern Co-op

Freshwater Fish. Brooke Bond

NEILSONS (Confectionery)

Qty		Date	Odds	Sets
50	Interesting Animals	1954	—	£1.75

NELSON LEE LIBRARY (Periodical)

| BF15 | Footballers ... ... | 1922 | £1.00 | £15.00 |
| BF6 | Modern British Locomotives ... ... | 1922 | £4.00 | £24.00 |

NESTLE LTD. (Chocolate)

L12	Animal Bars (Wrappers)	1970	—	£1.00
24	Animals of the World	1962	—	£6.00
P12	British Birds (Reward Cards)	1900	£6.00	—
49	Happy Families	1935	40p	£20.00
144	Pictorial World Atlas	1934	75p	—
100	Stars of the Silver Screen Vol. I	1936	60p	—
50	Stars of the Silver Screen Vol. II	1937	60p	—
136	This England	1936	25p	—
T24	Wild Animals Serie II	1910	£3.00	—
156	Wonders of the World Vol. I	1932	30p	—
144	Wonders of the World Vol. II	1933	30p	—

NEW ENGLAND CONFECTIONERY CO. (U.S.A.)

| M12 | Real Airplane Pictures ... ... | 1929 | 70p | £8.50 |
| 24 | Strange People of Many Lands ... ... | 1929 | £2.50 | — |

NEW HOLLAND MACHINE CO.

| P12 | Traction Engines ... ... | 1960 | £1.75 | £21.00 |

NEWS CHRONICLE (Newspaper)

L13	Barrow RFC	1955	—	£1.50
L14	Blackburn Rovers FC	1955	—	£2.50
L12	Bradford City FC	1955	—	£2.50
L11	Chesterfield FC	1955	—	£2.00
L12	Everton FC	1955	—	£2.50
L10	Everton FC (different back)	1955	—	£2.25
L15	Manchester City FC	1955	—	£3.00
L12	Rochdale F.C.	1955	—	£3.00
L14	Rochdale Hornets RFC	1955	—	£1.50
L13	Salford RFC	1955	—	£1.50
L17	Stockport County	1955	—	£2.00
L13	Sunderland	1955	—	£3.00
L13	Swinton RFC	1955	—	£1.25
L11	Workington AFC	1955	—	£1.50
L12	The Story of Stirling Moss	1955	£1.50	—

NEWTON, CHAMBERS & CO. (Toilet Rolls)

| P18 | More Rhyme Time (19-36) ... ... | 1934 | £1.50 | £27.00 |
| P18 | Nursery Rhymes (1-18) ... ... | 1934 | £1.50 | £27.00 |

NEW ZEALAND MEAT PRODUCERS BOARD

| X25 | Scenes of New Zealand Lamb ... ... | 1930 | £1.50 | £37.50 |

NORTHAMPTONSHIRE COUNTY CRICKET CLUB

| 30 | Northamptonshire Cricketers ... ... | 1985 | — | £7.50 |

NORTHERN CO-OPERATIVE SOCIETY LTD. (Tea)

Qty		Date	Odds	Sets
25	Birds	1963	60p	—
25	History of the Railways 1st Series	1964	—	£2.50
25	History of the Railways 2nd Series	1964	—	£5.00
25	Passenger Liners	1963	—	£1.00
25	Then & Now	1963	—	£3.00
25	Tropical Birds	1962	—	£2.00
25	Weapons of World War II	1962	—	£4.00
25	Wonders of the Deep	1965	—	£1.00

NORTON'S (Shop)

25	Evolution of the Royal Navy	1965	—	£12.50

NOSTALGIA REPRINTS

50	Cope's Golfers	1984	—	£6.00
238	County Cricketers (Taddy)	1987	—	£20.00
50	Cricketers 1896 (Wills)	1983	—	£6.00
50	Cricketers 1901 (Wills)	1984	—	£6.00
50	Military Series (Player)	1984	—	£6.00
18	Spurs Footballers (Jones)	1987	—	£1.50

NUGGET POLISH CO.

X30	Allied Series	1910	£7.50	—
50	Flags of all Nations	1925	£3.00	—
X40	Mail Carriers and Stamps	1910	£7.50	£300.00

NUNBETTA (Grocer)

25	Motor Cars	1955	£2.50	—

O.V.S. TEA

K25	Modern Engineering	1955	—	£2.50

TONY L. OLIVER (Commercial)

25	Aircraft of World War II	1964	60p	—
50	German Orders & Decorations	1963	—	£6.50
1	German Orders Advertisement Card	1963	—	40p
50	German Uniforms	1971	—	£3.50
M25	Vehicles of the German Wehrmacht	1965	—	£15.00

ORBIT (Commercial)

15	Engines of the L.N.E.R.	1986	—	£2.00
20	Famous Douglas Aeroplanes	1986	—	£2.00
28	Great Rugby Sides (NZ Tourists 1905)	1987	—	£2.00

OVALTINE (Beverage)

25	Do You Know?	1965	—	£5.00

OXO LTD. (Meat Extract)

K47	Advertisement Series	1926	£2.00	—
K20	British Cattle	1934	£1.50	£30.00
15	Bull Series	1937	£1.20	£18.00
K24	Feats of Endurance	1934	£1.25	£30.00
K20	Furs & Their Story	1932	£1.50	£30.00
K36	Lifeboats & Their History	1935	£1.75	£63.00
K30	Mystery Painting Pictures	1928	£1.50	£45.00
P6	Oxo Cattle Studies	1930	£8.00	—
25	Oxo Recipes	1936	£1.20	£30.00

P.M.R. ASSOCIATES LTD. (Commercial)

Qty		Date	Odds	Sets
25	England, The World Cup, Spain '82	1982	—	£1.00

H. J. PACKER LTD. (Confectionery)

K30	Footballers	1924	£7.50	—
50	Humorous Drawings	1936	£1.40	£70.00

PAGE WOODCOCK WIND PILLS

20	Humorous Sketches by Tom Browne	1902	£12.50	—

PALMER MANN & CO. LTD. (Salt)

24	Famous Cricketers	1950	*£5.00*	—
24	Famous Footballers	1950	*£3.50*	—
12	Famous Jets	1950	£3.00	—
12	Famous Lighthouses	1950	£2.50	—

PALS (Periodical)

BF27	Australian Sportsmen	1923	£2.50	£65.00
B8	Famous Footballers	1922	£2.00	—
BF12	Football Series	1922	£1.00	£12.00

PANINI (Commercial)
(Complete with Albums)

M220	A Team	1986	—	£10.00
M558	Football 81	1981	—	£10.00
M516	Football 82	1982	—	£10.00
M527	Football 83	1983	—	£10.00
M526	Football 84	1984	—	£10.00
M526	Football 85	1985	—	£10.00
M574	Football 86	1986	—	£10.00
M216	Masters of the Universe	1986	—	£10.00
M150	One Hundred Years of Coca Cola Advertising ...	1986	—	£12.50
M360	Pinnochio (Italian)	1985	—	£10.00
M180	Return of the Jedi	1980	—	£10.00
M210	Rugby 83 (French)	1983	—	£12.50
M256	Star Wars (Italian)	1978	—	£10.00
M204	Superman (Italian)	1979	—	£10.00
M400	Tarzan	1985	—	£10.00
M400	U.F.O.	1973	—	£10.00
M268	World of Cricket 83	1983	—	£12.50

JAMES PASCALL LTD. (Confectionery)

48	Boy Scout Series	1912	£3.50	—
24	British Birds	1925	80p	£20.00
30	Devon Ferns	1927	80p	£24.00
30	Devon Flowers	1927	80p	£24.00
24	Devon Worthies	1927	£1.00	£24.00
18	Dogs	1924	£1.60	£30.00
10	Felix the Film Cat	1928	£10.00	—
30	Flags & Flags with Soldiers	1905	£6.00	—
30	Glorious Devon	1929	£1.00	£30.00
36	Glorious Devon 2nd Series (Black Back)	1929	80p	£30.00

JAMES PASCALL LTD. (Confectionery)—cont.

Qty		Date	Odds	Sets
36	Glorious Devon 2nd Series (Green Back)	1929	£1.00	£36.00
36	Glorious Devon 2nd Series (non descriptive) ...	1929	£2.50	—
2	King George V & Queen Mary	1910	£15.00	—
44	Military Series	1912	£7.50	—
20	Pascall's Specialities	1926	£7.50	—
12	Royal Naval Cadet Series	1912	£7.50	—
?	Rulers of the World	1916	*£20.00*	—
28	Town and other Arms	1914	£7.50	—
50	Tricks & Puzzles	1926	£2.00	£100.00
?13	War Portraits	1915	*£10.00*	—

J. PATERSON & SON LTD. (Biscuits)

M48	Balloons	1960	—	£6.00

PATRICK (Garages)

T24	The Patrick Collection (Cars)	1986	—	£4.00
C24	The Patrick Collection (with coupons)	1986	—	£7.50

GEORGE PAYNE (Tea)

25	American Indian Tribes	1962	—	£3.00
25	British Railways	1962	—	£1.25
12	Characters from Dickens Works (numbered) ...	1912	£7.50	—
6	Characters from Dickens Works (unnumbered) ...	1912	£10.00	—
25	Dogs' Heads	1963	—	£2.00
25	Science in the 20th Century	1963	—	£1.00

PEEK FREAN & CO. (Biscuits)

X12	English Scenes	1884	£4.00	—
X4	Shakespeare Scenes	1884	£5.00	£20.00
X4	Views Abroad	1883	£7.50	£30.00

PENNY MAGAZINE

BF12	Film Stars	1931	£1.25	£15.00

PERFETTI (Gum)

40	Famous Trains	1983	80p	—

PETERKIN (Foods)

B8	English Sporting Dogs	1930	£6.00	—

PETPRO LTD.

35	Grand Prix Racing Cars	1966	—	£1.25

PHILADELPHIA CHEWING GUM CORP.

X88	War Bulletin	1965	40p	£35.00

PHILATELIC POSTCARD PUBLISHING CO. (Commercial)

Qty		Date	Odds	Sets
P10	Philatelic Anniversary Postcards Set 1	1983	—	£1.25

PHILLIPS (Tea)

25	Army Badges Past & Present	1964	—	£1.00
25	British Birds & Their Nests	1966	—	£15.00
25	British Rail	1965	—	£3.00

PLANET LTD. (Gum)

| X50 | Racing Cars of the World ... ... | 1965 | 75p | £37.50 |

PLANTERS NUT & CHOCOLATE CO. (U.S.A.)

| M25 | Hunted Animals ... ... | 1933 | 80p | £20.00 |

PLUCK (Periodical)

| BF27 | Famous Football Teams ... ... | 1922 | £1.00 | £27.00 |

POLAR PRODUCTS LTD. (Ice Cream, Barbados)

25	International Air Liners	1970	—	£5.00
25	Modern Motor Cars	1970	—	£5.00
25	Tropical Birds	1970	—	£4.00
25	Wonders of the Deep	1970	—	£4.00

POLYDOR LTD (Records)

| 16 | The Polydor Guitar Album ... ... | 1975 | — | £1.50 |

H. POPPLETON & SONS (Confectionery)

| 50 | Cricketers Series ... ... | 1926 | £12.00 | — |
| 16 | Film Stars Series ... ... | 1928 | £2.50 | |

POPULAR MOTORING (Periodical)

| L4 | P.M. Car Starter ... ... | 1972 | — | 75p |

POSTER STAMP ASSOCIATION

| 25 | Modern Transport ... ... | 1957 | — | £1.00 |

PRESCOTT (Confectionery)

| L36 | Speed Kings ... ... | 1966 | — | £3.00 |

PRESCOTT-PICKUP & CO. (Commercial)

P15	Charles & Diana in Canada	1983	—	£2.00
P60	Papal Visit	1982	—	£6.00
50	Railway Locomotives	1977	—	£2.50
P70	Royal Family—Birth of a Prince	1982	—	£8.00
P60	Thirty Years Elizabeth Regina	1982	—	£7.00

PRESTON DAIRIES (Tea)

| 25 | Country Life ... ... | 1966 | — | £1.00 |

PRICES PATENT CANDLE CO. LTD.

| P12 | Famous Battles ... ... | 1910 | £6.00 | £72.00 |

PRIMROSE CONFECTIONERY CO. LTD.

Qty		Date	Odds	Sets
24	Action Man	1976	50p	—
50	Amos Burke—Secret Agent	1970	—	£17.50
50	Andy Pandy	1960	—	£1.75
50	Bugs Bunny	1964	—	£2.50
50	Burke's Law	1967	75p	—
50	Chitty Chitty Bang Bang	1971	—	£1.75
50	Cowboy	1960	—	£2.50
25	Cup Tie Quiz	1973	—	£1.00
25	Dad's Army	1973	—	£1.00
50	Famous Footballers F.B.S.I.	1961	—	£3.00
25	Football Funnies	1974	—	£1.25
25	Happy Howlers	1975	—	£1.00
50	Joe 90	1969	—	£17.50
50	Krazy Kreatures from Outer Space	1970	—	£1.75
50	Laramie	1964	—	£6.00
50	Laurel & Hardy	1968	—	£4.00
M22	Mounties (Package Issue)	1960	£3.50	—
50	Popeye	1960	£2.00	—
50	Popeye 2nd Series	1961	15p	£7.50
50	Popeye 3rd Series	1962	—	£1.75
50	Popeye 4th Series	1963	—	£1.75
50	Queen Elizabeth II	1969	—	£3.50
50	Quick Draw McGraw	1964	—	£6.00
50	Space Patrol	1970	—	£2.50
50	Space Race	1969	—	£2.00
12	Star Trek	1971	—	£1.50
50	Superman	1968	—	£6.00
50	The Flintstones	1963	—	£1.50
50	Yellow Submarine	1968	—	£35.00
50	Z Cars	1968	—	£1.75

PRICE EDWARD THEATRE

XF?4	Josephine Baker Cards	1930	£6.00	—

S. PRIOR (Bookshop)

25	Do You Know?	1964	—	£10.00

PRIORY TEA CO. LTD.

50	Aircraft	1961	—	£3.50
50	Birds	1962	—	£6.00
24	Bridges	1960	—	£1.25
24	Cars	1958	£1.25	£30.00
50	Cars (Different)	1964	—	£5.00
50	Cycles & Motorcycles	1963	60p	£30.00
24	Dogs	1957	—	£1.00
24	Flowering Trees	1959	—	£1.00
24	Men at Work	1959	—	£1.50
24	Out & About	1957	—	£1.50
24	People in Uniform	1956	80p	£20.00
24	Pets	1957	—	£1.25
50	Wild Flowers	1963	40p	£20.00

PROPERT SHOE POLISH

Qty		Date	Odds	Sets
25	British Uniforms	1955	—	£1.50

PUKKA TEA CO. LTD.

50	Aquarium Fish	1961	—	£15.00

PYREX LTD. (Glassware)

P16	Guide to Simple Cooking	1976	—	£1.50

QUADRIGA (Commercial)

M126	Snooker Kings	1986	—	£5.00

QUAKER OATS

X12	Armour Through the Ages	1968	30p	£3.50
M4	Famous Puffers	1983	£2.00	£8.00
M54	Historic Arms of Merrie England	1938	40p	—
X8	Historic Ships	1967	£2.00	£16.00
M6	Honey Monster's Circus Friends	1985	35p	—
15	Honey Monster's Crazy Games Cards	1985	35p	—
M16	Jeremy's Animal Kingdom	1980	50p	£8.00
12	Monsters of the Deep	1984	40p	—
L6	Nature Trek	1976	20p	£1.25
X12	Prehistoric Animals	1967	£1.60	£20.00
X12	Space Cards	1968	£2.00	—
X12	Vintage Engines	1967	£2.00	£24.00

PACKAGE ISSUES

12	British Customs	1961	25p	£3.00
L36	British Landmarks	1961	30p	—
12	Characters in Literature	1961	50p	—
12	Exploration & Adventure	1974	50p	—
12	Famous Explorers	1961	30p	£3.50
12	Famous Inventors	1961	25p	£3.00
12	Famous Ships	1961	30p	—
12	Famous Women	1961	30p	£3.50
12	Fascinating Costumes	1961	25p	£3.00
12	Great Feats of Building	1961	25p	£3.00
L36	Great Moments of Sport	1961	50p	—
12	History of Flight	1961	30p	£3.50
12	Homes & Houses	1961	25p	£3.00
L36	Household Hints	1961	30p	—
X4	Minibooks	1969	£1.00	£4.00
12	National Maritime Museum	1974	75p	—
12	National Motor Museum	1974	75p	£9.00
12	On the Seashore	1961	25p	£3.00
L36	Phiz Quiz	1961	30p	—
L36	Railways of the World	1961	80p	—
L8	Return to Oz	1985	50p	—
12	Royal Airforce Museum	1974	75p	—
L12	Science & Invention	1974	50p	£6.00
L36	The Story of Fashion	1961	30p	—
12	The Wild West	1961	30p	£3.50
12	Weapons & Armour	1961	30p	£3.50

QUEEN ELIZABETH LAUNDRY

Qty			Date	Odds	Sets
45	Beauties	... ...	1912	£10.00	—

QUEENS OF YORK (Laundry)

30	Kings & Queens of England	... ...	1955	—	£15.00

QUORN SPECIALITIES LTD. (Foods)

25	Fish and Game	... ...	1963	£1.25	—

RADIO FUN (Periodical)

20	British Sports Stars	... ...	1956	—	£1.00

RADIO REVIEW (Periodical)

L36	Broadcasting Stars	... ...	1936	£1.25	£45.00
E20	Broadcasting Stars	... ...	1936	£2.00	£40.00

RALEIGH BICYCLES

L48	Raleigh the All Steel Bicycle	... ...	1957	—	£25.00

REDDINGS TEA CO.

25	Castles of Great Britain	... ...	1965	60p	£15.00
25	Cathedrals of Great Britain	... ...	1964	60p	£15.00
25	Heraldry of Famous Places	... ...	1966	60p	£15.00
48	Ships of the World	... ...	1964	—	£2.00
25	Stange Customs of the World	... ...	1970	—	£1.25
48	Warriors of the World	... ...	1962	50p	£25.00

REDDISH MAID CONFECTIONERY

50	Famous International Aircraft	... ...	1955	£1.00	£50.00
25	Famous International Athletes	... ...	1955	£1.50	—
25	International Footballers of Today	... ...	1955	£2.00	—

RED HEART (Pet Food)

P6	Cats	... ...	1954	—	£9.00
P6	Dogs	... ...	1953	—	£7.50
P6	Dogs 2nd Series	... ...	1953	—	£10.00
P6	Dogs 3rd Series	... ...	1954	—	£10.00

RED LETTER (Periodical)

P29	Charlie Chaplin Cards	... ...	1920	£4.00	—
M4	Luck Bringers (silk)	... ...	1924	£15.00	£60.00
X98	Midget Message Cards	... ...	1920	£1.50	—

REEVES LTD. (Confectionery)

25	Cricketers	... ...	1912	£12.50	—

REGENT OIL

X25	Do You Know?	... ...	1965	—	£1.00

RENATA GLASSO (Commercial, U.S.A.)

X55	Mars Attacks (reprints)	... ...	1984	—	£12.00
G4	Mars Attacks Premiums	... ...	1984	—	£2.00

RIDGWAY'S TEA

X20	Journey to the Moon	... ...	1958	£2.50	—

TYPE COLLECTING

There are now many collectors who concentrate on types either exclusively or in addition to their main collections. This involves keeping one or two cards from every series issued. Limitations of space and money make this a good compromise for many people, since they can have a limited goal, yet still providing a sufficient challenge to maintain their interest.

The advent of modern albums has eased one problem for type collectors, since they can now limit themselves to just one card per series, and still be able to see both front and back of that type. Further limitations may also be self-imposed by collecting the issues of just one country, or commodity. One collector 'only' collects one card from each manufacturer, while a lifetime could be spent just in trying to collect the different types issued by the tobacco firm of Wills!

The general collector can also acquire types as a method of identifying those series of which he wishes to obtain complete sets — and those that he wishes to avoid. It is also a useful idea to obtain type cards of all the varieties of one series, so that one can have a complete set of all the pictures and also a specimen of all the different backs that could be found with that front.

ERRORS & VARIETIES

In view of the enormous number of cards that has been produced, most of which have detailed descriptions, it is hardly surprising that mistakes occur occasionally. In some cases these were brought to light at an early stage, and a corrected card was also issued, but sometimes the error remained undetected until many years after the set appeared.

Some of the mistakes could best be described as 'Howlers', and among the best known are Carreras Figures of Fiction showing Uncle Tom with white feet, Pattreiouex Coastwise giving the date of the Battle of Trafalgar as 1812 and Player Sea Fishes with three versions of the Monk (or Angel) Fish, one of which states that it is inedible while another describes its flesh as 'quite wholesome'. Gallaher, in its Great War Series, showed a Tommy with his rifle sloped on the wrong shoulder, and Carreras Britains Defences No. 47 can be found with the picture upside down. Most of these have been illustrated elsewhere, so we have shown here a different selection, with no comments other than – find the mistake for yourself.

Varieties occur as the result of deliberate changes by the issuer. Common examples of this are the updating of army ranks and decorations, new sports statistics, and changes of rank or title caused by a death. The most fruitful series for a study of varieties are probably in the series of Guinea Gold cards and also Wills Transvaal series, where over 250 different cards can be collected within the 66 numbers of the series.

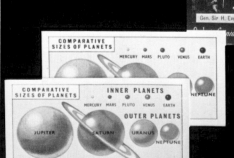

RINGTONS LTD. (Tea)

Qty		Date	Odds	Sets
25	Aircraft of World War II	1962	—	£7.50
25	British Cavalry Uniforms of the 19th Century ...	1971	—	£3.00
25	Do You Know?	1964	—	£1.00
25	Fruits of Trees & Shrubs	1964	—	£1.00
25	Headdresses of the World	1973	—	£1.00
25	Historical Scenes	1964	—	£1.25
25	Old England	1964	—	£1.00
25	People & Places	1964	—	£1.25
25	Regimental Uniforms of the Past	1966	—	£2.00
25	Sailing Ships Through the Ages	1967	—	£1.50
25	Ships of the Royal Navy	1961	—	£1.50
25	Sovereigns Consorts & Rulers 1st	1961	—	£3.00
25	Sovereigns Consorts & Rulers 2nd	1961	—	£3.00
25	The West	1968	—	£1.50
25	Then & Now	1970	—	£10.00
25	Trains of the World	1970	—	£1.00

RISCA TRAVEL AGENCY

25	Holiday Resorts	1957	—	£10.00

D. ROBBINS & CO. (Commercial, U.S.A.)

P24	Frontiers of Freedom	1942	—	£12.50
P24	Good Neighbors of the Americas	1942	—	£12.50
P24	Indians of the U.S.A.	1942	—	£20.00
P24	Modern Wonders of the World	1942	—	£12.50
P24	Our Friend—The Dog	1942	£1.25	—
P24	Story of Transportation	1942	—	£15.00

ROBERTSON LTD. (Preserves)

6	British Medals	1914	£10.00	—
10	Musical Gollywogs (Shaped)	1962	65p	£6.50
10	Sporting Gollywogs (Shaped)	1962	80p	£8.00

ROBERTSON & WOODCOCK LTD. (Confectionery)

50	British Aircraft Series	1930	£1.00	£50.00

ROBINSON BROS. & MASTERS (Tea)

25	Tea from the Garden to the Home	1930	£3.00	£75.00

ROBINSON'S BARLEY WATER

X30	Sporting Records (with folder)	1983	—	£1.50

ROCHE & CO. LTD. (Matches)

K49/50	Famous Footballers	1927	£1.25	—

THE ROCKET (Periodical)

BF11	Famous Knockouts	1923	£1.50	£16.50

ROSSI'S (Ice Cream)

M48	Flags of the Nations	1975	10p	£4.00
	Album		—	50p
25	The History of Flight 1st Series	1963	—	£4.00
25	The History of Flight 2nd Series	1963	—	£4.00
25	World's Fastest Aircraft	1964	—	£2.50

ROWNTREE & CO. (Confectionery)

Qty		Date	Odds	Sets
K12	British Birds (Packet Issue)	1955	—	£2.50
25	Celebrities	1905	£10.00	—
X8	Circus Cut-outs	1960	£1.50	£12.00
M20	Merrie Monarchs	1978	—	£2.00
M18	Prehistoric Animals	1978	—	£1.50
L6	Punch & Judy Show	1976	—	£2.00
X42	Railway Engines (Caramac)	1976	—	£5.00
M10	Texan Tall Tales of the West	1977	50p	£5.00
48	The Old & The New	1934	£1.50	—
120	Treasure Trove Pictures	1932	50p	—
24	York Views	1924	£5.00	—

ROYAL NATIONAL LIFEBOAT INSTITUTION

M16	Lifeboats	1979	—	75p

ROYAL SOCIETY FOR PREVENTION OF ACCIDENTS

24	Modern British Cars	1954	40p	£10.00
22	Modern British Motor Cycles	1953	80p	£17.50
25	New Traffic Signs	1958	—	£2.50
24	Veteran Cars 1st Series	1955	40p	£10.00
24	Veteran Cars 2nd Series	1957	40p	£10.00

ROYAL LEAMINGTON SPA

25	Royal Leamington Spa	1975	—	£1.00

RUBY (Periodical)

X10	Famous Beauties of the Day	1923	£2.00	£20.00
X6	Famous Film Stars	1923	£2.00	—

S & B PRODUCTS

?69	Torry Gillick's Internationals	1951	£2.00	—

SAGION STUFFING

28	Dominoes Without the Dot	1939	12p	£3.50

J. SAINSBURY LTD. (Groceries)

M12	British Birds	1924	£3.00	£36.00
M12	Foreign Birds	1924	£3.00	£36.00

ST. GEORGE'S HALL

50	War Portraits	1916	£17.50	—

SANDERS BROS. (Custard)

25	Birds, Fowls, Pigeons & Rabbits	1925	£1.50	—
20	Dogs	1926	£1.00	£20.00
25	Recipes	1924	£1.20	£30.00

SANITARIUM HEALTH FOOD CO. (New Zealand)

X12	Animals of New Zealand	1974	—	£3.50
L30	Another Look at New Zealand	1971	—	£2.50
L30	Antarctic Adventure	1972	—	£3.50
X12	Bush Birds of New Zealand	1981	—	£2.50
L20	Cars of the Seventies	1976	—	£2.50

SANITARIUM HEALTH FOOD CO. (New Zealand)—cont.

Qty		Date	Odds	Sets
L20	Conservation—Caring for Our Land	1974	—	£2.00
L20	Discover Indonesia	1977	—	£2.00
L24	Famous New Zealanders	1971	—	£2.50
M30	Fascinating Orient	1974	—	£2.00
M20	History of Road Transport in New Zealand	1979	—	£4.00
X12	Jet Aircraft	1974	—	£3.50
L20	Looking at Canada	1978	—	£2.00
L25	National Costumes of the Old World	1968	—	£3.50
X12	New Zealand Lakes, Series 2	1978	—	£2.50
L30	New Zealand National Parks	1973	—	£4.00
L20	New Zealand's Booming Industries	1975	—	£1.50
M30	New Zealand To-Day	1974	—	£3.00
L20	N.Z. Energy Resources	1976	—	£2.50
M20	N.Z. Rod and Custom Cars	1979	—	£4.00
X12	N.Z. Waterfalls	1981	—	£2.50
X12	N.Z.R. Steam Engines	1976	—	£4.00
X12	Our Fascinating Fungi	1980	—	£2.50
M20	Our South Pacific Island Neighbours	1974	—	£3.00
L20	Spectacular Sports	1974	—	£2.50
L20	Super Cars	1972	—	£3.50
TS16	The Mysterious East	1964	—	£4.00
L20	The Story of New Zealand Aviation	1977	—	£3.00
L20	The Story of New Zealand in Stamps	1977	—	£4.00
L20	Timeless Japan	1975	—	£2.50
TS16	Veteran & Vintage Cars	1964	—	£6.00
L20	Vintage Cars	1973	—	£5.00
X12	Wild Flowers of N.Z.	1979	—	£2.50

SAVOY PRODUCTS LTD. (Foods)

Qty		Date	Odds	Sets
M56	Aerial Navigation	1926	60p	£35.00
M56	Aerial Navigation Series B	1927	60p	£35.00
M56	Aerial Navigation Series C	1928	60p	£35.00
M56	Famous British Boats	1928	60p	£35.00

SCANLEN'S (Gum, Australia)

Qty		Date	Odds	Sets
M172	Cricket Series (including album)	1982	—	£12.50
M172	Cricket Series No. 2 (including album)	1983	—	£12.50
X90	World Series Cricket	1982	—	£10.00

THE SCHOOL FRIEND (Periodical)

Qty		Date	Odds	Sets
L6	Famous Film Stars	1927	£2.00	—
X10	Popular Girls of Cliff House School	1922	£5.00	—
XF6	Popular Pictures	1923	£1.50	—

THE SCHOOLGIRL (Periodical)

Qty		Date	Odds	Sets
BF12	Zoological Studies	1923	£1.25	£15.00

THE SCHOOLGIRLS WEEKLY (Periodical)

Qty		Date	Odds	Sets
XF1	HRH The Duke of York	1922	—	£3.00
XF4	Popular Pictures	1922	£2.00	£8.00

SCOTTISH DAILY EXPRESS

Qty		Date	Odds	Sets
X24	Scotcards (Soccer)	1972	80p	£20.00

THE SCOUT (Periodical)

Qty		Date	Odds	Sets
L9	Birds' Eggs	1925	£1.50	£13.50
M12	Railway Engines	1924	£2.50	£30.00

SCRAPBOOK MINICARDS

27	Pendon Museum (model railway etc.)	1978	—	£1.00

SECRETS (Periodical)

K52	Film Stars (Miniature Playing Cards)	1935	50p	—

SELLOTAPE PRODUCTS LTD. (Adhesive Tape)

35	Great Homes & Castles	1974	—	£5.00

SEYMOUR MEAD & CO. LTD. (Tea)

24	The Island of Ceylon	1964	—	£1.00

SHARMAN (Newspapers)

T24	Golden Age of Flying	1979	—	£2.00
T24	Golden Age of Motoring	1979	—	£2.00
T24	Golden Age of Steam	1979	—	£2.00

EDWARD SHARP & SONS (Confectionery)

20	Captain Scarlet	1970	£1.50	£30.00
25	Hey Presto I	1970	—	£1.00
K53	Miniature Playing Cards	1924	£1.50	—
100	Prize Dogs	1924	£2.00	—

SHELL (Oil)

M16	Animals (3-D)	1975	50p	£8.00
14	Bateman Series	1930	£3.50	£50.00
P20	Great Britons	1972	15p	£3.00
K16	Man in Flight (medals) including Mount	1970	50p	£8.00
M16	Wonders of the World (3-D)	1976	—	£5.00

AUSTRALIAN ISSUES

M60	Beetle Series (301-360)	1962	—	£7.50
M60	Birds (121-180)	1960	—	£12.50
M60	Butterflies and Moths (181-240)	1960	—	£7.50
M60	Citizenship Series	1965	—	£7.50
M60	Discover Australia with Shell	1959	—	£20.00
M60	Meteorlogy Series (361-420)	1963	—	£7.50
M60	Pets (481-540)	1964	—	£10.00
M60	Shells, Fish and Coral (61-120)	1959	—	£12.50
M60	Transportation Series (241-300)	1961	—	£12.50

NEW ZEALAND ISSUES

B48	Aircraft of the World	1970	—	£2.00
B60	Cars of the World	1970	—	£3.00
B48	Racing Cars of the World	1970	—	£3.50
40	Vintage Cars (Transfers)	1970	—	£3.00

SHELLEY'S ICE CREAM

25	Essex—County Champions	1984	16p	£4.00

SHEPHERD'S DAIRIES

100	War Series	1915	£4.00	—

SHERMANS POOLS LTD.

Qty		Date	Odds	Sets
P8	Famous Film Stars	1940	15p	£1.25
P37	Famous Teams	1938	£1.00	£40.00
P2/37	Famous Teams (Aston Villa/Blackpool)	1938	—	25p
P38	Searchlight on Famous Players	1937	£1.25	—

SHIPTON

75	Trojan Gen Cards	1959	50p	£37.50

SHUREYS PUBLICATIONS LTD.

P?750	Views (Various Printings)	1906	50p	—

SILVER KING & CO. (Theatrical)

1	Advertisement Card	1905	—	£5.00

SINGER SEWING MACHINE CO. (U.S.A.)

53	Beauties (Playing card inset)	1898	£7.50	—
P36	Costumes of All Nations	1892	£3.50	£125.00
P18	Costumes of All Nations (Different)	1894	£6.00	£110.00

SKETCHLEY CLEANERS

25	A Nature Series	1960	—	£3.00
25	Communications	1960	—	£4.00
25	Tropical Birds	1960	—	£5.00

SLADE & BULLOCK LTD. (Confectionery)

25	Cricket Series	1924	*£25.00*	—
25	Football Terms	1924	£7.50	—
25	Modern Inventions	1925	£4.00	£100.00
20	Now & Then Series	1925	£5.00	—
25	Nursery Rhymes	1925	*£10.00*	—
25	Science & Skill Series	1925	£5.00	—
25	Simple Toys & How to Make Them	1925	£6.00	—

P. SLUIS (Bird Food)

X30	Tropical Birds	1962	—	£3.50

SMART NOVELS (Periodical)

BF12	Stage Artistes & Entertainers	1924	£1.25	—

JOHN SMITH (Brewers)

P5	Limericks (Beer Mats)	1976	—	£1.50

SNAP CARDS (Gum)

L50	ATV Stars 1st Series	1960	50p	£25.00
L48	ATV Stars 2nd Series	1959	30p	£15.00
L50	Associated Rediffusion Stars	1960	50p	£25.00
L50	Dotto	1959	35p	£17.50

H. A. SNOW (Films)

12	Hunting Big Game in Africa	1923	£3.00	—

SOCCER BUBBLE GUM

M48	Soccer Teams No. 1 Series	1960	—	£7.00
M48	Soccer Teams No. 2 Series	1961	50p	£24.00

SODASTREAM (Confectionery)

Qty		Date	Odds	Sets
25	Historical Buildings	1957	—	£1.00

SOMPORTEX LTD. (Gum Vending)

L60	Famous TV Wrestlers	1966	£1.00	£60.00
X60	Film Scene Series James Bond 007	1966	£1.25	—
L72	John Drake Danger Man	1966	£1.25	—
L50	The Exciting World of James Bond 007 ...	1965	£1.25	—
L72	The Saint	1967	£1.40	—
L72	Thunderball	1967	40p	£30.00
X73	Thunderbirds (Coloured)	1967	£1.20	£85.00
L72	Thunderbirds (Black/White)	1967	£1.20	£85.00
X72	Thunderbirds (Black/White)	1967	£1.00	£72.00
X36	Weirdies	1968	50p	£18.00
26	You Only Live Twice (Film Strips)	1969	£2.00	—

SONNY BOY

50	Railway Engines	1960	—	£2.00

SOUTH WALES CONSTABULARY

X36	British Stamps	1983	—	£6.00
X36	Merthyr Tydfil Borough Council	1987	—	£7.50
X37	Payphones Past and Present	1987	—	£7.50
X36	Ryhmney Valley	1986	—	£6.00
X35	The '82 Squad (Rugby)	1982	50p	£25.00

SPAR GROCERS

X30	Disney on Parade	1972	—	£7.50

SPILLERS NEPHEWS (Biscuits)

25	Conundrum Series	1910	£10.00	—
40	Views of South Wales & District	1910	£8.00	—

SPORT AND ADVENTURE (Periodical)

M46	Famous Footballers	1922	£1.00	£46.00

SPRATTS PATENT LTD. (Pet Food)

K100	British Bird Series (Numbered)	1935	£1.00	—
K50	British Bird Series (Unnumbered)	1935	80p	—
42	British Birds	1926	£1.40	£60.00
36	Champion Dogs	1926	£2.00	—
K20	Fish	1935	£6.00	—
K100	Poultry Series	1935	£1.75	—
25	The Bonzo Series	1924	£2.00	£50.00

STAMP CORNER

25	American Indian Tribes	1963	—	£12.50

STAR JUNIOR CLUB

10	Animals	1960	60p	£6.00
10	Sports & Games (Numbered)	1960	70p	£7.00
5	Sports & Games (Unnumbered)	1960	80p	£4.00

STAVELEYS (Shop)

24	World's Most Beautiful Birds	1924	£3.00	—

STOKES & DALTON (Cereals)

Qty		Date	Odds	Sets
M20	The Crimson Cobra	1950	75p	£15.00

STOLL (Films)

25	Stars of To-day	1930	£3.50	—
25	The Mystery of Dr. Fu-Manchu	1930	£5.00	—

STOLLWERCK (Chocolate)

T144	Animal World	1902	60p	£85.00
F?100	Views of the World	1915	£3.00	—

THE SUN (Newspaper)

M134	Football Swap Cards	1970	15p	£20.00
M52	Gallery of Football Action	1975	60p	£30.00
M6	How to Play Football	1975	70p	£4.00
M54	Page 3 Playing Cards	1979	—	£4.00
1000	Soccercards	1980	—	£25.00
P50	3D Gallery of Football Stars	1975	40p	—

SUNBLEST TEA

25	Inventions & Discoveries 1st Series	1960	—	£4.00
25	Inventions & Discoveries 2nd Series	1960	—	£4.00
25	Prehistoric Animals 1st Series	1960	—	£2.00
25	Prehistoric Animals 2nd Series	1960	—	£2.00

SUNBLEST (Australia)

M24	Sports Action Series	1975	—	£4.00
M25	Sunblest Explorer Cards	1975	—	£3.00

SUNDAY EMPIRE NEWS

48	Famous Footballers of Today (Durling)	1953	£1.25	£60.00

SUNDAY STORIES (Periodical)

M5	Flags (Silk)	1916	£6.00	—
M6	The King & His Soldiers (Silk)	1916	£6.50	—

SWEETACRE (Confectionery, Australia)

48	Aircraft of the World	1932	75p	—
36	Cricketers (Minties)	1926	£5.00	£180.00
24	Cricketers (Caricatures)	1938	£7.50	—
48	Favourite Dogs	1932	£1.50	—
32	Prominent Cricketers (33-64)	1932	£2.00	£65.00
48	Sports Champions	1930	£1.50	—
48	Steamships of the World	1932	75p	£36.00
32	Test Records (1-32)	1932	£2.00	£65.00
48	This World of Ours	1932	£1.50	—

SWEETULE PRODUCTS LTD. (Confectionery)

18	Aircraft (Packet)	1954	£3.00	£54.00
25	A Nature Series	1960	—	£1.50
25	Animals of the Countryside	1959	—	£1.00
25	Archie Andrews Jokes	1957	£1.50	—
25	Birds & Their Eggs	1954	—	£1.00
25	Birds & Their Eggs (Black Back)	1959	—	£2.00

SWEETULE PRODUCTS LTD. (Confectionery)—cont.

Qty		Date	Odds	Sets
25	Birds & Their Eggs (Blue Back)	1959	—	£2.00
25	Birds & Their Haunts	1958	£2.00	—
52	Birds, Fish & Flowers (P/C Inset)	1961	—	£6.00
25	Birds of the British Commonwealth (Black Back)	1954	—	£1.00
25	Birds of the British Commonwealth (Blue Back)	1954	—	£1.25
M12	Coronation Series (Packet)	1953	£3.50	—
25	Do You Know?	1963	—	£1.25
25	Family Crests	1961	—	£1.50
25	Famous Sports Records	1957	—	£2.00
25	Football Club Nicknames	1959	—	£2.00
K18	Historical Cars & Cycles	1957	—	£1.25
18	Home Pets (Packet)	1954	£3.50	—
25	International Footballers (Packet)	1962	£2.50	£62.50
25	Junior Service Quiz	1959	—	£1.00
18	Landmarks of Flying (Packet)	1961	£2.50	£45.00
50	Modern Aircraft	1954	—	£1.75
25	Modern Transport	1955	—	£1.00
18	Motor Cars (Packet)	1952	*£3.50*	
50	Motor Cycles Old & New	1963	—	£20.00
30	National Flags & Costumes	1962	—	£5.00
25	Naval Battles	1959	—	£1.25
25	Products of the World	1958	—	£1.00
18	Railway Engines—Past & Present (Packet)	1953	£3.00	£54.00
25	Sports Quiz	1958	—	£1.50
1	Stamp Card (Real Stamp Attached)	1962	—	15p
25	Stamp Series	1961	—	£1.50
25	The Wild West (Black Back)	1960	—	£3.00
25	The Wild West (Blue Back)	1960	—	£1.00
X30	Trains of the World	1960	—	£20.00
25	Treasure Island	1957	—	£2.00
25	Tropical Birds	1954	—	£1.00
25	Vintage Cars	1964	—	£1.50
25	Weapons of Defence	1959	—	£1.00
25	Wild Animals	1958	—	£1.00
25	Wild Flowers	1961	—	£1.00
25	Wonders of the World	1956	—	£1.00

SWETTENHAM (Tea)

Qty		Date	Odds	Sets
25	Aircraft of the World	1959	—	£3.50
25	Animals of the Countryside	1959	—	£1.25
25	Birds & Their Eggs	1958	—	£1.00
25	British Coins & Costumes	1958	—	£1.50
25	Butterflies & Moths	1958	—	£1.00
25	Evolution of the Royal Navy	1957	—	£1.00
25	Into Space	1959	—	£1.00
24	The Island of Ceylon (Conqueror Tea)	1964	£1.00	£24.00
25	Wild Animals	1958	—	£4.00

W. SWORD & CO. (Biscuits)

Qty		Date	Odds	Sets
25	British Empire at Work	1925	*£5.00*	—
20	Dogs	1926	£5.00	—
20	Inventors & their Inventions	1926	£5.00	—
25	Safety First	1927	£5.00	—

W. SWORD & CO. (Biscuits)—cont.

Qty		Date	Odds	Sets
25	Sports & Pastimes Series	1926	£6.00	—
25	Vehicles of all Ages	1924	£5.00	—
25	Zoo Series (brown)	1928	£4.00	—
25	Zoo Series (coloured)	1928	£5.00	—

TEACHER'S WHISKY

L12	Scottish Clans & Castles (circular)	1955	50p	£6.00

TEASDALE & CO. (Confectionery)

50	Cinema Stars (Anon)	1935	£2.00	—
25	Great War Series	1916	£10.00	—

TETLEY TEA

48	British Birds	1970	—	£25.00

TEXACO PETROL

12	Texaco Trophy Cricket Cards	1984	—	£1.00

D. C. THOMSON & CO. LTD. (Periodical)

L30	Adventure Pictures	1929	£1.25	£37.50
B16	Badges of the Fighting Fliers	1939	£1.00	£16.00
P26	Battles for the Flag	1939	£1.50	—
K80	Boys of All Nations	1936	40p	—
20	British Birds & Their Eggs	1930	£1.00	£20.00
F11	British Team of Footballers	1923	80p	£9.00
L20	Canvas Masterpieces (Silk)	1925	£5.00	—
16	Catch-My-Pal Cards	1939	75p	£12.00
X12	Coloured Photos of Star Footballers	1927	£2.00	—
64	County Cricketers	1955	£1.00	£65.00
16	Cricket Crests	1934	£3.50	£54.00
KF8	Cricketers	1923	£1.25	£10.00
X24	Cricketers	1933	£4.00	£96.00
P16	Cup Tie Stars of all Nations	1962	£1.00	—
12	Dandy Dogs	1928	£2.00	—
K28	Dominoes—School Caricatures	1936	£1.00	—
20	Easy Scientific Experiments	1930	£1.00	£20.00
BF18	Famous British Footballers (English)	1923	60p	£10.00
K80	Famous Feats	1937	40p	—
25	Famous Footballers	1955	50p	£12.50
24	Famous Footballers (Different)	1956	50p	£12.00
20	Famous Liners	1930	£1.50	£30.00
L32	Famous Ships	1931	£2.00	—
P12	Famous Teams in Football History	1961	£1.25	£15.00
P16	Famous Teams in Football History, 2nd	1962	£1.00	£16.00
16	Flags of All Nations	1934	£1.00	£16.00
K80	Flags of the Sea	1937	40p	—
KF137	Footballers	1923	40p	—
X8	Footballers	1933	£2.00	£16.00
F18	Footballers	1923	65p	£11.50
K52	Footballers—Hunt the Cup Cards	1937	75p	£40.00
24	Footballers—Motor Cars (Double-Sided)	1929	£2.50	—
BF22	Footballers—Signed Real Photos (English) ...	1923	60p	£13.50
F40	Football Photos	1925	£2.00	—

217

D. C. THOMSON & CO. LTD. (Periodical)—cont.

Qty		Date	Odds	Sets
48	Football Stars	1957	50p	£24.00
44	Football Stars of 1959	1959	50p	£22.00
K60/64	Football Team Cards	1934	35p	£21.00
64	Football Tips & Tricks	1955	30p	£20.00
L32	Football Towns & Their Crests	1931	£2.00	—
T12	Great Captains	1972	£1.50	—
12	Guns in Action	1938	75p	£9.00
M8	Hidden Treasure Clue Cards	1930	£7.50	—
P16	International Cup Teams	1964	£1.00	£16.00
6	Ju Jitsu Cards	1925	£2.50	£15.00
24	Motor Bike Cards	1926	£2.50	£60.00
20	Motor Cycles	1930	£2.50	£50.00
K100	Motor Cars	1934	40p	—
11	Mystic Menegerie	1925	£3.00	—
36	1930 Speedway Stars	1930	£2.00	£72.00
K80	Punishment Cards	1936	40p	—
12	Queer Animals	1928	£1.25	£15.00
16	Queer Birds	1934	£1.00	£16.00
K80	Secrets of Cricket	1936	75p	—
36	Spadgers Monster Collection of Spoofs	1936	£1.00	—
48	Speed	1937	50p	£24.00
12	Speedsters of the Wilds	1928	£1.25	—
48	Stars of Sport & Entertainment	1960	40p	£20.00
8/12	Star Footballers (metal)	1932	£5.00	—
P22	Star Teams of 1961	1961	80p	£17.50
20	The Wireless Telephone	1930	£1.25	£25.00
32	The World's Best Cricketers (Green Back)	1932	75p	£24.00
36	The World's Best Cricketers (Mauve Back)	1930	£3.00	£110.00
72	The World's Best Cricketers	1958	£1.00	£72.00
X12	The World's Biggest	1937	£4.00	£50.00
24	This Year's Top Form Footballers	1924	60p	£15.00
10	Vanguard Photo Gallery	1923	£5.00	—
96	VP Flips	1925	60p	—
24	Warrior Cards (Sectional Back)	1929	75p	£18.00
K28	Warrior Cards (Domino Back)	1936	75p	£21.00
K80	Warrior Cards	1937	40p	—
20	Why?	1930	£1.00	£20.00
K28	Wild West Dominoes	1936	£1.00	£28.00
20	Wonders of the Rail	1930	£2.00	£40.00
20	Wonders of the World	1930	£1.00	£20.00
64	World Cup Footballers	1958	60p	£37.50
M72	World Cup Stars	1971	70p	£50.00

THURMER & SYMES (Biscuits)

B96	Ocean Giants	1954	£1.25	—

TIMARU MILLING CO. (Cereals, New Zealand)

36	Focus on Fame	1948	—	£6.50
37	Peace & Progress	1947	—	£6.50
36	Victory Album Cards	1946	—	£10.00

TIMES CONFECTIONERY CO. LTD.

Qty		Date	Odds	Sets
BF24	Roy Rogers—In Old Amarillo (Plain Back)	1955	—	£1.00
B24	Roy Rogers—In Old Amarillo (Printed Back) ...	1955	—	£2.50
BF24	Roy Rogers—South of Caliente (Plain Back) ...	1955	—	£1.00
B24	Roy Rogers—South of Caliente (Printed Back) ...	1955	—	£2.50

TIMPERLEY CARD COLLECTORS (Club)

Qty		Date	Odds	Sets
10	Timperley Types	1980	—	£5.00
10	Timperley Types Second Series	1981	—	£3.50
10	Timperley Types Third Series	1981	—	£3.50
10	Timperley Types Fourth Series	1982	—	£3.00
10	Timperley Types Fifth Series	1982	—	£3.00
10	Timperley Types Sixth Series	1983	—	£3.00
10	Timperley Types Seventh Series	1983	—	£3.00

TIP TOP (Ice Cream, New Zealand)

Qty		Date	Odds	Sets
M10	Galactic Bar	1977	—	£5.00
M15	R2D2 Space Ice	1977	—	£7.50

TIT-BITS (Periodical)

Qty		Date	Odds	Sets
K54	Pin-Ups (P/C Inset)	1976	—	£2.50
TF17	Star Cover Girls	1953	£1.50	—
T12	Tit-Bits Clubs	1977	—	£3.50

CHOCOLAT TOBLER LTD.

Qty		Date	Odds	Sets
50	Famous Footballers	1939	£2.00	—
T192	General Interest Series	1900	60p	£120.00

TOMMY GUN (Toys)

Qty		Date	Odds	Sets
50	Medals (Plain Back)	1971	—	£1.75

TOM THUMB (New Zealand)

Qty		Date	Odds	Sets
M24	Supercars	1980	—	£3.00

TONIBELL (Ice Cream)

Qty		Date	Odds	Sets
12	Action Soldiers	1976	—	£1.25
M20	Banknotes	1974	12p	£2.50
L12	Beautiful Butterflies	1974	12p	£1.50
M20	County Badge Collection	1974	12p	£2.50
25	Did You Know?	1963	—	£1.00
L12	Did You Know?	1975	30p	—
X12	England's Soccer Stars	1970	75p	£9.00
D19	Famous Sports Trophies	1976	—	£5.00
D12	Farmyard Stencils	1977	—	£3.00
X12	Horses in the Service of Man	1984	50p	£6.00
M24	1st Division Football League Club Badges	1972	60p	£15.00
25	Inventions that Changed the World	1963	—	£1.25
X10	Junior Champs	1983	30p	£3.00
M24	Kings of the Road	1977	40p	—
K36	Team of all Time	1971	60p	—
25	The World's Passenger Liners	1963	—	£1.25
25	This Changing World (With line)	1963	—	£2.00
25	This Changing World (Without line)	1963	—	£2.50
25	Wonders of the Heavens	1963	—	£3.00

TOP FLIGHT (Confectionery)

Qty		Date	Odds	Sets
25	Top Flight Stars	1959	—	£2.00

TOPICAL TIMES (Periodical)

		Date	Odds	Sets
M6	Football Teams (metel)	1924	£4.00	£24.00
BF8	Football Teams	1924	£2.00	
BF10	Footballers (Pairs)	1924	£1.00	£10.00
E12	Footballers, Panel Portraits	1932	£1.50	£20.00
E24	Footballers, Panel Portraits	1933	£1.25	—
E14	Footballers, Panel Portraits	1934	£1.00	£14.00
E14	Footballers, Panel Portraits ...	1935	£1.25	—
E16	Footballers, Panel Portraits coloured	1936	£1.50	£24.00
E14	Footballers, Panel Portraits	1938	£1.00	£14.00
E16	Footballers, Panel Portraits	1939	£1.00	£16.00
E8	Footballers, Special issue (coloured)	1934	£2.50	£20.00
E8	Footballers, Triple Portraits	1937	£2.00	£16.00
L24	Great Players	1938	60p	£15.00
C24	Miniature Panel Portraits	1937	60p	£15.00
C24	Stars of To-day	1938	60p	£15.00

TOP NOTE SLIDES

		Date	Odds	Sets
P9	Pop Singers	1952	£2.50	—

TOPPS CHEWING GUM INC.

		Date	Odds	Sets
X99	Autos of 1977	1977	40p	—
X132	Battlestar Galactica	1979	10p	£10.00
X66	Bay City Rollers	1978	20p	£13.50
X49	Comic Book Heroes	1977	40p	£20.00
X220	Footballers (Red Back)	1975	15p	£33.00
X88	Footballers (Scottish, Blue Back)	1975	30p	—
X330	Footballers (Blue Back)	1976	12p	£40.00
X132	Footballers (Scottish, Red Back)	1976	30p	—
X330	Footballers (Red Back)	1977	12p	£40.00
X132	Footballers (Scottish, Yellow Back)	1977	30p	—
X396	Footballers (Orange Back)	1978	10p	£15.00
X132	Footballers (Scottish Green Back)	1978	15p	—
X396	Footballers (Pale Blue Back)	1979	10p	£40.00
X132	Footballers (Scottish, Red Back)	1979	12p	—
X66	Footballers (Pink Back)	1980	12p	£8.00
X65	Footballers (Blue Back)	1981	12p	—
E18	Football Posters	1980	12p	—
X21	Funny Puzzles	1978	30p	—
L41	Garbage Pail Kids 1st series A	1986	—	£7.50
L41	Garbage Pail Kids 1st series B	1986	—	£7.50
L42	Garbage Pail Kids 2nd series A	1986	—	£7.50
L42	Garbage Pail Kids 2nd series B	1986	—	£10.00
L57	Garbage Pail Kids 3rd series A	1987	—	£7.50
L71	Garbage Pail Kids 3rd series B	1987	—	£10.00
L48	Garbage Pail Kids 4th series A	1987	—	£7.50
L76	Garbage Pail Kids 4th series B	1987	—	£10.00
X49	Marvel Super Heroes	1980	—	£6.00
X66	Planet of the Apes	1974	15p	£10.00
X72	Railway Quiz see A. & B.C.	1959	—	
X50	Shocking Laffs	1977	20p	—
X88	Star Trek, The Motion Picture	1980	—	£8.00

TOPPS CHEWING GUM INC.—cont.

Qty		Date	Odds	Sets
X66	Star Wars (1-66)	1978	10p	£6.00
X66	Star Wars (1A-66A)	1978	10p	—
X66	Superman the Movie 1st Series (1-66)	1979	—	£4.00
X66	Superman the Movie 2nd Series (67-132) ...	1979	—	£4.00
X88	The Black Hole	1980	10p	£5.00
X42	Wanted Posters	1978	25p	—

U.S. ISSUES

Qty		Date	Odds	Sets
X66	Baby	1985	—	£4.50
X88	Buck Rogers in the 25th Century	1979	—	£4.00
X55	Cats (humorous)	1983	—	£5.00
X77	Close Encounters	1982	—	£3.50
X88	Creature Feature	1980	—	£6.00
X19	Diplomat Soccer Series	1981	—	£3.50
X36	Donkey Kong	1982	—	£3.00
X96	E.T.	1982	—	£4.00
X66	Funny Valentines	1960	—	£15.00
X82	Gremlins	1984	—	£5.00
X88	Indiana Jones	1984	—	£5.00
X70	Jaws 2	1978	—	£4.00
X44	Jaws 3-D	1983	—	£5.00
X88	Masters of the Universe	1984	—	£5.00
X66	Michael Jackson	1984	—	£4.00
G13	Michael Jackson Giant Stickers Series 3	1984	—	£4.00
X99	Mork and Mindy	1978	—	£4.00
X55	Mysteries of India	1967	—	£12.50
X88	Raiders of the Lost Ark	1981	—	£6.00
G12	Smurf Tattoos	1983	—	£2.00
X132	Star Wars—Return of the Jedi	1983	—	£5.00
X23	Stickers	1983	—	£1.50
X132	Star Wars—Return of the Jedi II	1983	—	£5.00
X88	Superman 2	1981	—	£5.00
X99	Superman 3	1983	—	£5.00
X66	The 'A' Team	1983	—	£5.00
X84	The Black Hole	1979	—	£4.00
X132	The Empire Strikes Back, 1st Series	1980	—	£6.00
X88	The Empire Strikes Back, 3rd Series	1980	—	£6.00
X55	Weird Wheels	1980	—	£4.00

TOP SELLERS (Commercial)

Qty		Date	Odds	Sets
M54	Crazy Stickers	1975	—	£2.50
P100	Superstars	1975	—	£10.00

JOHN TORDOFF & SON LTD. (Tea)

Qty		Date	Odds	Sets
25	Safety First	1926	£3.00	£75.00
25	The Growth and Manufacture of Tea	1926	£4.00	—

TOTAL PETROL

Qty		Date	Odds	Sets
X25	Return to Oz	1985	—	£1.50

TOWER TEA

Qty		Date	Odds	Sets
24	Illustrated Sayings	1910	£12.50	—

TREBOR/SHARP (Confectionery)

Qty		Date	Odds	Sets
25	Famous Pets	1972	—	£1.00

TRENOUTHS (Shop)

24	World's Most Beautiful Butterflies	1924	£3.00	—

TRUCARDS (Commercial)

M30	Animals	1972	—	£1.00
M30	Battle of Britain	1972	—	£1.00
M30	Flowers	1972	—	£1.00
M30	History of Aircraft	1972	—	£1.00
M30	Sport	1972	—	£1.00
M30	Veteran and Vintage Cars	1972	—	£1.50
M30	World War I	1972	—	£1.00
M30	World War II	1972	—	£1.00

TUCKETT'S (Confectionery)

25	Photos of Cricketers	1925	£15.00	—
50	Photos of Film Stars	1935	£3.00	—
25	Photos of Footballers	1925	£7.50	—

W. & E. TURNER (Shoes)

20	War Pictures	1915	£5.00	—

TWININGS TEA

30	Rare Stamps	1960	30p	£9.00
30	Rare Stamps 2nd Series	1960	—	£1.50
30	Rare Stamps 2nd Series (Red Overprint)	1961	—	£1.00

TYDOL GASOLINE (U.S.A.)

X40	Aeroplanes	1937	—	£50.00

TYPHOO TEA LTD.

36 Page Illustrated Reference Book—£2.25

25	Aesop's Fables	1924	£1.00	£25.00
25	Ancient & Annual Customs	1922	60p	£15.00
T25	Animal Friends of Man	1927	£2.00	£50.00
T25	Animal Offence & Defence	1926	50p	£12.50
T25	A Tale of Two Cities	1931	£1.20	£30.00
24	British Birds & Their Eggs	1914	£4.00	£100.00
T25	British Birds & Their Eggs	1936	30p	£7.50
29/30	British Empire at Work	1925	70p	£20.00
30	British Empire at Work Continuation Card ...	1925	£6.00	—
1	British Empire at Work Last Chance Card ...	1925	—	£5.00
25	Calendar 1934	1933	£10.00	—
25	Calendar 1936	1935	£6.00	—
T1	Calendar 1937	1936	—	£3.50
T25	Characters from Shakespeare	1937	24p	£6.00
25	Common Objects Highly Magnified	1925	60p	£15.00
25	Conundrums	1915	£8.00	—
24	Do You Know?	1962	—	£1.00
T25	Famous Voyages	1934	50p	£12.50
M20	Flags & Arms of Countries	1916	£6.00	—
24	Great Achievements	1962	—	£10.00

TYPHOO TEA LTD.—cont.

Qty		Date	Odds	Sets
T25	Historic Buildings	1936	50p	£12.50
T25	Homes of Famous Men	1934	30p	£7.50
T25	Horses	1935	40p	£10.00
T25	Important Industries of the British Empire	1939	16p	£4.00
T25	Interesting Events in British History	1938	16p	£4.00
T25	John Halifax—Gentleman	1932	£1.00	£25.00
T25	Lorna Doone	1930	£1.60	£40.00
10	Nursery Rhymes	1914	£12.00	—
24	Our Empire's Defenders	1916	£12.50	—
48	Puzzle Series	1913	£12.50	—
T30	Robin Hood & His Merry Men	1928	£2.00	£60.00
M12	The Amazing World of Dr Who	1976	£1.00	£12.00
T30	The Story of David Copperfield	1929	£1.00	£30.00
T25	The Swiss Family Robinson	1935	16p	£4.00
24	Travel Through the Ages	1962	—	£1.00
T25	Trees of the Countryside	1938	16p	£4.00
T25	Whilst We Sleep	1928	80p	£20.00
24	Wild Flowers	1961	—	£1.00
T25	Wild Flowers in their Families	1936	16p	£4.00
T25	Wild Flowers in their Families 2nd Series	1937	16p	£4.00
T25	Wonder Cities of the World	1933	60p	£15.00
M24	Wonderful World of Disney	1975	—	£15.00
T25	Work on the Farm	1933	80p	£20.00
25	Zoo Series	1932	30p	£7.50

PACKAGE ISSUES

Qty		Date	Odds	Sets
20	By Pond & Stream	1955	15p	£3.00
20	Common British Birds	1955	15p	£3.00
20	Costumes of the World	1955	15p	£3.00
24	Do You Know?	1962	20p	£5.00
20	Famous Bridges	1955	15p	£3.00
20	Famous Buildings	1955	15p	£3.00
24	Famous Football Clubs	1962	20p	£5.00
24	Famous Football Clubs, 2nd Series	1963	25p	£6.00
35	Football Club Plaques	1973	75p	—
24	Football Stars, New Series	1973	40p	£10.00
24	Great Voyages of Discovery ·	1962	25p	£6.00
24	International Football Stars	1964	30p	£7.00
24	International Football Stars, 2nd Series	1969	50p	£12.00
24	100 Years of Great British Achievements	1972	30p	£7.00
20	Pets	1955	15p	£3.00
20	Some Countryside Animals	1955	15p	£3.00
20	Some Popular Breeds of Dogs	1955	20p	£4.00
20	Some World Wonders	1955	15p	£3.00
24	Travel Through the Ages	1962	20p	£5.00
20	Types of Ships	1955	15p	£3.00
20	Wild Animals	1955	15p	£3.00
24	Wild Flowers	1961	20p	£5.00

PREMIUM ISSUES

Qty		Date	Odds	Sets
E24	Famous Football Clubs	1964	£4.00	—
E24	Famous Football Clubs, 2nd Series	1965	£2.50	—
E24	Football Stars	1973	£2.50	—
G24	Great Voyages of Discovery	1967	£1.50	—

TYPHOO TEA LTD.—cont.

Qty		Date	Odds	Sets
E24	International Football Stars, 1st Series	1969	£3.00	—
E24	International Football Stars, 2nd Series	1969	£3.00	
G24	100 Years of British Achievements	1972	—	£12.00

TYSON & CO. (Soap)

28	Semaphore Signals	1912	£7.50	—

UNION JACK (Periodical)

BF6	Monarchs of the Ring	1923	£1.25	£7.50
B8	Police of All Nations	1922	£2.00	£16.00

UNITED AUTOMOBILE SERVICES

25	Castles (Series No. 1)	1925	£3.00	—
25	Churches (Series No. 2)	1925	£3.00	—
25	Places of Interest (Series No. 4)	1925	£3.00	—
25	"United" (Series No. 3)	1925	£3.00	—

UNITED CONFECTIONERY CO.

50	Wild Animals of the World	1905	£5.00	—

UNITED DAIRIES

25	Aquarium Fish	1962	—	£1.50
25	Birds & Their Eggs	1961	—	£2.00
25	British Uniforms of the 19th Century	1962	—	£2.50
25	The Story of Milk	1966	—	£3.00
25	The West	1963	—	£2.50

UNIVERSAL AUTOMATICS LTD.

X30	Trains of the World	1958	—	£7.50

UNIVERSAL CIGARETTE CARD CO. LTD.

15	Australian Cricket Team 1905	1986	—	£2.50
13	Car Registration Nos. (Irish)	1987	—	£3.00
15	English Cricketers of 1902	1987	—	£2.50

VAL GUM

L144	Animals of the World	1954	50p	—
L144	Birds of the World	1954	50p	—
L292	Film Stars	1954	50p	—
L50	Footballers	1935	£2.50	—
L48	Natural History Sketches	1954	£1.00	—
L72	Popeye	1954	£1.00	£72.00
L?	Shirley Temple Cards	1935	£2.00	—

VAUX BREWERIES

M30	Footballers	1987	—	£6.00

VENNALL'S STORES

24	World's Most Beautiful Birds	1924	£4.00	—

VENORLANDUS LTD. (Commercial)

M48	Our Heroes, World of Sport	1979	—	£4.00

LITERATURE

Unlike stamps or coins, it was not necessary to keep exact records of cigarette cards as they were issued and therefore, particularly in the case of the earlier series, information has had to be painstakingly assembled over a period of years by the recording of cards as they are discovered by collectors. The Cartophilic Society of G.B. Ltd. has shouldered the burden of publishing most of the research on card series in its Reference Books (see page 7). Information on new issues and previously unrecorded items is coming in at such a rate that the World Tobacco Index Part 5 is now well on the way to be published.

Several more specialised works have also been produced by dealers and private individuals. These include the invaluable L.C.C.C. Handbooks Parts 1 and 2, which are an essential complement to the World Index, and two books recently published by Murray Cards – British Silk Issues and the 254 page Listing of Cricket Cigarettes & Trade Cards.

There have been few works published of a general nature, and second hand copies of obsolete titles are eagerly sought. A new book is however now available – the Story of Cigarette Cards, by Martin Murray. This contains over 80 pages of illustrations, and full details appear on page 9. An inexpensive alternative is the album issued by Jacob's Club Biscuits – Famous Picture Cards from History, including reproductions from 32 different series.

NOVELTIES

MODERN OCEAN GREY HOUND.

THE SPORTSMAN
Strood

In an effort to attract buyers to their products some manufacturers used a considerable amount of ingenuity in their card issues. Moving away from the 'stiffener' image the American firm Kinney issued several die cut sets in shapes such as musical instruments, clocks and fans. A larger set of shapes was also issued by Gail & Ax. Other unusual issues in the great period of American cards include booklets by Duke, folding and transparent cards by Kinney and spinning cards by Consolidated.

In Britain the most unusual series is of real gramophone records featuring talks by personalities from show business and sport issued by the Record Cigarette Co. in 1934. Wills issued a number of sectional series, designed to be joined together to form a large picture. Other unusual ideas include cards demonstrating golf strokes (by Cotton) which were to be held together with an elastic band and then flicked to give the impression of an action shot; a Godfrey Phillips set which when moistened displays different colours for a racing game; and a set of cards by Bocnal which when heated became luminous.

Different materials have been used other than card such as the Whitbread Inn Signs printed on aluminium, Nabisco Soldiers on plastic and Wills Miniatures on metal; silks and similar materials were extensively used and occupy a separate page of this volume. Metal pins to go in the lapel were issued by the American Tob. Co. and Wills, while there were even metal toy soldiers given with Greys Cigarettes.

VERKADE'S FABRIEKEN N.V. (Biscuits, Holland)

Qty		Date	Odds	Sets
T140	De Bloemen En Haar Vrienden	1933	—	£8.00
T140	De Boerderij	1935	—	£12.00
T138	Hans De Torenkraai	1936	—	£8.00
T132	Kamerplanten	1928	—	£15.00
T126	Mijn Aquarium	1925	—	£12.50
T126	Vetplanten	1926	—	£10.00

VICTORIA GALLERIES
Officially authorised reprints of Imperial Tobacco Co. Series

L25	Aviary and Cage Birds (Player)	1987	—	£6.25
L24	Cats (Player)	1986	—	£6.25
L25	Dogs (Wills)	1987	—	£6.25
L25	Famous Golfers (Wills)	1987	—	£6.25
L25	Game Birds and Wild Fowl (Player)	1987	—	£6.25
L25	Golf (Player)	1986	—	£6.25
L25	Racing Yachts (Player)	1987	—	£6.25
L25	Rigs of Ships (Wills)	1987	—	£6.25

CHOCOLAT DE VILLARS

24	British Birds & their Eggs	1926	£1.00	£24.00

VOMO AUTOMATICS

X50	Flags of the World	1965	30p	£15.00

JONATHAN WALES LTD.

25	The History of Flight 1st Series	1963	£2.00	—
25	The History of Flight 2nd Series	1963	£2.00	—

WALKER, HARRISON & GARTHWAITE LTD. (Dog Food)

M15	Dogs	1902	£6.00	—

T. WALL & SONS (Ice Cream)

24	Do You Know?	1965	—	£1.50
36	Dr Who Adventure	1966	60p	£20.00
48	Moon Fleet	1967	—	£2.50
M6	Prehistoric Animals (Magicards)	1971	—	75p
P6	Sea Creatures	1971	—	75p
20	Skateboard Surfer	1978	—	£1.00

WALTERS PALM TOFFEE

50	Some Cap Badges of Territorial Regiments	1938	20p	£10.00

WAND CONFECTIONERY LTD.

X10	Chubby Checker—How to do the Twist	1964	£3.00	—
25	Commemoration Stamp Series	1963	£1.40	£35.00
X35	Pop D.J.'s	1964	£1.20	£42.00
25	They Gave Their Name	1963	—	£5.00
23/25	They Gave Their Name	1963	—	£1.00

WARWICK DISTRICT COUNCIL

30	England's Historic Heartland	1980	—	£1.25

WATFORD BISCUIT CO.

Qty		Date	Odds	Sets
KF48	Cinema Stars	1952	—	£10.00

WEBCOSA & CO.

| X20 | Trail Town ... ... | 1963 | 75p | £15.00 |

WEEKLY WELCOME (Periodical)

| 12 | Lest We Forget Cards ... ... | 1916 | £4.00 | — |

WEETABIX LTD. (Cereals)

TS25	Animal Cards	1962	—	£1.25
T28	Asterix—His Friends & Foes	1976	15p	£4.00
T18	Batman and Wonderwoman	1979	30p	£6.00
TS25	British Bird Cards	1962	70p	—
TS25	British Cars	1963	£1.00	—
L25	Conquest of Space, Series A	1959	—	£4.00
L25	Conquest of Space, Series B	1959	—	£4.00
T25	Dr Who (Coloured Background)	1977	—	£15.00
T24	Dr Who (White Background)	1975	—	£15.00
T18	Flash Gordon	1981	30p	£5.00
T18	Huckleberry Hound	1977	30p	£5.00
T18	Mickey Mouse's Playmates	1978	40p	£7.50
TS25	Our Pet Cards	1961	—	£1.50
T18	Robin Hood	1980	30p	£5.00
T18	Star Trek	1979	50p	£9.00
T18	Superman	1978	40p	£7.50
L25	The Western Story	1959	—	£1.25
TS25	Thrill Cards	1960	75p	—
P5	Weeta-Cards	1987	—	£2.50
TS25	Working Dog Cards	1961	—	£2.00
T18	World of Sport	1986	—	£5.00

JAMES O. WELSH (Confectionery, U.S.A.)

| 50 | Comics ... ... | 1950 | — | £60.00 |

WELSH RUGBY UNION

| 50 | Great Welsh Rugby Players ... ... | 1981 | — | £2.00 |

WESTCO (Confectionery)

| F60 | Westco Autocards ... ... | 1954 | £2.50 | — |

J. WEST FOODS LTD.

| M8 | Famous Sea Adventures ... ... | 1972 | — | 75p |

WEST LONDON SYNAGOGUE

50	Jewish Life in Many Lands	1961	—	£7.50
50	Jewish Symbols & Ceremonies	1961	—	£3.00
25/50	Jewish Symbols & Ceremonies	1961	—	£1.00

WEST MIDLANDS POLICE

| X36 | Pictorial History of Walsall & District ... ... | 1986 | — | £12.50 |

WESTON BISCUIT CO. LTD. (Australia)

| L24 | Veteran & Vintage Cars, 1st Series ... ... | 1961 | — | £12.00 |
| L24 | Veteran & Vintage Cars 2nd Series ... ... | 1962 | — | £2.00 |

WHEATLEY & SONS

Qty		Date	Odds	Sets
24	World's Most Beautiful Birds	1924	£3.00	—

WEST RIDING COUNTY COUNCIL

20	Health Cards	1924	£2.00	£40.00

WHITBREAD & CO. LTD. (Brewers)

M1	Duke Without a Head	1958	—	£1.25
M50	Inn Signs, 1st Series (Metal)	1951	£1.00	£50.00
M50	Inn Signs, 2nd Series (Metal)	1951	£1.00	£50.00
M50	Inn Signs, 3rd Series (Metal)	1952	£1.00	£50.00
M50	Inn Signs, 3rd Series (Card)	1952	£1.25	£62.50
M50	Inn Signs, 4th Series	1952	£1.00	£50.00
M50	Inn Signs, 5th Series	1953	£1.00	£50.00
M25	Inn Signs, Bournemouth	1973	£1.20	£30.00
M25	Inn Signs, Devon & Somerset	1973	£1.00	£25.00
M25	Inn Signs, Isle of Wight	1974	£1.20	£30.00
M25	Inn Signs, Kent	1973	£1.20	—
M15	Inn Signs, London	1973	75p	—
M10	Inn Signs, London (Different)	1974	£1.00	—
M25	Inn Signs, Marlow	1973	£1.20	—
M25	Inn Signs, Portsmouth	1973	£1.20	—
M4	Inn Signs, Special Issue	1955	£1.25	£5.00
M25	Inn Signs, Stratford-Upon Avon	1974	£1.20	£30.00
M25	Inn Signs, West Pennines	1973	£1.20	—
M25	Maritime Inn Signs	1974	20p	£5.00
M1	The Britannia Inn (Plain back)	1958	—	£15.00
M1	The Britannia Inn (Printed back)	1958	—	£25.00
M1	The Railway	1958	—	£2.00
M1	The Startled Saint	1958	—	£15.00

WHITE FISH AUTHORITY

25	The Fish We Eat	1954	—	£1.00

WHITEHAVEN LIBRARY

M6	The Port of Whitehaven	1978	—	£1.00

WHITEHEAD (Lollies)

X25	Kings & Queens	1980	—	£1.00

WIKO (Confectionery, Germany)

50	Soldaten Der Welt	1969	—	£2.00

WILCOCKS & WILCOCKS LTD. (Tea)

25	Birds	1965	60p	—
25	British Cavalry Uniforms of the 19th Century ...	1963	—	£4.00
25	Garden Flowers	1964	—	£1.25
25	Passenger Liners	1967	—	£6.00
25	People & Places	1966	—	£1.00
25	Tropical Birds	1965	—	£2.00
25	Wonders of the Deep	1965	—	£1.50
25	Wonders of the World	1971	—	£2.50

A. S. WILKIN LTD. (Confectionery)

25	Into Space	1960	—	£2.00

WILKINSON LTD. (Tools)

Qty		Date	Odds	Sets
K4	Wilkinson Tools	1962	30p	£1.20

W. R. WILKINSON & CO. (Confectionery)

B25	Footballers	1956	£4.00	—

WIMPY (Restaurants)

M20	Super Heroes Super Villains	1979	40p	£8.00

WOMAN'S FRIEND (Periodical)

K52	Fortune Telling Cards	1925	60p	—

WOMAN'S OWN (Periodical)

F8	Film Stars	1955	£1.50	—

WOODCOCK'S XL STORES

24	World's Most Beautiful Fishes	1925	£3.50	—

G. WOODHEAD & SONS (Tea)

25	Types of British Soliders	1916	£10.00	—

WRIGHTS BISCUITS LTD.

24	Marvels of the World	1954	—	£1.00
24	Mischief Goes to Mars (Mischief Club)	1954	—	£2.50
24	Mischief Goes to Mars (Wright at side)	1954	—	£1.00
24	Mischief Goes to Mars (Wright at base)	1954	—	£2.50

YOUNG BRITAIN (Periodical)

BF15	Favourite Cricketers Series (in Pairs)	1922	£2.50	£37.50

SPECIAL OFFERS

10 different pre 1940 sets, our selection (no pages)	**£15.00**
35 different post 1945 sets, our selection	**£10.00**
100 different post 1945 sets, our selection (including the above 35)	**£35.00**
8 different sets of Trucards	**£3.00**
10 different Brooke Bond sets (our selection)	**£6.00**
125 post war type cards from 125 different series	**£2.50**
Liebig starter pack. Our 1987 Catalogue + 15 sets	**£10.00**
40 different tobacco advertising inserts	**£4.00**
12 different cardboard cigarette packets	**£2.00**
8 different Bassett Sweet Cigarette Packets	**£1.00**

"NOSTALGIA" REPRINTS

An exciting concept for collectors. Reproductions of Classic cards sets, all of which are almost impossible to obtain, at a price that everyone can afford.

These cards are of the highest quality, and the latest technology has been used to recreate as closely as possible the beauty of the originals. They have received universal acclaim in the cigarette card world, and are indeed becoming collector's items in their own right.

Because of the difficulty of distinguishing our reproductions from the originals each reprint has 'A Nostalgia Reprint' printed on the back of the card.

TITLES CURRENTLY AVAILABLE

Taddy County Cricketers

15	Derbyshire
15	Essex
16	Gloucestershire
15	Hampshire
15	Kent
15	Lancashire
14	Leicestershire
15	Middlesex
15	Northamptonshire
14	Nottinghamshire
15	Somersetshire (sic)
15	Surrey
15	Sussex
15	Warwickshire
14	Worcestershire
15	Yorkshire

ONLY £1.50 per County. Or all 238 cards for £20.00

Cope	50 Cope's Golfers	£6.00
Jones Bros.	18 Spurs Footballers	£1.50
Player	50 Millitary Series	£6.00
Wills	50 Cricketers 1896	£6.00
Wills	50 Cricketers 1901	£6.00

OTHER REPRINTS AVAILABLE

I.T.C. Canada

45	Hockey Players		1987 —	£7.50
36	Hockey Series		1987 —	£7.50

Player

L25	Aviary & Cage Birds		1987 —	£6.25
L24	Cats		1986 —	£6.25
L25	Game Birds & Wild Fowl		1987 —	£6.25
L25	Golf		1986 —	£6.25
L25	Racing Yachts		1987 —	£6.25

Wills

L25	Dogs		1987 —	£6.25
L25	Famous Golfers		1987 —	£6.25
L25	Rigs of Ships		1987 —	£6.25

Bubbles

X66	Mars Attacks		1984 —	£12.00

ORDER FORM

To Murray Cards (International) Ltd., 51 Watford Way, Hendon Central, London NW4 3JH.

Please supply the following items in connection with your special introductory offer.

Complete Sets

ISSUER	SERIES TITLE	PRICE

Albums (Please specify album and cover only covers, and page sizes)

TOTAL _____

LESS 10% _____

Odd cards (listed on separate sheet of paper) ....

Books (specify title and price).

GRAND TOTAL _____

1. I enclose a remittance for this amount.
2. Please charge my Access/Visa account

Card number ....

Expiry date................................

NAME...

ADDRESS...

....

....

SPECIAL INTRODUCTORY OFFER

The quality of our cards and of our service is second to none. In order to introduce ourselves to new clients, and as a 'Thank You' to existing customers, we are offering a ten per cent discount on any one order for complete sets of cards and albums upon presentation of the voucher below.

Just work out what you would like to order, and send us your list. Deduct the 10% and send your cheque for the balance (or you can pay by Credit Card), together with the voucher printed below. Orders for odd cards and books may be placed at the same time, but please remember that these must be at the normal Catalogue prices.

EXAMPLES

(1)	Set Wills Soldiers of the World	£400.00
	SAVING 10%	£40.00
	Send Voucher and pay ONLY	£360.00
(2)	Sets. Carreras Do You Know	£4.00
	Gallaher Trains of the World	£12.00
	Ogden Foreign Birds	£17.50
		£33.50
	2 Nostalgia albums with slipcases	£20.00
		£53.50
	SAVING 10%	£5.35
		£48.15
	World Index Part 1	£15.00
	Send voucher and pay ONLY	£63.15

Remember. You can order as little or as much as you like for the voucher offer, but an order of £50.00 will more than recover the cost of the Catalogue. For this reason we must restrict the offer to one voucher for each customer.

For your convenience you may detach this complete page and use the order form on the reverse.

MONEY-SAVING VOUCHER

To Murray Cards (International) Ltd., 51 Watford Way, London NW4 3JH.

Please send me the goods shown overleaf/separately. I wish to claim the special 10% discount on all the complete sets and albums listed. This is the only voucher I have returned.

NAME.. ADDRESS..................................

....

DATE.. ....

Offer valid 1st January to 30th September 1988.

232